Solutions Manual for
COLLEGE PHYSICS
4th edition

Franklin Miller, Jr.
Kenyon College

HARCOURT BRACE JOVANOVICH, INC.
New York   Chicago   San Francisco   Atlanta

Cover photo: Manfred Kage from Peter Arnold

ISBN: 0-15-511735-1

Printed in the United States of America

PREFACE

Solutions to Problems

This manual contains solutions for all numerical problems in *College Physics*, Fourth Edition. Not all of these solutions will be used by all instructors. I have had in mind the needs of the inexperienced teacher, and if I have erred, it has been on the side of abundance and attention to details of the solutions.

The numbering of the problems in the text has been carefully considered. In many cases, problems of similar content are numbered in succession, so that an instructor can assign either the odd-numbered problem (for which the answer is in the text) or the even-numbered problem (for which no answer is in the text). Similarly, in the chapters on mechanics I have paid attention to the distribution of problems stated in metric and in British units.

For the non-numerical questions at the ends of chapters, the comments in this manual range from simple statements of answers to extensive background information. These comments are not intended dogmatically; they are not to be passed on verbatim to the student but rather should serve to focus on the intention of the question.

Organization of the Course

It would be presumptuous for an author to dictate the detailed organization of a physics course. Nevertheless, for what they are worth, I give two suggestions that have proved valid in my own teaching of elementary physics from *College Physics*.

First, a realistic timetable must be drawn up at the start of the school year that will allow adequate time for basic atomic and nuclear physics (Chapters 27, 28, and 30). The entire Chapter 29 (Atomic Structure) can be considered to be "For Further Study," although Sec. 29-7 on x rays can be assigned separately if desired. If, as often happens, a last-minute curtailment is unavoidable due to accumulated slipping behind during the year, let this affect only Chapter 29 (Atomic Structure), Chapter 31 (Applied Nuclear Physics), and, perhaps, Chapter 26 (Applied Optics). The text builds toward fundamental atomic and nuclear physics. We would be doing a great disservice to liberal arts students as well as premedical and other preprofessional students if we allowed them to leave their college physics course without reaching significantly into contemporary physics.

Second, I strongly urge that the assignment in the mathematical appendix mentioned on p. 799 be made at the first or second class meeting. It seems to be a deadly bore, and naturally we want to get on with "real physics." However, I have tried it both ways in my own classes and have found a significantly better performance by students in classes that review arithmetic and algebra at the very start *as an assignment*—not on a "do it if you feel like it" basis. Refer the student to p. 799: "Solve as many of these problems as you need to, until you are sure that you could do one more of them with little hesitation or anguish. Then you will be able to devote your valuable time and energy to thinking about *physics*, instead of continually wasting your time on what is merely routine." By the terms of this suggestion, a well-prepared student will spend practically no time on this assignment and will not be forced to do a lot of busywork. On the other hand, the poorly prepared student will gain immensely by studying Sections A1, A2, A3, and B1 as the first assignment of the course.

Mathematical Level

The text, like the earlier editions, is written for students who bring to the course no mathematics beyond high-school algebra. Don't be misled by the appearance of derivatives and integral signs. In the main body of the Fourth Edition we use limits of ratios; this is pedagogically sound. There is no reason not to call these ratios by the name "derivatives." Note, however, that *formulas* for derivatives are used only in the optional For Further Study sections. Throughout, I have reinforced the definition of a derivative by repeatedly stating a result first as the limit of a ratio and then (in the next line) in the derivative notation (see pp. 31, 34, 115, 126, 173, 187, 316, 379, 408, 490). Similarly, the definite integral is repeatedly defined and redefined as the limit of a sum (pp. 33, 35, 120, 421, 422, 489, 554, 735). With this reinforcement the text does, I believe, satisfy the needs of mathematically naive students. There is no need to omit or soft-pedal this kind of non-formal calculus, which is explained in the text with the help of high-school algebra and graphical interpretations. The text is therefore suitable for the usual "non-calculus" course in elementary physics.

References; Films

The effect on students of end-of-chapter references in an elementary text is uncertain. Instructors agree that these references *should* be there; they also agree that it is difficult to get students to use them. I believe that instructors should call attention to specific references from time to time, perhaps by assigning occasional 5-minute reports to be given to the class by selected students. Somehow, the entire class must know about the existence of the list of references, as a first step toward voluntary use of them.

Listed among the references are film loops produced by various physicists. It is impractical to give in the References the many sources of supply for these film loops; instructors who use loops will know where to get them. If freely available to students, film loops are useful for review purposes as well as supplementary study. In my college we have two automatic projectors. One is used by instructors wishing to illustrate a point in a lecture. The other is kept on a table in an alcove in a hallway near open shelves containing about 120 loops. Students can project loops of their own choice during their free periods or in the evening. In some institutions a similar free-choice facility is maintained in the library. It is not uncommon for an instructor to show a loop during class lecture and then assign the same loop for closer individual study to be made before the next class meeting.

The solutions to the problems have been carefully checked. I would be grateful for any reports of residual errors or inaccuracies either in the solutions manual or in the text itself.

Franklin Miller, Jr.
Kenyon College
Gambier, Ohio 43022

CONTENTS

Chapter 1   The Nature of Physics

Questions

1-2 The message would give the retem in terms of the wavelength of the krypton line mentioned on p. 6. The Martians would know krypton as "the 36th element in the periodic table."

1-3 $A = \frac{1}{2}bh$, where a is the base and h the height. The dimensional formula is $[A] = [L]^2$.

1-5 At this time, only the dimensional consistency of the formula is being checked. The formula is, in fact, also quantitatively correct (Prob. 3-C4).

1-6 The centime has a mass equal to the mass of the quantity of water contained in two cubes, each having edges equal to one 4 billionth of the circumference of the earth.

1-7 A metric ton (tonne) is 2204.6 lb (p. 8; see also Table 4 of the Appendix, p. 803). This is 205 lb greater than an ordinary ton (10%). A "long ton" used in commerce is 2240 lb, which is 2% greater than a metric ton.

Chapter 2   Structure and Properties of Matter

Questions

2-1 29 electrons; 27 electrons; 34 neutrons; 36 neutrons; 29 protons; 65 nucleons; 65; 29; 29.

2-2 The attractive nuclear force between the protons, and that between the protons and the neutrons, is of overriding importance at nuclear distances of the order of 10^{-14} m. See p. 760.

2-3 10 moles; 6×10^{24} molecules.

2-4 In 10 moles of H_2O there are $20 \times 6 \times 10^{23}$ hydrogen *atoms* and $10 \times 6 \times 10^{23}$ oxygen atoms.

2-5 A kilogram of iron.

2-6 A proton and a neutron; nuclear force.

2-7 $^{238}_{92}U$ has 3 more neutrons than does $^{235}_{92}U$.

Multiple Choice

2-8 (*b*);   **2-9** (*c*);   **2-10** (*a*);   **2-11** (*a*);   **2-12** (*c*);   **2-13** (*c*).

Problems

2-A1 3.156×10^7 s/y.

2-A2 1.58×10^9 in.

2-A3 $m = (9 \times 10^3 \text{ m}^3)(1.293 \text{ kg/m}^3) = 1.16 \times 10^4 \text{ kg} \doteq 11.6$ tonnes.

2-A4 Sp. grav. $= (1.977 \times 10^{-3} \text{ g/cm}^3)/(1.293 \times 10^{-3} \text{ g/cm}^3) = 1.53$.

2-A5 $m = Vd = (50 \text{ m}^3)(0.14 \times 1.293 \text{ kg/m}^3) = 9.05$ kg.

2-A6 Sp. grav. of tungsten hexafluoride is $(12.9 \times 10^{-3})/(1.293 \times 10^{-3}) = 10.0$.

2-A7 $V = m/d = (960 \text{ g})/(1.040 \text{ g/cm}^3) = 923 \text{ cm}^3$.

2-A8 (a) $m = Vd = (2.4 \times 10^{12} \text{ cm}^3)(2.7 \text{ g/cm}^3) = 6.48 \times 10^{12} \text{ g}$;   (b) 6.48×10^9 kg;
(c) 6.48×10^6 tonnes.

2-A9 The density of nuclear matter is about $2 \times 10^{14} \text{ g/cm}^3$ (p. 21). Hence $m = (0.01 \times 10^{-1} \text{ cm})^3(2 \times 10^{14} \text{ g/cm}^3) = 2 \times 10^5 \text{ g} = 200$ kg. Only an exceptional athlete could lift this speck of nuclear matter. The world records for weight lifting depend on the type of lift employed. At the 1976 Olympics in Montreal, Vasili Alexeev set a world record for the clean-and-jerk of 255 kg.

2-B1 $m = Vd = (10^{-2} \text{ cm}^3)(7.86 \text{ g/cm}^3) = 7.86 \times 10^{-2}$ g. We use the atomic weight of iron (Periodic Table, p. 805) and Avogadro's number:

$$N = \left(6.02 \times 10^{23} \frac{\text{atoms}}{\text{mole}}\right)\left(\frac{1 \text{ mole}}{55.847 \text{ g}}\right)(7.86 \times 10^{-2} \text{ g}) = 8.47 \times 10^{20} \text{ atoms}.$$

2-B2 (a) $(40 \times 10^3 \text{ g})\left(\frac{6.02 \times 10^{23} \text{ molecules}}{18 \text{ g}}\right) = 1.33 \times 10^{27}$ water molecules in the body.   (b) Assuming perfect mixing, the water in Socrates' libation has been greatly diluted: $N = \left(\frac{60 \text{ g}}{10^{24} \text{ g}}\right)(1.33 \times 10^{27}) = 80\ 000$ molecules.

2-B3 $(1.008 \text{ g})/(6.02 \times 10^{23}) = 1.67 \times 10^{-24}$ g. Strictly speaking, the atomic weight of neutral H should be decreased by the mass of one electron; this mass is only $1/1837$ of a proton mass and can be neglected, to 3 significant figures.

2-B4 $m = (10^6 \text{ atoms})\left(\frac{197 \text{ g/mole}}{6.02 \times 10^{23} \text{ atoms/mole}}\right) = 3.27 \times 10^{-16}$ g.

2-B5 $\left(\frac{0.05 \times 10^{-3} \text{ g}}{1 \text{ m}^3}\right)(450 \text{ cm}^3)\left(\frac{1 \text{ m}}{10^2 \text{ cm}}\right)^3\left(\frac{6.02 \times 10^{23} \text{ atoms}}{58.7 \text{ g}}\right) = 2.3 \times 10^{14}$ atoms.
Use the atomic weight of nickel from the Periodic Table, p. 805.

2-B6 Total mass is $(10 \text{ l})(1.00 \text{ kg/l}) + (5 \text{ l})(1.26 \text{ kg/l}) = 16.30$ kg; $d = (16.30 \text{ kg})/(15 \text{ l}) = 10.8$ kg/l; sp. grav. $= 10.8$.

2-B7 Volume of the coin is calculated to be 0.62344 cm^3.
(a) Canadian coin: $(0.62344 \text{ cm}^3)(8.90 \text{ g/cm}^3) = 5.549$ g
(b) U. S. coin: $\frac{1}{4}(0.62344 \text{ cm}^3)(8.90 \text{ g/cm}^3) = 1.406$ g
$\qquad\qquad \frac{3}{4}(0.62344 \text{ cm}^3)(8.93 \text{ g/cm}^3) = \underline{4.176 \text{ g}}$
$\qquad\qquad\qquad\qquad\qquad\qquad\qquad\qquad\quad 5.582$ g

The difference is 0.03 g, or 30 mg. Density values to 3 significant figures are adequate for this "yes or no" question.

2-B8 $(0.19)(10) + (0.81)(11) = 10.81$.

2-B9 (a) $(1000 \text{ cm}^3)(0.791 \text{ g/cm}^3) = 791$ g.   (b) $\left(\frac{6.02 \times 10^{23} \text{ molecules}}{46 \text{ g}}\right)(791 \text{ g})$
$= 1.04 \times 10^{25}$ molecules.

2-B10 $\left(\frac{0.238 \text{ kg}}{1 \text{ mole}}\right)\left(\frac{1 \text{ mole}}{6.02 \times 10^{23} \text{ atoms}}\right) = 3.95 \times 10^{-25}$ kg/atom.

2-B11 $238/0.0476 = 56/0.0112 = 5000$ in each box.

2-C1 $V = m/d = (2 \times 10^{30} \text{ kg})/(2 \times 10^{17} \text{ kg/m}^3) = 10^{13} \text{ m}^3$. From $V = \frac{1}{6}\pi D^3$, the diameter D of the sphere is 2.67×10^4 m, or 26.7 km.

2-C2   The thickness t is given by volume/area:

$$t = \left(\frac{5.00 \text{ cm}^3}{4 \times 10^3 \text{ m}^2} \right) \left(\frac{1 \text{ m}}{100 \text{ cm}} \right)^3 = 1.25 \times 10^{-9} \text{ m}$$

This is 12.5 angstroms. This molecular dimension is some 10 times larger than the separation of atomic planes in Fig. 2-1 because each molecule of the "organic oil" consists of many atoms. A thickness of 10–15 Å is usually obtained in the laboratory if oleic acid is allowed to spread out on a water surface.

Chapter 3   Kinematics—The Description of Motion

Questions

3-1   Equations (b) and (d) are dimensionally incorrect; (a) and (c) *may* be correct. Actually, only (c) is quantitatively correct.

3-2   You could only measure an average velocity $\Delta s / \Delta t$ over some small interval of time and of displacement. As $\Delta t \rightarrow 0$, uncertainties in both Δs and Δt would become greater. This has nothing to do with the Heisenberg uncertainty principle.

3-3   The odometer measures distance, a scalar quantity.

3-4   As seen from the plane, the package falls vertically downward. As seen from the automobile, the package travels in a parabolic path, with an initial horizontal velocity 20 m/s in a backward direction.

3-5   The runner's center of mass will follow a parabolic path; if his speed does not change, the horizontal component of velocity must decrease, and thus the center of mass will arrive at the bag later than if there had been no jump. However, if the runner dives at the bag, his finger tips may well reach the bag enough in advance of his center of mass to make the maneuver worthwhile.

Multiple Choice

3-6 (c);   3-7 (b);   3-8 (b);   3-9 (a);   3-10 (b);   3-11 (b).

Problems

3-A1   (a) $\dfrac{440 \text{ km}}{5.5 \text{ h}} = 80$ km/h;   (b) $\left(80 \dfrac{\text{km}}{\text{h}} \right) \left(\dfrac{1 \text{ mi}}{1.609 \text{ km}} \right) = 49.7$ mi/h;

     (c) $\left(80 \dfrac{\text{km}}{\text{h}} \right) \left(\dfrac{5280 \text{ ft}}{1.609 \text{ km}} \right) \left(\dfrac{1 \text{ h}}{3600 \text{ s}} \right) = 72.9$ ft/s.

3-A2 $s = vt = \left(88.5 \dfrac{\text{km}}{\text{h}} \right) \left(\dfrac{1000 \text{ m}}{1 \text{ km}} \right) \left(\dfrac{1 \text{ h}}{3600 \text{ s}} \right) (0.25 \text{ s}) = 6.15$ m.

3-A3 (a) $\left(4\ \dfrac{m}{day}\right)\left(\dfrac{1\ km}{1000\ m}\right)\left(\dfrac{1\ day}{24\ h}\right) = 1.67 \times 10^{-4}\ km/h$;

$\left(4\ \dfrac{m}{day}\right)\left(\dfrac{1\ mi}{1609\ m}\right)\left(\dfrac{1\ day}{24\ h}\right) = 1.04 \times 10^{-4}\ mi/h$;

$\left(4\ \dfrac{m}{day}\right)\left(\dfrac{1\ ft}{3.048\ m}\right)\left(\dfrac{1\ day}{86\ 400\ s}\right) = 1.52 \times 10^{-4}\ ft/s$;

(b) $a = \dfrac{\Delta v}{\Delta t} = \left(-3\ \dfrac{m}{day}\right) / (2\ min) = -1.50\ m/day\cdot min$;

$\left(-1.50\ \dfrac{m}{day\cdot min}\right)\left(\dfrac{1\ day}{86\ 400\ s}\right)\left(\dfrac{1\ min}{60\ s}\right) = -2.89 \times 10^{-7}\ m/s^{2}$.

3-A4 (a) 34 m/s;   (b) 0;   (c) 15 m/s.   [Estimate instantaneous velocities from the slope of a tangent to the graph; average velocity is the slope
of a chord drawn between two points.]

3-A5 (a) 20 m/s;   (b) 0.   See comments on **3-A4**.

3-A6 (a) At $t = 2.5$ s;   (b) at $t = 0.5$ s;   (c) yes, at about $t = 2$ s, 3.5 s, 4.8 s,
5.7 s;   (d) 2.4 m/s^{2};   (e) about 28 m.   [The displacement in part
(e) is found by graphical integration: from $t = 0$ to $t = 4$, we count about 28
squares under the graph (with due allowance for portions of squares); each
square is $(2\ m/s)(0.5\ s) = 1.0$ m. Some data on tests of dolphins are given
by T. G. Lang and K. Pryor in "Hydrodynamic Performance of Porpoises
(*Stenella attenuata*)," *Science*, **152**, 531 (1966).]

3-A7 $\dfrac{(8.4 - 12.0)\ m/s}{180\ s} = 0.02\ m/s^{2}$, westward.

3-A8 (a) $v = v_0 + at = (9.8\ m/s^{2})(3\ s) = 29.4\ m/s$;   (b) $v = (9.8\ m/s^{2})(4\ s) = 39.2$
m/s;   (c) $v_{av} = \tfrac{1}{2}(v_0 + v) = \tfrac{1}{2}(29.4 + 39.2)\ m/s = 34.3\ m/s$;   (d) $s = v_{av}t$
$= (34.3\ m/s)(1\ s) = 34.3$ m.

3-A9 (a) Use $v_{av} = s/t$; speeds are $(100\ m)/(10.0\ s) = 10.00\ m/s$, and $(100\ m)/$
$(10.5\ s) = 9.52\ m/s$.   (b) After 10.0 s, the slow runner has moved through
a distance $(9.52\ m/s)(10.0\ s) = 95.2$ m; the runners are separated by 4.8 m.

3-A10 (a) $v = 12.8\ m/s + (-9.8\ m/s^{2})(1\ s) = +3.0\ m/s$ (upward);   (b) $v = 12.8$
m/s $+ (-9.8\ m/s^{2})(2\ s) = -6.8\ m/s$ (downward).

3-A12 $F_x = 11.3$ lb; $v_x = 15.45$ ft/s.

3-A15 (a) 18 blocks;   (b) 1.4 blocks SW from the starting point.   [Read the
problem carefully and draw a street map of the city. Main Street runs E–W;
Center Avenue runs N–S.]

3-A16 $(300\ m/s)\cos 60° = 150\ m/s$.

3-A17 (a) $(320\ km/h)\cos 45° = 212\ km/h$;   (b) $-212\ km/h$.

3-A18 (a) 40 ft/s;   (b) 50 ft/s;   (c) $(30\ ft)/(40\ ft/s) = 0.75$ s.

3-A19 (a) 3600 m/s + 470 m/s = 4070 m/s;   (b) 3600 m/s − 470 m/s = 3130 m/s;
(c) so they can be aimed eastward, out over the Atlantic.

3-B1 (a) Total time was $\dfrac{800\ km}{500\ km/h} + 0.4\ h + \dfrac{800\ km}{600\ km/h} = 3.33$ h; average speed

was $\dfrac{1600\ km}{3.33\ h} = 480\ km/h$;   (b) The plane's air speed was 550 km/h, and
the wind velocity was 50 km/h.

3-B2 350 m/s.   [The bullet takes 0.25 s to reach the target; the sound travels
175 m in 0.50 s.]

3-B3 Time to fall: $s = \tfrac{1}{2}gt^{2}$; $t = \sqrt{\dfrac{2s}{g}} = \sqrt{\dfrac{2(30.0\ m)}{9.8\ m/s^{2}}} = 2.47$ s; time for sound to

return: $t = \dfrac{30\ m}{340\ m/s} = 0.09$ s; total time is 2.56 s.

3-B4 (a) $\left(45.06 \dfrac{m}{s}\right)\left(\dfrac{1 \text{ mi/h}}{0.4470 \text{ m/s}}\right) = 100.8$ mi/h;   (b) $\dfrac{18.5 \text{ m}}{45.06 \text{ m/s}} = 0.411$ s;

(c) $a = \dfrac{v^2}{2s} = \dfrac{(45.06 \text{ m/s})^2}{2(0.08 \text{ m})} = 1.27 \times 10^4 \text{ m/s}^2.$ [Thrown pitches passing over the plate were measured under game conditions on September 7, 1974 by scientists from the Electronics Research Division of Rockwell International. Infrared radiation of wavelength 10.59 μm from a low-power CO_2 laser was beamed from the press box and reflected straight back by the approaching ball. The Doppler frequency shift measured the component of velocity parallel to the beam direction; the angles needed to determine the actual velocity of the ball were obtained by direct tape-measure survey of Anaheim Stadium.]

3-B5 $v^2 = v_0^2 + 2as$; $s = \dfrac{(88 \text{ ft/s})^2 - (44 \text{ ft/s})^2}{2(4.4 \text{ ft/s}^2)} = 660$ ft.

3-B6 $t = \dfrac{19 \text{ m/s} - 9 \text{ m/s}}{2.5 \text{ m/s}^2} = 4.0$ s; $s = v_{av}t = (14 \text{ m/s})(4 \text{ s}) = 56$ m.

3-B7 $v^2 = v_0^2 + 2as$; $0 = v_0^2 + 2(-9.8 \text{ m/s}^2)(2.4 \text{ m})$; $v_0 = 6.86$ m/s.

3-B8   The first stone has fallen for $(14.7 \text{ m/s})/(9.8 \text{ m/s}^2) = 1.50$ s, and during this time has fallen $\frac{1}{2}(9.8 \text{ m/s}^2)(1.5 \text{ s})^2 = 11.025$ m. The second stone, in 0.50 s, has fallen $\frac{1}{2}(9.8 \text{ m/s}^2)(0.5 \text{ s})^2 = 1.225$ m. The distance between the stones is 11.025 m − 1.225 m = 9.80 m.

3-B9   (a) 36 ft;   (b) 1.5 s;   (c) 3.0 s;   (d) 48 ft/s.

3-B10   If the downward direction is chosen to be the + direction, then   (a) $v = v_0 + at = 6 \text{ ft/s} + (32 \text{ ft/s}^2)(2 \text{ s}) = 70$ ft/s;   (b) $s = v_0t + \frac{1}{2}at^2 = (6 \text{ ft/s})(2 \text{ s}) + \frac{1}{2}(32 \text{ ft/s}^2)(2 \text{ s})^2 = 76$ ft. Since the helicopter has descended 12 ft, the bag is now 64 ft below the helicopter. Alternatively, relative to the helicopter $v_0 = 0$, hence the relative separation is given by $\frac{1}{2}(32 \text{ ft/s}^2)(2 \text{ s})^2 = 64$ ft.

3-B11   (a) 58 ft/s (downward);   (b) 64 ft below the helicopter.   It is instructive to note that relative to the helicopter, the displacement is the same as in Prob. **3-B10**, since the initial velocity relative to the helicopter is 0 in both problems.

3-B12 $v^2 = v_0^2 + 2as$; $0^2 = v_0^2 + 2(-9.8 \text{ m/s}^2)(8 \text{ m})$; $v_0 = 12.5$ m/s.

3-B13   Choose the + direction to be upward (the opposite choice gives the same results). The times are most easily calculated in two steps. For the ball thrown downward,

$$v = \sqrt{v_0^2 + 2as} = \sqrt{(64 \text{ ft/s})^2 + 2(-32 \text{ ft/s}^2)(-80 \text{ ft})} = 96 \text{ ft/s}.$$

Thus $v_{av} = \frac{1}{2}(64 + 96) \text{ ft/s} = 80$ ft/s; $t = s/v_{av} = (80 \text{ ft})/(80 \text{ ft/s}) = 1$ s. For the ball thrown upward, the height of rise is found from $v^2 = v_0^2 + 2as$; $0^2 = (64 \text{ ft/s})^2 + 2(-32 \text{ ft/s}^2)s$; $s = 64$ ft above the balcony. This ball therefore falls 144 ft to the ground, in a time given by $t = \sqrt{2s/a} = \sqrt{2(-144 \text{ ft})/(-32 \text{ ft/s}^2)} = 3$ s. When it strikes the ground its speed is $\sqrt{2as} = \sqrt{2(-144 \text{ ft})(-32 \text{ ft/s}^2)} = 96$ ft/s. (The two times can also be found as the positive roots of quadratic equations based on $s = v_0t + \frac{1}{2}at^2$.) In summary: (a) The second ball strikes the ground 4 s after the first one, and   (b) each ball strikes the ground with a speed of 96 ft/s.   (c) Using $s = v_0t + \frac{1}{2}at^2$ we can calculate the position of each ball at $t = 1$ s; the first ball is at − 80 ft (just striking the ground), and the second ball is at +48 ft. The balls are 128 ft apart. [After studying Chap. 6, the student will see that the two answers in part (b) are equal by the law of conservation of energy.]

3-B14 $t = \sqrt{2(0.25 \text{ ft})/(32 \text{ ft/s}^2)} = 0.125$ s.

3-B15 To acquire a speed of 9.8 m/s, the car would have to fall from a height given by $s = (v^2 - v_0^2)/2a = (9.8 \text{ m/s})^2/(19.6 \text{ m/s}^2) = 4.9$ m.

3-B16 At impact, $v = \sqrt{2(81 \text{ ft})(32 \text{ ft/s}^2)} = 72$ ft/s. The ball rebounds at $\frac{3}{4}(72 \text{ ft/s})$ = 54 ft/s. Height of rise is $s = (v^2 - v_0^2)/2a = -(54 \text{ ft/s})^2/2(-32 \text{ ft/s}^2)$ = 45.6 ft.

3-B17 Time to accelerate is $t = (44 \text{ ft/s})/(6 \text{ ft/s}^2) = 7.333$ s; during this time the car travels $s = v^2/2a = (44 \text{ ft/s})^2/2(6 \text{ ft/s}^2) = 161.33$ ft. Time to stop: $t = (44 \text{ ft/s})/(8 \text{ ft/s}^2) = 5.50$ s; during this time the car travels $s = (44 \text{ ft/s})^2/2(8 \text{ ft/s}^2) = 121.00$ ft. Finally, we find that the car travels at constant speed of 44 ft/s for a distance $(800 - 161.33 - 121.00)$ ft = 517.67 ft; this requires $(517.67 \text{ ft})/(44 \text{ ft/s}) = 11.77$ s. The total time is $(7.33 + 11.77 + 5.50)$ s = 24.6 s.

3-B18 $a = v^2/2s = (12 \text{ m/s})^2/2(1 \text{ m}) = 72 \text{ m/s}^2$.

3-B19 (a) v_{av} was $(225 \text{ m})/(5 \text{ s}) = 45$ m/s. Hence, using $v_{av} = (v_0 + v)/2$ we find $v_0 = 2v_{av} - v = 2(45 \text{ m/s}) - 30 \text{ m/s} = 60$ m/s.
(b) $a = (v - v_0)/t = (30 \text{ m/s} - 60 \text{ m/s})/(5 \text{ s}) = -6 \text{ m/s}^2$.

3-B20 At the base of the mast. This question is discussed again in Sec. 7-3, Galilean Relativity, on pp. 151-52.

Prob. 3-B21

3-B21 v_{AE} = velocity of air relative to earth = ?
v_{PE} = velocity of plane relative to earth
        = 226 km/h, NE
v_{PA} = velocity of plane relative to air
        = 160 km/h, eastward.
The vector diagram must be constructed so the sequence of subscripts is correct: $v_{PA} + v_{AE}$ = v_{PE}. The diagram shows that v_{AE} = 160 km/h, northward.

3-B22 The vector sum is $v_{HA} + v_{AE} = v_{HE}$. From the diagram, (a) v_{HE} = 75 km/h, 37° E of N; (b) (75 km/h)(0.20 h) = 15 km.

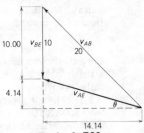
Prob. 3-B22

3-B23 From the vector diagram, $\tan \theta = 4.14/14.14$; $\theta = 16.3°$. $v_{AE} = \sqrt{(14.14)^2 + (4.14)^2} = 14.7$ m/s, 16° N of W.

3-B24 Draw a vector diagram of velocities to find v_{SE}, the velocity of the swimmer relative to the earth. (a) $\theta = 30°$; swimmer heads 30° upstream. (b) $v_{SE} = \sqrt{3} = 1.73$ m/s; (c) $t = (320)/(1.73 \text{ m/s}) = 185$ s; (d) time to swim 320 m downstream is $(320 \text{ m})/(3 \text{ m/s})$ = 107 s; time to swim 320 m upstream is $(320 \text{ m})/(1 \text{ m/s}) = 320$ s. Total time for the round trip is 427 s. Round trip straight across and back requires 2(185 s) = 370 s. Straight across and back is 57 s faster. [This problem serves as background for the discussion of the Michelson-Morley experiment (p. 154).]

Prob. 3-B23

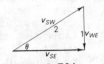
Prob. 3-B24

3-B25 The swimmer's velocity relative to the water is $\sqrt{5}$ = 2.23 m/s; the distance is $(320\text{ m})(\sqrt{5}/2)$ = $160\sqrt{5}$ m. Time to cross is $(160\sqrt{5}\text{ m})/(\sqrt{5}\text{ m/s})$ = 160 s. More simply, the eastward component of velocity is just 2 m/s, and hence to travel 320 m eastward requires $(320\text{ m})/(2\text{ m/s})$ = 160 s.

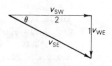

Prob. 3-B25

3-B26 $t = \sqrt{2s/a} = \sqrt{2(0.75\text{ m})/(9.8\text{ m/s}^2)}$ = 0.391 s. Range is $v_0 t = (0.6\text{ m/s})(0.391\text{ s})$ = 0.234 m.

3-B27 (a) To reach the highest point, where $v_y = 0$, requires 0.30 s. Using $v = v_0 + at$ gives $0 = v_{0y} + (-9.8\text{ m/s}^2)(0.30\text{ s})$; $v_{0y} = 2.94$ m/s. (b) $H = \frac{1}{2}at^2 = \frac{1}{2}(9.8\text{ m/s}^2)(0.30\text{ s})^2$ = 0.441 m. (c) $v_{0y}/v_{0x} = \tan 30°$, whence $v_{0x} = (2.94\text{ m/s})/(\tan 30°)$ = 5.09 m/s. The range is $R = v_{0x}t = (5.09\text{ m/s})(0.60\text{ s})$ = 3.06 m.

3-B28 The bullet is in the air for $t = (300\text{ m})/(600\text{ m/s})$ = 0.50 s. During this time the bullet falls $s = \frac{1}{2}at^2 = \frac{1}{2}(9.8\text{ m/s}^2)(0.50\text{ s})^2$ = 1.23 m. The bullet strikes a point 1.23 m below the target.

3-B29 The time of flight is twice the time to fall 2.54 cm (1 in.); $2\sqrt{2(2.54\text{ cm})/(980\text{ cm/s}^2)}$ = 0.144 s. $v_{0x} = (100\text{ m})/0.144\text{ s}$ = 694 m/s. Strictly speaking, one should also take account of the vertical component of the velocity: $v_{0y} = \sqrt{2gH} = \sqrt{2(980\text{ cm/s}^2)(2.54\text{ cm})}$ = 70 cm/s. The muzzle velocity is therefore $\sqrt{(694)^2 + (0.7)^2}$ m/s, but this is essentially the same as the horizontal component.

3-B30 (a) $t = \sqrt{2h/g} = \sqrt{2(3\text{ m})/(9.8\text{ m/s}^2)}$ = 0.7825 s; $R = (2.5\text{ m/s})(0.7825\text{ s})$ = 1.96 m. (b) $v_x = 2.50$ m/s; $v_y = \sqrt{2(9.8\text{ m/s}^2)(3\text{ m})}$ = 7.67 m/s.

3-B31 (a) $t = \sqrt{2s/a} = \sqrt{2(100\text{ ft})/(32\text{ ft/s}^2)}$ = 2.50 s; (b) from the 45° angle, the range is seen to be 100 ft. Thus, $v_0(2.50\text{ s})$ = 100 ft; v_0 = 40 ft/s. (c) $v_y = (32\text{ ft/s}^2)(2.50\text{ s})$ = 80 ft/s; v_x = 40 ft/s; $\tan\theta = v_x/v_y$, whence θ = 27° from the vertical.

3-B32 From Eq. 3-18, $R = (v_0^2/g)\sin 2\theta$, which is a maximum for θ = 45° (see Prob. 3-C16). Thus, $v_0^2 = Rg$. If the boy throws the ball upward at v_0, the height of rise would be given by $v_0^2 = 2gH'$; $H' = v_0^2/2g = Rg/2g = R/2$.

3-B33 $t = (10\text{ m})/(8\text{ m/s})$ = 1.25 s; $H = \frac{1}{2}(9.8\text{ m/s}^2)(1.25\text{ s})^2$ = 7.66 m.

3-B34 (a) $t = 2(19.6\text{ m/s})/(9.8\text{ m/s}^2)$ = 4.0 s; (b) $R = (40\text{ m/s})(4.0\text{ s})$ = 160 m; (c) $H = v_{0y}^2/2g = (19.6\text{ m/s})^2/2(9.8\text{ m/s}^2)$ = 19.6 m; (d) $v_0 = \sqrt{(19.6)^2 + (40)^2}$ = 44.5 m/s.

3-B35 Time to maximum height is 1 s; $v_{0y} = (9.8\text{ m/s}^2)(1\text{ s})$ = 9.8 m/s. $v_{0x} = (40\text{ m})/(2\text{ s})$ = 20.0 m/s. $\tan\theta = (9.8\text{ m/s})/(20.0\text{ m/s})$, whence θ = 26°. $v = \sqrt{(9.8)^2 + (20.0)^2}$ = 22.3 m/s, 26° above the horizontal.

3-B36 Equate the time for horizontal motion to the time for vertical motion:
$$\frac{42\text{ m}}{v_0\cos 20°} = \frac{2v_0\sin 20°}{9.8\text{ m/s}^2}; \quad v_0 = 25.3\text{ m/s}.$$

3-B37 (a) Time to reach maximum height is $t = \sqrt{2s/a} = \sqrt{2(0.60\text{ m})/(9.8\text{ m/s}^2)}$ = 0.350 s. $v_{0y} = (9.8\text{ m/s}^2)(0.350\text{ s})$ = 3.43 m/s; $v_0 = v_{0y}/\sin 20° = (3.43\text{ m/s})/\sin 20°$ = 10.0 m/s. Next we find $v_{0x} = v_0\cos 20°$ = 9.42 m/s. (b) Time in air is 0.700 s; $R = (9.42\text{ m/s})(0.700\text{ s})$ = 6.59 m.

3-B38 The range, for any given angle of takeoff, is proportional to v_0^2/g (Eq. 3-18). Hence, since g is $\frac{1}{6}$ as much, the range is 6 times as great. (The jumper is in the air 6 times as long.)

3-B39 (a) The time in the air is not affected by the mid-flight correction. From $v = v_0 + at$ we find $t = (160\ \text{ft/s})/(32\ \text{ft/s}^2) = 5$ s to the top; total time in the air is 10 s. (b) The rocket moves for 5 s at a horizontal speed of 160 ft/s and lands 800 ft downrange. (c) At $t = 7$ s, $y = v_{0y}t + \frac{1}{2}at^2 = (160\ \text{ft/s})(7\ \text{s})$ $+ \frac{1}{2}(-32\ \text{ft/s}^2)(7\ \text{s})^2 = 336$ ft; (it has fallen 64 ft below its maximum height in the 2 s after firing the retrorocket). Also, $x = v_{0x}t = (160\ \text{ft/s})(2\ \text{s}) = 320$ ft. The rocket is 336 ft above the ground, 320 ft downrange.

3-C1 Yes, the passenger can catch the train, in 6 s. If displacements are measured from the passenger's initial position, we have $s_1 = 8t$ (for passenger) and $s_2 = 30 + 0t + \frac{1}{2}(1)t^2$ (for train). Equate s_1 and s_2, obtaining $t^2 - 16t + 60 = 0$; $t = 6$ s or 10 s. The second answer is the time at which the rear end of the train would catch up with the passenger if he kept on running instead of climbing aboard at the earliest opportunity.

3-C2 No, he is 1 s too slow. He runs the first $(5280 - 1480)$ ft in 190 s at a constant speed of $3800/190 = 20$ ft/s. During the next 10 s he runs a distance $s = v_0t + \frac{1}{2}at^2 = (20\ \text{ft/s})(10\ \text{s}) + \frac{1}{2}(1\ \text{ft/s}^2)(10\ \text{s})^2 = 250$ ft. His final speed is $v = v_0 + at = 20\ \text{ft/s} + (1\ \text{ft/s}^2)(10\ \text{s}) = 30$ ft/s. He now travels the remaining 1230 ft at 30 ft/s, which requires 41 s. Total time is $(190 + 10 + 41)\ \text{s} = 4$ min, 1 s.

3-C3 (a) The car has to travel 75 ft farther than the truck, during the time required to pull alongside. $70t + \frac{1}{2}(6)t^2 = 70t + 75$; $t = 5$ s. (b) $v = v_0 + at = 70\ \text{ft/s} + (6\ \text{ft/s}^2)(5\ \text{s}) = 100$ ft/s; this is 30 ft/s relative to the truck. (c) $s = v_0t + \frac{1}{2}at^2 = (70\ \text{ft/s})(5\ \text{s}) + \frac{1}{2}(6\ \text{ft/s}^2)(5\ \text{s})^2 = 425$ ft. (d) $s = v_0t = (70\ \text{ft/s})(5\ \text{s}) = 350$ ft.

3-C4 $s = v_0t + \frac{1}{2}at^2$, also $v_0 = v - at$. Combining these to eliminate v_0 gives, after simplification, $s = vt - \frac{1}{2}at^2$.

3-C5 (a) $s = v_0t + \frac{1}{2}at^2$ yields $48 = 64t - 16t^2$, or $t^2 - 4t + 3 = 0$. The two roots of this quadratic equation are $t = 1$ s, $t = 3$ s. (b) $v^2 = v_0^2 + 2as$ yields $v = \pm\sqrt{(64)^2 + 2(-32)(48)} = \pm\sqrt{1024} = \pm32$ ft/s. (c) The velocity is +32 ft/s when the ball passes the 48 ft level on the way up (at $t = 1$ s), and is -32 ft/s when it passes the 48 ft level on the way down (at $t = 3$ s).

3-C6 A straightforward method uses two equations. Let t be the time to the top of the window. Then $h = 4.9t^2$; also $h + 1.8 = 4.9(t + 0.1)^2$. Solve simultaneously to get $t = 1.787$ s and $h = 15.64$ m. Another method uses $v_0 = \sqrt{2gh}$ for the velocity at the top of the window. Then, from $s = v_0t + \frac{1}{2}at^2$ we have $1.8 = (\sqrt{2(9.8)h})(0.1) + \frac{1}{2}(9.8)(0.1)^2$, which yields $h = 15.64$ m.

3-C7 For the vertical motion, $v_{0y} = (8.00\ \text{m/s})\sin 30° = 4.00$ m/s. The final vertical displacement is -3 m. Thus, from $s = v_0t + \frac{1}{2}at^2$, we obtain $-3 = 4t + \frac{1}{2}(-9.8)t^2$; $4.9t^2 - 4t - 3 = 0$; $t = 1.29$ s. Ignore the negative solution for t, which could refer to an imaginary motion of the diver up from the water to pass the springboard at $t = 0$.

3-C8 Here $v_{0x} = 10\sin 30° = 6$ ft/s; $v_{0y} = 10\cos 37° = 8$ ft/s. $-4 = 6t - 16t^2$; $t = 0.7215$ s. $R = (8\ \text{ft/s})(0.7215\ \text{s}) = 5.77$ ft.

3-C9 Here $v_{0y} = 98\sin 30° = 49$ m/s. Consider only the vertical motion. $-120 = 49t + \frac{1}{2}(-9.8)t^2$; the positive root is $t = 12.0$ s.

3-C10 $v_{0x} = 24\cos 30° = 20.78$ m/s; $v_{0y} = 24\sin 30° = 12.00$ m/s. For the vertical motion, $-20 = 12t + \frac{1}{2}(-9.8)t^2$; $t = 3.587$ s. (a) Range $= (20.78\ \text{m/s})(3.587\ \text{s}) = 74.5$ m. (b) $v_y^2 = v_{0y}^2 + 2ay = (12\ \text{m/s})^2 + 2(-9.8\ \text{m/s}^2)(-20\ \text{m}) = 536$ m^2/s^2. Also, $v_x^2 = v_{0x}^2 = (20.78\ \text{m/s})^2 = 432\ \text{m}^2/\text{s}^2$. The final speed is $v = \sqrt{v_x^2 + v_y^2} = \sqrt{432 + 536} = 31.1$ m/s.

3-C11 The vertical rise of the ball is 3.048 m $- 2.000$ m $= 1.048$ m.

vertical motion: $1.048 = (v_0 \sin 60°)t + \frac{1}{2}(-9.8)t^2$

horizontal motion: $6.000 = (v_0 \cos 60°)t$

Solve simultaneously (substitute t from the second equation into the first equation) to obtain $v_0 = 8.69$ m/s.

3-C12 $t = \sqrt{2h/g} = \sqrt{2(1\text{ m})/(9.8\text{ m/s}^2)} = 0.452$ s.   (a) $v_0 = (1.2\text{ m})/(0.452\text{ s}) = 2.66$ m/s.   (b) $v_x = 2.66$ m/s (at all times). When the angle is 45°, v_y is also 2.66 m/s. Then $s = v_y^2/2g = (2.66\text{ m/s})^2/2(9.8\text{ m/s}^2) = 0.36$ m below the table top. The ball is 0.64 m above the floor.

3-C13 Using data from Example 3-14, we have $x = 20t$, $y = -16t^2$, and the equation of the path is $y = -\frac{1}{25}x^2$, a parabola.

3-C14 The height of rise involves only v_{0y}, which is $v_0 \sin \theta$. Using $v^2 = v_0^2 + 2as$ gives $0^2 = (v_0 \sin \theta)^2 + 2(-g)H$, which yields $H = (v_0^2/2g) \sin^2 \theta$.

3-C15 $\tan \phi = \frac{1}{2} \tan \theta$.   [$\tan \phi = H/(R/2) = 2H/R$, where H is shown in Fig. 3-25. Calculate H from $(v_0 \sin \theta)^2 = 2gH$; R is given by Equation 3-18 on p. 47. Use $\sin \theta/\cos \theta = \tan \theta$.]

3-C16 Using the identity $\sin 2\theta = 2 \sin \theta \cos \theta$, Eq. 3-18 becomes $R = (v_0^2/g) \sin 2\theta$. For a given v_0, the range is a maximum if $\sin 2\theta = 1$, whence $\theta = 45°$.

3-C17 (a) m, m/s, m/s².   (b) $v = ds/dt = 40 - 10t$ (see Table, p. 797). At $t = 2$, $v = 20$ m/s.   (c) $s(3) - s(2) = 275$ m $- 260$ m $= 15$ m.   (d) $a = d^2s/dt^2 = -10$ m/s².

3-C18 (a) 17.4;   (b) 17.04;   (c) 17.008. The derivative at $t = 3$ s is $ds/dt = 8t - 7 = 24 - 7 = 17$ m/s (exactly).

3-C19 Formal integration (Table, p. 798) gives

$$\int_2^3 (t^2 - 3)\,dt = \left[\frac{t^3}{3} - 3t\right]_2^3 = \left(\frac{27}{3} - 9\right) - \left(\frac{8}{3} - 6\right) = 3.33 \text{ m}.$$

Chapter 4   Dynamics

Questions

4-1 The essential point of this question and the next three questions is that Newton's third law applies to forces which mutually act on *different* bodies. In Ques. 4-1, the statement is false, because it is an example of the second law (both forces act on the book). In Ques. 4-2a, this *is* an example of the third law. In Ques. 4-3, the answer is "yes," but only one of the forces acts *on the cart*, so there is a net force on the cart. In Ques. 4-4, the net force on the horse is forward, since the force of the ground on the horse is greater than the force of the cart on the horse.

4-5 Mass: kilogram, gram. Weight: pound, dyne, newton, ounce.

4-6 The object of greater weight also had greater inertia, in strict proportion, and so received the same acceleration.

4-7 To compare weights, a spring balance or an equal-arm balance could be used. These would also be suitable for comparing gravitational mass, since m in $W = mg$ refers to gravitational mass. Inertial masses can be compared directly only through experiments involving Newton's second law directly (as in Eq. 4-3) or indirectly (the momentum experiment on p. 118, or the mass balance on p. 215).

4-8   On earth, the weight of the ball bearings causes just enough frictional force (see p. 88) so that the net force is zero, and no motion takes place. In interstellar space, the balls essentially "float" on the metal surface, and the gravitational attraction between the balls is not balanced out by friction. If two steel balls, each of radius 1 cm, are initially at rest with their centers 20 cm apart, the time for a collision (in interstellar space) works out to be about 13 hours.

4-9   Weight on earth = (36 kg)(9.8 m/s^2); weight on moon is $\frac{1}{6}$ as much, i.e., 58.8 N. Mass on moon is same as on earth, i.e., 36 kg.

4-10   (a) Only if friction is negligible would the two tensions be the same. With friction, for any car the tension F_1 in the forward coupling is greater than F_2 in the rear coupling, so that $F_1 = F_2 + f$, and net $F = 0$.   (b) If the train is accelerating in a forward direction, $F_1 - F_2$ must be even greater than in part (a). If the train has negative acceleration (e.g., coasting to a halt), it *is* possible for the tensions in all couplings to be the same, namely, zero.

4-11   Force of log acting on the ground is 800 N in a forward direction.

4-12   During a quick jerk, the inertia of the ball keeps it from moving far enough to snap the top thread. During a steady pull, the tension in the top thread always exceeds that in the bottom thread by an amount equal to the weight of the ball.

4-13   By Newton's third law, the force of the monkey on the mirror is equal and opposite to the force of the mirror on the monkey. The pulley transmits the force of the monkey on the mirror and reverses its direction. Hence, the monkey and the mirror always have accelerations that are equal in both magnitude and direction. Even if the monkey lets go and freely falls, the mirror also freely falls.

4-14   The two triangles have equal bases, AB and CD, and their altitudes (the dotted line through the sun) are the same.

Multiple Choice

4-15 (c);   4-16 (a);   4-17 (b);   4-18 (a);   4-19 (b);   4-20 (c).

Problems

4-A1   Net F = 12 000 dyn − 9000 dyn = 3000 dyn, downward.
4-A3   Net F = 5000 lb − 1200 lb = 3800 lb, upward.
4-A4 a = (20 N)/(5 kg) = 4 m/s^2.
4-A5 m = (200 dyn)/(50 cm/s^2) = 4 g.
4-A6 F = (2.5 kg)(4 m/s^2) = 10 N.
4-A7 F = (80 g)(30 cm/s^2) = 2400 dyn.

4-A8   Here and elsewhere it is convenient to consider the gravitational field strength at the earth's surface to be 9.8 N/kg, which is equivalent to the acceleration of a freely falling body of 9.8 m/s^2.
$m = (98\ \text{N})/(9.8\ \text{N/kg}) = 10\ \text{kg};\ a = F/m = (40\ \text{N})/(10\ \text{kg}) = 4\ \text{m/s}^2$.

4-A9   Use $m = W/g$ for the mass of the car.
$$a = \frac{F}{m} = \frac{360\ \text{lb}}{(640\ \text{lb})/(32\ \text{ft/s}^2)} = 18\ \text{ft/s}^2.$$

4-A10 $F = ma = (40\ \text{kg})(-0.5\ \text{m/s}^2) = -20\ \text{N}$.

4-A11 $F = 2^2$ as much, i.e., $4 \times 200\ \text{N} = 800\ \text{N}$.

4-A12   Distance is doubled; F is $\frac{1}{4}$ as much, i.e., $\frac{1}{4}(132\ \text{N}) = 33\ \text{N}$.

4-B1 $a = (\text{net } F)/m = (19.6\ \text{N} - 8.6\ \text{N})/(2\ \text{kg}) = 5.5\ \text{m/s}^2$, downward.

4-B2 $\dfrac{\text{net } F}{W/g} = \dfrac{180\ \text{lb} - 135\ \text{lb}}{(180\ \text{lb})/(32\ \text{ft/s}^2)} = 8\ \text{ft/s}^2$, downward.

4-B3   (a) $\dfrac{\text{net } F}{W/g} = \dfrac{9000\ \text{lb} - 8000\ \text{lb}}{(8000\ \text{lb})/(32\ \text{ft/s}^2)} = 4\ \text{ft/s}^2$, upward;   (b) $s = \frac{1}{2}at^2$
$= \frac{1}{2}(4\ \text{ft/s}^2)(2\ \text{s})^2 = 8\ \text{ft}$.

4-B4   (a) $a = (\text{net } F)/m = (800\ \text{N} - 300\ \text{N})/(2000\ \text{kg}) = 0.25\ \text{m/s}^2$;   (b) $s = v_0 t$
$+ \frac{1}{2}at^2 = (20\ \text{m/s})(8\ \text{s}) + \frac{1}{2}(0.25\ \text{m/s}^2)(8\ \text{s})^2 = 168\ \text{m}$.

4-B5   (a) $v_{av} = 15\ \text{km/h};\ s = v_{av}t = (15\ \text{km/h})(21/60\ \text{h}) = 5.25\ \text{km}$;

(b) $a = \dfrac{v^2 - v_0^2}{2s} = \dfrac{0^2 - (30\ \text{km/h})^2}{2(5.25\ \text{km})} = 85.7\ \text{km/h}^2 = \left(85.7\ \dfrac{\text{km}}{\text{h}^2}\right)\left(\dfrac{1\ \text{h}}{3600\ \text{s}}\right)^2\left(\dfrac{10^3\ \text{m}}{1\ \text{km}}\right)$

$= 6.61 \times 10^{-3}\ \text{m/s}^2$. Net $F = ma = (2.50 \times 10^8\ \text{kg})(6.61 \times 10^{-3}\ \text{m/s}^2) = 1.65$
$\times 10^6\ \text{N}$. The force of friction is 1650 kN. The problem of stopping a large supertanker in case of emergency is a serious one. As we see from this problem, the tanker cannot be stopped in less than a few kilometers. It will be useful to return to this problem after studying Chap. 6, using Newton's second law in a different form:
$$\text{impulse} = \text{change of momentum}$$
$$Ft = \Delta(mv)$$
$$F(21\ \text{min})\left(\frac{60\ \text{s}}{1\ \text{min}}\right) = (2.50 \times 10^8\ \text{kg})\left(30\ \frac{\text{km}}{\text{h}}\right)\left(\frac{10^3\ \text{m}}{1\ \text{km}}\right)\left(\frac{1\ \text{h}}{3600\ \text{s}}\right)$$
$$F = 1.65 \times 10^6\ \text{N}$$

4-B6   *Panic stop*: $a = (-3000\ \text{N})/(1000\ \text{kg}) = -3\ \text{m/s}^2$; distance to stop is
$$s = \frac{v^2 - v_0^2}{2a} = \frac{0^2 - (10\ \text{m/s})^2}{2(-3\ \text{m/s}^2)} = 16.7\ \text{m}$$
Thus a panic stop is impossible within the allotted 15 m.
Step on the gas: $a = (+1000\ \text{N})/(1000\ \text{kg}) = +1\ \text{m/s}^2$. To clear the intersection, the driver must travel $15 + 55 = 70$ m in 6 s. Calculate the distance the driver can travel in 6 s:
$s = v_0 t + \frac{1}{2}at^2 = (10\ \text{m/s})(6\ \text{s}) + \frac{1}{2}(1\ \text{m/s}^2)(6\ \text{s})^2 = 78\ \text{m}$
The car is 8 m past the intersection when the light goes red. Alternatively, one can calculate the time required to clear the intersection, which turns out to be 5.49 s (0.51 s to spare).

4-B7 $F = ma = (0.06\ \text{kg})\left(\dfrac{70\ \text{m/s}}{2 \times 10^{-4}\ \text{s}}\right) = 2.1 \times 10^4\ \text{N} = 21\ \text{kN}$.

4-B8 $v_1 = \sqrt{2gh} = \sqrt{2(9.8\ \text{m/s}^2)(30\ \text{m})} = -24.25\ \text{m/s}$ (downward).
$v_2 = (0.80)(24.25\ \text{m/s}) = +19.45\ \text{m/s}$ (upward). The change in velocity is
$+43.65\ \text{m/s}$. Now find the force: $F = ma = (0.5\ \text{kg})\left(\dfrac{43.65\ \text{m/s}}{2 \times 10^{-3}\ \text{s}}\right) = 1.09$
$\times 10^4\ \text{N} = 10.9\ \text{kN}$.

4-B9 $a = v^2/2s = (800 \text{ m/s})^2/2(0.8 \text{ m}) = 4 \times 10^5 \text{ m/s}^2$; $F = (10^{-2} \text{ kg})(4 \times 10^5 \text{ m/s}^2)$ $= 4 \times 10^3 \text{ N}$.

4-B10 (a) $v_0 = (5 \text{ m})/(0.2 \text{ s}) = 25 \text{ m/s}$; $a = v^2/2s = (25 \text{ m/s})^2/2(0.8 \text{ m}) = 390 \text{ m/s}^2$; $F = ma = (0.60 \text{ kg})(390 \text{ m/s}^2) = 234 \text{ N}$. (b) During 0.2 s, the vertical droop of the ball is $s = \frac{1}{2}gt^2 = \frac{1}{2}(9.8 \text{ m/s}^2)(0.2 \text{ s})^2 = 0.196 \text{ m}$.

4-B11 (a) $a = \Delta v/\Delta t = (70 \text{ m/s})/(10^{-3} \text{ s}) = 7 \times 10^4 \text{ m/s}^2$; $F = ma = (0.160 \text{ kg})$ $\cdot(7 \times 10^4 \text{ m/s}^2) = 1.12 \times 10^4 \text{ N} = 11.2 \text{ kN}$. (b) By Newton's third law, the force of the ball on the bat is also of magnitude 11.2 kN.

4-B12 (a) $a = (150 \text{ N})/(0.05 \text{ kg}) = 3000 \text{ m/s}^2$; $v = \sqrt{2as} = \sqrt{2(3000 \text{ m/s}^2)(0.6 \text{ m})}$ $= 60 \text{ m/s}$. (b) If fired straight upward at 60 m/s, the height of rise of the arrow would be found from $v_0^2 = 2gh$; $h = (60 \text{ m/s})^2/2(9.8 \text{ m/s}^2) = 184 \text{ m}$.

4-B13 The acceleration is $v^2/2s = (40 \text{ ft/s})^2/2(20 \text{ ft}) = 40 \text{ ft/s}^2$. In this problem we use W/g for the mass.

(a) Force on the car: $F = (W/g)(a) = \left(\dfrac{3200 \text{ lb}}{32 \text{ ft/s}^2}\right)(40 \text{ ft/s}^2) = 4000 \text{ lb}$

(b) Force on the driver: $F = \left(\dfrac{160 \text{ lb}}{32 \text{ ft/s}^2}\right)(40 \text{ ft/s}^2) = 200 \text{ lb}$.

4-B14 $F = ma = (3.4 \text{ kg})(1078 \text{ m/s}^2) = 3.67 \times 10^3 \text{ N}$ or 3.67 kN.

4-B15 (a) $a = (v^2 - v_0^2)/2s = \dfrac{(6 \text{ m/s})^2 - (50 \text{ m/s})^2}{2(20 \text{ m})} = -61.6 \text{ m/s}^2$, upward;

(b) $F = (75 \text{ kg})(61.6 \text{ m/s}^2) = 4620 \text{ N}$.

4-B16 The net force on the woman is 40 lb, downward. This is less than her weight, so her acceleration is less than g. Using W/g for her mass, we have

net $F = \left(\dfrac{W}{g}\right)a$; (40 lb) $= \left(\dfrac{100 \text{ lb}}{32 \text{ ft/s}^2}\right)a$; $a = 12.8 \text{ ft/s}^2$.

4-B17 Let T be the tension in the rope. The acceleration is $(3 \text{ m/s})/(0.6 \text{ s})$ $= 5 \text{ m/s}^2$. net $F = ma$ becomes $T - (30 \text{ kg})(9.8 \text{ m/s}^2) = (30 \text{ kg})(5 \text{ m/s}^2)$, whence $T = 444 \text{ N}$.

4-B18 $a = (-9 \text{ N})/(30 \text{ kg}) = -0.3 \text{ m/s}^2$; this is a negative acceleration, due to friction. $v^2 = v_0^2 + 2as = (4 \text{ m/s})^2 + 2(-0.3 \text{ m/s}^2)(20 \text{ m})$; $v = 2 \text{ m/s}$. [Since the energy method will not be introduced until Chap. 6, a direct solution is made by first finding the acceleration. See Prob. 6-B21.]

4-B19 First find the upward acceleration: $a = 2s/t^2 = 2(0.15 \text{ m})/(0.1 \text{ s})^2 = 30 \text{ m/s}^2$. Now net $F = ma$ becomes $T - (5 \text{ kg})(9.8 \text{ m/s}^2) = (5 \text{ kg})(30 \text{ m/s}^2)$; $T = 199 \text{ N}$.

4-B20 First find the acceleration, using W/g for mass. Net $F = ma$ becomes

$108\,000 \text{ lb} - 96\,000 \text{ lb} = \left(\dfrac{96\,000 \text{ lb}}{32 \text{ ft/s}^2}\right)a$; $a = 4 \text{ ft/s}^2$. Now find t from $t = \sqrt{2s/a}$ $= \sqrt{2(80 \text{ ft})/(4 \text{ ft/s}^2)} = 6.32 \text{ s}$. The early moments of the launching of a spacecraft are indeed majestically slow.

4-B21 $14\,000 \text{ N} - (1000 \text{ kg})(9.8 \text{ m/s}^2) = (1000 \text{ kg})a$; $a = 4.20 \text{ m/s}^2$.

4-B22 (a) Isolate the log as a freebody: $T - 600 \text{ N} = (400 \text{ kg})(2 \text{ m/s}^2)$; $T = 1400 \text{ N}$. (b) Consider the entire system (log + tractor): $F - 600 \text{ N} = (400 \text{ kg} + 800 \text{ kg})$ $\cdot(2 \text{ m/s}^2)$; $F = 3000 \text{ N}$. As a check, isolate the tractor as a freebody, and use the tension found in part (a): $F - 1400 \text{ N} = (800 \text{ kg})(2 \text{ m/s}^2)$; $F = 3000 \text{ N}$.

4-B23 (a) $F - 500 \text{ N} = (500 \text{ kg} + 300 \text{ kg})(2 \text{ m/s}^2)$; $F = 2100 \text{ N}$. (b) horse: $2100 \text{ N} - T = (500 \text{ kg})(2 \text{ m/s}^2)$; $T = 1100 \text{ N}$; stoneboat: $T - 500 \text{ N} = (300 \text{ kg})$ $\cdot(2 \text{ m/s}^2)$; $T = 1100 \text{ N}$.

4-B24 Consider the whole system: net $F = (W/g)a$ becomes

$100 \text{ lb} - 60 \text{ lb} = \left(\dfrac{100 \text{ lb}}{32 \text{ ft/s}^2}\right)a$; $a = 8 \text{ ft/s}^2$.

$v = v_0 + at = 5 \text{ ft/s} + (-8 \text{ ft/s}^2)(3 \text{ s}) = -19 \text{ ft/s}$ (downward).

4-B25 (a) $3(9.8)$ N $- 1(9.8)$ N $= (3$ kg $+ 1$ kg$)a$; $a = 4.9$ m/s^2.   (b) Isolate the 3 kg body: $3(9.8)$ N $- T = (3$ kg$)(4.9$ m/s$^2)$; $T = 14.7$ N.   (c) Isolate the 1 kg body: $T - 1(9.8)$ N $= (1$ kg$)(4.9$ m/s$^2)$; $T = 14.7$ N. These tensions are equal in magnitude, illustrating Newton's third law.

4-B26 (a) $10(9.8)$ N $= (30$ kg $+ 10$ kg$)a$; $a = 2.45$ m/s^2.   (b) $t = \sqrt{2s/a} =$ $= \sqrt{2(0.3 \text{ m})/(2.45 \text{ m/s}^2)} = 0.495$ s.   (c) Isolate the 30 kg block: $T = (30$ kg$)(2.45$ m/s$^2) = 73.5$ N; or isolate the 10 kg block: $10(9.8)$ N $- T$ $= (10$ kg$)(2.45$ m/s$^2)$; $T = 73.5$ N.   (d) After the block hits the pulley and is at rest, the tension in the cord is $10(9.8)$ N $= 98$ N.

4-B27 (a) Consider the whole system (using W/g for the mass):

$$5 \text{ lb} - 3 \text{ lb} = \left(\frac{(5 + 3) \text{ lb}}{32 \text{ ft/s}^2} \right) a; \; a = 8 \text{ ft/s}^2;$$

$t = \sqrt{2s/a} = \sqrt{2(9 \text{ ft})/(8 \text{ ft/s}^2)} = 1.50$ s.

(b) Isolate the 5 lb body:

$$5 \text{ lb} - T = \left(\frac{5 \text{ lb}}{32 \text{ ft/s}^2} \right)(8 \text{ ft/s}^2); \; T = 3.75 \text{ lb}.$$

(c) Isolate the 3 lb body:

$$T - 3 \text{ lb} = \left(\frac{3 \text{ lb}}{32 \text{ ft/s}^2} \right)(8 \text{ ft/s}^2); \; T = 3.75 \text{ lb}.$$

These tensions are equal in magnitude, illustrating Newton's third law.

4-B28 By Newton's third law, the force of the ground on the sprinter is 400 lb, upward and to the right, the horizontal component is $(400 \text{ lb}) \cos 60° = 200$ lb (forward). $F = (W/g)a$; $a = Fg/W = (200 \text{ lb})(32 \text{ ft/s}^2)/(160 \text{ lb}) = 40$ ft/s^2.

4-B29 Use the Periodic Table (p. 805) to find the atomic weights. 1 mole of iron is 0.05585 kg; 1 mole of aluminum is 0.02698 kg.

$$F = \left(6.67 \times 10^{-11} \; \frac{\text{N·m}^2}{\text{kg}^2} \right) \frac{(0.05585 \text{ kg})(0.02698 \text{ kg})}{(1 \text{ m})^2} = 1.01 \times 10^{-13} \text{ N}.$$

4-B30 $F = \left(6.67 \times 10^{-11} \; \dfrac{\text{N·m}^2}{\text{kg}^2} \right) \dfrac{(1.67 \times 10^{-27} \text{ kg})(9.11 \times 10^{-31} \text{ kg})}{(5.29 \times 10^{-11} \text{ m})^2} = 3.63 \times 10^{-47} \text{ N}.$

As we see in Chap. 17, the electric force between the proton and electron is far greater than the gravitational force (Prob. 17-B1).

4-B31 The mass of each ball is found from the density (Table 2-1): $m = \frac{4}{3} \pi (0.10 \text{ m})^3 (7860 \text{ kg/m}^3) = 32.9$ kg.

$$F = \left(6.67 \times 10^{-11} \; \frac{\text{N·m}^2}{\text{kg}^2} \right) \frac{(32.9 \text{ kg})(32.9 \text{ kg})}{(0.2 \text{ m})^2} = 1.81 \times 10^{-6} \text{ N} = 0.181 \text{ dyn}.$$

4-B32 (a) The rocket's distance from the center of the earth has been doubled, so its weight is $\frac{1}{4}(980 \text{ N}) = 245$ N.   (b) $a = F/m = (245 \text{ N})/(100 \text{ kg}) = 2.45$ m/s^2. The acceleration is $\frac{1}{4}g$ since the weight is $\frac{1}{4}$ of its value at the earth's surface.

4-B33 At the surface, the weight of a test body of mass m is mg_P; equate this to the gravitational force Gmm_P/r_P^2 and simplify. The test mass m cancels out.

4-B34 $[G] = [\text{M}^{-1}\text{L}^3\text{T}^{-2}] = [\text{F}^{-1}\text{L}^4\text{T}^{-4}]$.

4-B35 $\dfrac{m \text{ earth}}{m \text{ sun}} = \dfrac{6 \times 10^{24} \text{ kg}}{2 \times 10^{30} \text{ kg}} = 3 \times 10^{-6}$; the factor is 1.000003. The correction can *not* be neglected if data to 1 part in a million are used.

4-B36 As in Prob. 4-9,
  field due to sun: 6.0×10^{-3} N/kg (same as before)
  field due to moon: 0.5×10^{-3} N/kg (same as before).
The field due to the earth is different; the distance from earth is now 5.0 $\times 10^8$ m instead of 3×10^8 m; the field is $(3/5)^2$ as much, i.e., $\frac{9}{25}(4.5 \times 10^{-3}$

N/kg) = 1.6×10^{-3} N/kg. Taking due account of relative directions (for P between moon and sun) we obtain the resultant field: $(+6.0 - 0.5 - 1.6) \times 10^{-3}$ N/kg = 3.9×10^{-3} N/kg, directed toward the sun. We return to this situation in Prob. 8-B36.

4-C1   (a) $a = (-1200 \text{ N})/(500 \text{ kg}) = -2.4 \text{ m/s}^2$; $v = \sqrt{v_0^2 + 2as}$
$= \sqrt{(40 \text{ m/s})^2 + 2(-2.4 \text{ m/s}^2)(300 \text{ m})} = 12.65 \text{ m/s}$.   ($b$) $s = v_0 t + \frac{1}{2}at^2$;
$300 = 40t + \frac{1}{2}(-2.4)t^2$.   The smallest of the two roots of the quadratic equation is $t = 11.40$ s. The driver makes it, with 0.40 s to spare.

4-C2   (a) net $F = ma$; $120 \text{ N} = (20 \text{ kg} + 10 \text{ kg})a$;
$a = 4 \text{ m/s}^2$.   (b) Isolate the 10 kg box:
$F = (10 \text{ kg})(4 \text{ m/s}^2) = 40 \text{ N}$. As a check,
isolate the 20 kg box: $120 \text{ N} - F = (20 \text{ kg})$
$\cdot(4 \text{ m/s}^2)$; $F = 40 \text{ N}$.   (c) Acceleration
is now 4 m/s^2 to the left. Isolate either
box, obtaining 80 N for the force between
them.

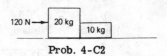

Prob. 4-C2

4-C3   The acceleration of this Atwood's machine is given by net $F = ma$, applied to the whole system, using W/g for the mass:
$$(15 - 5) \text{ lb} = \left(\frac{(15 + 5) \text{ lb}}{32 \text{ ft/s}^2}\right)a; \quad a = 16 \text{ ft/s}^2$$
After release, the 15 lb object falls 2 ft to the floor, acquiring a velocity $v = \sqrt{2as} = \sqrt{2(16 \text{ ft/s}^2)(2 \text{ ft})} = 8 \text{ ft/s}$. Now the cord becomes slack and the 5 lb object is on its own, projected upward at 8 ft/s from a position 4 ft above the floor. Again using $v^2 = v_0^2 + 2as$, we obtain $s = -v_0^2/2a$ $= -(8 \text{ ft/s})^2/2(-32 \text{ ft/s}^2) = 1 \text{ ft}$. The final maximum height of the object is 5 ft above the floor. The pulley is high enough to allow this.

4-C4   Data given in the problem show that the buckets collide after the heavy one falls 5.5 m and the light one rises 5.5 m. The acceleration of the system is given by $(12 - 9) \text{ N} = (12 \text{ kg} + 9 \text{ kg})a$; $a = \frac{3}{21}(9.8 \text{ m/s}^2) = 1.40 \text{ m/s}^2$. Then $t = \sqrt{2s/a} = \sqrt{2(5.5 \text{ m})/(1.40 \text{ m/s}^2)} = 2.80$ s.

4-C5   (a) Consider the whole system, with an added force due to friction: $98 \text{ N} - 38 \text{ N} = (40 \text{ kg})a$; $a = 1.50 \text{ m/s}^2$.   (b) $t = \sqrt{2s/a} = \sqrt{2(0.30 \text{ m})/(1.50 \text{ m/s}^2)}$ $= 0.632$ s.   (c) Isolate the 10 kg block: $98 \text{ N} - T = (10 \text{ kg})(1.50 \text{ m/s}^2)$; $T = 83 \text{ N}$.   (d) When stopped, $T = 98 \text{ N}$, as in Prob. 4-B26.

4-C6   This combines an Atwood's machine problem and a projectile problem. For the system of two balls, $a = mg/(m + m)$; $a = \frac{1}{2}g = 16 \text{ ft/s}^2$; the time it takes for the system to move 2 ft is $t = \sqrt{2s/a} = \sqrt{2(2 \text{ ft})/(16 \text{ ft/s}^2)} = 0.50$ s. This is the time it takes for A to reach the floor. The velocity of both balls is now $v = at = (16 \text{ ft/s}^2)(0.50 \text{ s}) = 8.0 \text{ ft/s}$. Ball B coasts at this speed for 2 ft, which requires 0.25 s. Finally, ball B becomes a projectile and is in the air for $\sqrt{2(2 \text{ ft})/(32 \text{ ft/s}^2)} = 0.354$ s. The total time for B to reach the floor is 0.50 s + 0.25 s + 0.35 s = 1.10 s. The range $R = v_x t = (8 \text{ ft/s})(0.354 \text{ s})$ = 2.83 ft.

4-C7   (a) $(12 \text{ N})/(4.0 \text{ kg}) = 3.0 \text{ m/s}^2$.   ($b$) The coupling supplies the net force on the two rear cars; $T = (1.6 \text{ kg})(3.0 \text{ m/s}^2) = 4.80$ N.

4-C8   First, the acceleration of the system is found: $(10 - 6)9.8 \text{ N} = 16a$, $a = \frac{1}{4}g$ $= 2.45 \text{ m/s}^2$. This is very similar to the problem of finding the time in the air of a projectile that is thrown to a height h; it is twice the time $\sqrt{2h/g}$ for the projectile to fall from a height h. Here the total time is $2\sqrt{2s/a}$ $= 2\sqrt{2(2 \text{ m})/(2.45 \text{ m/s}^2)} = 2.56$ s. If desired, the required initial velocity can be found from $0^2 = v_0^2 + 2(-2.45 \text{ m/s}^2)(2 \text{ m})$; $v_0 = 3.13$ m/s.

4-C9   (a) Consider the system as a whole: the net downward force is $(30)9.8$ N $- 114$ N $= 294$ N $- 114$ N $= 180$ N. Thus $a = (180$ N$)/(30$ kg$) = 6$ m/s^2 (downward); $s = \frac{1}{2}at^2 = \frac{1}{2}(6$ m/s$^2)(0.50$ s$)^2 = 0.75$ m (downward).   (b) Isolate the 15 kg block: $T + 15(9.8)$ N $- 114$ N $= (15$ kg$)(6$ m/s$^2)$; $T = 57$ N. As a check, isolate the chain and bottom block, considered as a single entity: $(13)9.8$ N $- T = (15$ kg$)(6$ m/s$^2)$; $T = 57$ N.

4-C10   Range is proportional to $1/g$, hence $\Delta R/R = \Delta g/g$. Here $\Delta g/g = 2.22/981.91 = 2.26 \times 10^{-3}$, or $2.22/979.69 = 2.27 \times 10^{-3}$. It doesn't much matter which $\Delta g/g$ is used; the change in range is $(18.31$ m$)(2.26 \times 10^{-3}) = 0.041$ m $= 4.1$ cm farther.

4-C11   net $F = \dfrac{W}{g}a$; 100 lb $- 64$ lb $= \left(\dfrac{64 \text{ lb}}{32 \text{ ft/s}^2}\right)a$; $a = 18$ ft/s^2. $t = \sqrt{2s/a}$
$= 2(9$ ft$)/(18$ ft/s$^2) \doteq 1.0$ s.

4-C12   This consists of four Atwood's machine problems. For the first trip,
350 lb $- 210$ lb $= \left(\dfrac{350 \text{ lb} + 210 \text{ lb}}{32 \text{ ft/s}^2}\right)a$; $a = 8$ ft/s^2, and $t = \sqrt{2s/a}$
$= \sqrt{2(36 \text{ ft})/(8 \text{ ft/s}^2)} = 3.00$ s. Similarly, the other trips require 3.35 s, 2.60 s, and 1.50 s; the total time is 10.45 s.

Chapter 5   Statics

Questions

5-1   The train is in (dynamic) equilibrium, since its acceleration is 0. The condition for equilibrium of a point ($\Sigma \mathbf{F} = 0$) can be applied because the weight can be considered as a single force concentrated at the center of gravity (see Fig. 5-1).

5-2   No; at the highest point the instantaneous velocity is 0 but the acceleration is 9.8 m/s^2, downward.

5-4   The tower is in stable equilibrium, because the line of action of the weight (acting at the c.g.) passes into the ground at a point within the base area.

5-5   The freight train of Ques. 5-1 is in motion, yet it is in equilibrium. The baseball of Ques. 5-2 is at rest (instantaneously) but is not in equilibrium; its acceleration is -9.8 m/s^2 throughout the motion.

5-6   Statics is the case where the acceleration has a special value, namely 0.

5-8   To a first approximation, the force of friction depends only on the nature of the surface (coefficient of friction) and the normal force. The dependence on velocity of the relative motion of the surfaces is usually small (see, however, References 4–8 on p. 113).

5-9   The *coefficient* of friction depends on the roughness of the surfaces. To a first approximation, the coefficient is independent of the normal force or the velocity of slip.

5-10   At the center of the hole.

Multiple Choice

5-11 (a);   5-12 (c);   5-13 (a);   5-14 (c);   5-15 (c);   5-16 (a).

Problems

5-A1   (a) (50 N) cos 45° = 35.4 N;   (b) (50 N) cos 30° = 43.3 N.
5-A2   (a) (300 km/h) cos 30° = 260 km/h;   (b) (300 km/h) cos 15° = 290 km/h.
5-A3 $F = \sqrt{(30)^2 + (40)^2} = 50$ units; tan θ = 30/40; θ = 37° above the horizontal.
5-A4 $F = \sqrt{(80\text{ lb})^2 + (60\text{ lb})^2} = 100$ lb; tan θ = 60/80; θ = 37° E of N.
5-A5 F cos 25° = 40 lb; F = 44.1 lb.
5-A6   The resultant of all three forces is downward, along the pole.
5-A7   The wire makes an angle of 60° with the horizontal; F_x = (1200 N) cos 60° = 600 N.
5-A8   (135 lb)(0.08) = 10.8 lb.
5-A9 μ_s = (13.5 lb)/(135 lb) = 0.10.
5-A10   Using μ_k = 0.1 gives F = (250 N)(0.1) = 25 N.
5-A11   Clockwise.
5-A12   Using lever arms relative to an axis through the upper right corner gives the following torques: (a) (8 lb)(1 ft) = 8 lb·ft;   (b) (8 lb)(4 ft) = 32 lb·ft; (c) (8 lb)(0 ft) = 0;   (d) (8 lb)(4 cos 30° ft) = 27.7 lb·ft.
5-A13   (100 lb)(7 ft) = 700 lb·ft, clockwise. The vector representation of this torque is into the plane of the paper.
5-A14   (1.1 N)(cos 20°)(8 cm) = 8.27 N·cm = 0.0827 N·m.
5-A15   About point A: clockwise torques = (133 lb)(17.3 ft) + (100 lb)(7 ft) = 3000 lb·ft; counterclockwise torques = (300 lb)(10 ft) = 3000 lb·ft.

5-B1   1.69 dyn, 20.3° E of N, or 69.7° N of E.
5-B3 ΣF_x = 0 + 2.00 dyn − 1.414 dyn = 0.586 dyn; ΣF_y = 3.00 dyn + 0 − 1.414 dyn = 1.586 dyn. $F = \sqrt{(0.586\text{ dyn})^2 + (1.586\text{ dyn})^2} = 1.69$ dyn; tan θ = F_y/F_x = 1.586/0.586; θ = 69.7° N of E.
5-B4   112 lb, 17° N of W.
5-B5 ΣF_x = 0 − 50 lb − 56.57 lb = −106.57 lb; ΣF_y = 90 lb + 0 − 56.57 lb = 33.43 lb; $F = \sqrt{(-106.57\text{ lb})^2 + (33.43\text{ lb})^2} = 111.7$ lb; tan θ = 33.43/106.57; θ = 17.4° N of W.

5-B7   Component method: Let T_1 be the tension in AC, and T_2 be the tension in AB. ΣF_x = 0 gives $0.707T_2 = 0.866T_1$; ΣF_y = 0 gives $0.707T_2 + 0.500T_1 = 50$ lb. Solve simultaneously, obtaining T_1 = 36.6 lb, T_2 = 44.8 lb. Vector triangle: The resultant of $\mathbf{T_1}$ and $\mathbf{T_2}$ must be a vertical vector of magnitude 50 lb. The law of sines gives $T_1/\sin 45° = T_2 \sin 60° = 50/\sin 75°$.

Prob. 5-B7

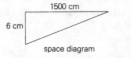

Prob. 5-B8

5-B8 Half the weight of the bird is borne by the upward component of the tension in each wire. First, use the Pythagorean theorem to find the hypotenuse of the space triangle to be 1500.002 cm (a negligible stretch). By similar triangles, $T/(2.5 \text{ N}) = (1500.002 \text{ cm})/(6 \text{ cm})$; $T = 625$ N.

5-B9 The vertical component of the tension F in the slanting string equals 98 N, the ball's weight: $F \cos 60° = 98$ N; $F = 196$ N. Balancing horizontal components gives $T = F \sin 60° = (196 \text{ N})$ $\cdot \sin 60° = 170$ N. Alternatively, the force diagram shows that $(98 \text{ N})/T = \tan 30°$; $T = (98 \text{ N})/ \tan 30° = 170$ N.   [See Prob. 5-C8 for an extension of this problem, also Prob. 8-C5.]

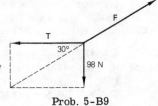

Prob. 5-B9

5-B10 250 N.   [The same as the answer to Example 5-1; the trunk is in dynamic equilibrium in each case. The speed is of no consequence for the problem.]

5-B11 Since the plane is frictionless, **R** is perpendicular to the plane. The force triangle gives $F = (500 \text{ N}) \tan 30°$ $= 289$ N.

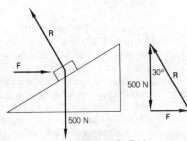

Prob. 5-B11

5-B12 The downward force is $9.8m$ (in newtons); the horizontal force is (0.4) $\cdot (98 \text{ N}) = 39.2$ N. The resultant must be at 30° downward to the left, to balance the force of the slanting string. Hence, $(9.8m)/(39.2 \text{ N}) = \tan 30°$; $m = 2.31$ kg.

5-B13 Use μ_k for both surfaces. The top block exerts a frictional force (to the right) on the bottom block, and the floor also exerts a frictional force to the right. Apply net F $= ma$ to the bottom block: $F - 0.4(6)9.8$ N $- 0.4(16)9.8$ N $= (10 \text{ kg})(2 \text{ m/s}^2)$; $F = 106$ N.

5-B14 The upward component of F must balance the weight and also overcome friction; $F \cos 30° = 5 \text{ lb} + (F \sin 30°)(0.2)$; $F = 6.53$ lb.

5-B15 The downhill component of the weight of the book is 7.5 N and the normal component of the weight is $(15 \text{ N}) \cos 60° = 12.99$ N. We need 7.5 N of friction; $f = \mu_s F_n$; $7.5 = 0.3$ $\cdot (F + 12.99 \text{ N})$; $F = 12.01$ N.

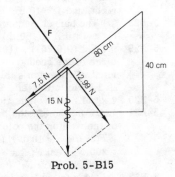

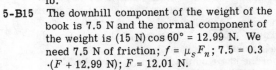

Prob. 5-B15

5-B16 $x_{c.g.} = \dfrac{(600 \text{ lb})(2 \text{ ft}) + (1500 \text{ lb})(3 \text{ ft}) + (100 \text{ lb})(5 \text{ ft})}{(600 + 1500 + 100) \text{ lb}} = 2.82$ ft.

5-B17 $x_{c.g.} = \dfrac{(6 \text{ N})(25 \text{ cm}) + (4 \text{ N})(75 \text{ cm}) + (2 \text{ N})(125 \text{ cm})}{(6 + 4 + 2) \text{ N}} = 58.3$ cm.

5-B18 Torques about Dick's end: $F_T(8 \text{ m}) = (150 \text{ N})(4 \text{ m}) + (400 \text{ N})(3 \text{ m})$; F_T $= 225$ N; torques about Tom's end: $F_D(8 \text{ m}) = (150 \text{ N})(4 \text{ m}) + (400 \text{ N})(5 \text{ m})$; $F_D = 325$ N. As a check, the total upward force exerted by Tom and Dick is 550 N, which equals the total weight that is supported.

5-B19 $(200 \text{ lb})x = (100 \text{ lb})(10 \text{ ft} - x)$; $x = 3.33$ ft.

5-B20 $(20 \text{ lb})(2 \text{ in.}) + F(7 \text{ in.}) = (15 \text{ lb})(9 \text{ in.}); F = 13.6 \text{ lb.}$

5-B21 $(20 \text{ lb})(2 \text{ in.}) + F(12 \text{ in.}) = (15 \text{ lb})(9 \text{ in.}); F = 7.9 \text{ lb}$, downward.

5-B22 By similar triangles, the weight of the trunk has components 300 N down the plane and 400 N normal to the plane. The mass of the trunk is $(500/g)$ kg. (a) net $F = 400 \text{ N} - 300 \text{ N} = 100 \text{ N}$, upward along the plane; (b) $a = (100 \text{ N})/(500/g \text{ kg}) = \frac{1}{5}g = 1.96 \text{ m/s}^2$; (c) 400 N.

5-B23 The net force is $340 \text{ lb} - 0.6(400 \text{ lb}) = 100 \text{ lb}$. The sledge is not in equilibrium. From net $F = (W/g)a$, we obtain $a = (\text{net } F)(g/W) = (100 \text{ lb})(32 \text{ ft/s}^2)/(400 \text{ lb}) = 8 \text{ ft/s}^2$. Since the net force is $\frac{1}{4}$ the sledge's weight, its acceleration is $\frac{1}{4}g$.

5-B24 (a) $(800 \text{ N}) \cos 60° = 400 \text{ N}$; (b) since the force along the slope must be $(800 \text{ N}) \sin 60° = 693 \text{ N}$, and the rope supplies 500 N, the force of friction is $693 \text{ N} - 500 \text{ N} = 193 \text{ N}$, upward along the slope.

5-B25 First find the acceleration: $400 \text{ N} - 0.3(80)9.8 \text{ N} = (80 \text{ kg})a$; $a = 2.06 \text{ m/s}^2$. $s = \frac{1}{2}at^2 = \frac{1}{2}(2.06 \text{ m/s}^2)(3 \text{ s})^2 = 9.27 \text{ m}$. See Prob. 5-B26 where the rope is not horizontal.

5-B26 The rope supplies a forward force of 346 N and an upward force of 200 N. The weight of the box is 784 N. Now apply Newton's second law: $346 \text{ N} - 0.3(784 \text{ N} - 200 \text{ N}) = (80 \text{ kg})a$; $a = 2.14$ m/s^2; $s = \frac{1}{2}at^2 = \frac{1}{2}(2.14 \text{ m/s}^2)(3 \text{ s})^2 = 9.63 \text{ m}$. Note that although only a component of the rope tension is effective in a forward direction, the acceleration is greater than in Prob. 5-B25, because the upward component of the rope tension reduces the normal force and thus reduces the frictional drag.

Prob. 5-B26

5-B27 $T(4 \text{ ft}) = (10 \text{ lb})(5.4 \text{ ft}); T = 13.5 \text{ lb.}$ The components at the base are $H = 13.5 \text{ lb}$, to the right, and $V = 10 \text{ lb}$, upward.

5-B28 (a) The barrel rests on the ground at a point that is 12 in. out from the curb. (b) $F(18 \text{ in.}) = (150 \text{ lb})(12 \text{ in.}); F = 100 \text{ lb.}$

5-B29 (a) $F(6 \text{ ft})(0.707) = (10 \text{ lb})(4 \text{ ft}); F = 9.43 \text{ lb}$ to the left. (b) The horizontal force of the ground on the hoe is $9.43 \text{ lb} - (10 \text{ lb})(0.707) = 2.36 \text{ lb}$ to the right. By Newton's third law, the horizontal force of the hoe on the ground is 2.36 lb to the left, a push.

5-B30 2 kg of milk weighs 19.6 N; $(19.6 \text{ N})(33 \text{ cm}) = (B \sin 10°)(8 \text{ cm}); B = 466 \text{ N.}$

5-B31 Let F be the tension in the guy wire, H and V the components of the force of the wall on the pole. (a) $(200 \text{ N})(3 \cos 30° \text{ m}) + (500 \text{ N})(6 \cos 30° \text{ m}) = F(3 \text{ m}); F = 1039 \text{ N}$ (rounded to 1040 N). (b) $H = F = 1039 \text{ N}$, $V = 500 \text{ N} + 200 \text{ N} = 700 \text{ N}; R = \sqrt{(1039)^2 + (700)^2} = 1253 \text{ N}$ (rounded to 1250 N). $\tan \theta = (700 \text{ N})/(1039 \text{ N}); \theta = 34°$ above the horizontal.

5-B32 By subtraction, the force of the chair on the head is found to be 71 lb. $(110 \text{ lb})x = (71 \text{ lb})(65 \text{ in.}); x = 42 \text{ in.}$

5-B33 Torques about the head: $F_1(200 \text{ cm}) = (200 \text{ N})(100 \text{ cm}) + (500 \text{ N})(70 \text{ cm})$; $F_1 = 275 \text{ N}$. Torques about the feet: $F_2(200 \text{ cm}) = (200 \text{ N})(100 \text{ cm}) + (500 \text{ N}) \cdot (130 \text{ cm}); F_2 = 425 \text{ N}$. As a check, $275 \text{ N} + 425 \text{ N} = 700 \text{ N}$, the total weight supported.

5-B34 Use the Pythagorean theorem to find that the ladder rests on the wall at a point 4 m above the ground. From $\Sigma F_y = 0$, $V = 800$ N; from $\Sigma F_x = 0$, $H = P$. Since the ladder is about to slip, we are getting the maximum force of static friction; $H = \mu_s V = (0.45)(800\ \text{N}) = 360$ N. Thus $P = 360$ N. Now balance the torques about the foot of the ladder: (200 N) $\cdot(1.5\ \text{m}) + (600\ \text{N})x = (360\ \text{N})(4\ \text{m})$; $x = 1.90$ m. Use similar triangles to find $L = \frac{5}{3}x = 3.17$ m.

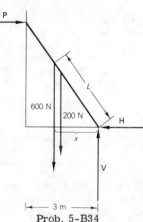

Prob. 5-B34

5-B35 The height of the ladder against the wall is $(20\ \text{ft})\sin 30°$. Balance the torques about the foot of the ladder (with the horizontal push P equal to the horizontal force of the ground): $(80\ \text{lb})(4\cos 30°\ \text{ft}) = H(20\sin 30°\ \text{ft})$; $H = 27.7$ lb. $\Sigma F_y = 0$ gives $V = 80$ lb. Hence $\mu_s = (27.7\ \text{lb})/(80\ \text{lb}) = 0.346$.

5-B36 (a) Assume that the block is stationary. Then, for $W = 60$ lb, the tensions in the cords are 75 lb (to the left) and 60 lb (to the right). The force of friction must be 75 lb − 60 lb = 15 lb (to the right). This is certainly possible, since the *maximum* force of static friction is 0.40(100 lb) = 40 lb. (b) If the block is about to move, the magnitude of f is 40 lb. Block about to move to the left: $W + 40\ \text{lb} - 75\ \text{lb} = 0$; $W = 35$ lb. Block about to move to the right: $W - 40\ \text{lb} - 75\ \text{lb} = 0$; $W = 115$ lb. Thus for the block to remain stationary, W can lie between 35 lb and 115 lb. Unstable equilibrium is also possible: For 35 lb $\le W \le$ 45 lb, and for 105 lb $\le W \le$ 115 lb, the block *can* be at rest, but since $\mu_k < \mu_s$, it is in unstable equilibrium, and if set into motion the block would be accelerated. For instance, if $W = 38$ lb, only 30 lb of kinetic friction would act toward the right on a *moving* block, and the net force on the system would be 75 lb − 30 lb − 38 lb = 7 lb to the left.   [See also Prob. 5-B37.]

5-B37 The block is moving to the left (see Prob. 5-B36), and $f = 0.30(100\ \text{lb}) = 30$ lb. Apply Newton's second law to the entire system, using W/g for mass:
$$75\ \text{lb} - 30\ \text{lb} - 25\ \text{lb} = \left(\frac{75\ \text{lb} + 100\ \text{lb} + 25\ \text{lb}}{32\ \text{ft/s}^2}\right)a;\ a = 3.2\ \text{ft/s}^2.\ v = \sqrt{2as}$$
$$= \sqrt{2(3.2\ \text{ft/s}^2)(4\ \text{ft})} = 5.06\ \text{ft/s}.$$

5-B38 (a) If the tension in the guy wire is T, the vertical component, acting at the top outside corner of the sign, is $0.6T$. Balance torques about the pin: $(0.6T)(8\ \text{ft}) = (120\ \text{lb})(4\ \text{ft})$; $T = 100$ lb.   (b) At the pin, $H = 0.8T = 80$ lb; $V = 120\ \text{lb} - 0.6T = 120\ \text{lb} - 60\ \text{lb} = 60$ lb. Hence $R = \sqrt{H^2 + V^2} = \sqrt{(80)^2 + (60)^2} = 100$ lb, at an angle 37° above the horizontal. As a check, note that the vectors **R**, **T**, and **W** intersect at a point (as must always be the case if only three forces act on a rigid body).

5-B39 The component of tension that is perpendicular to AC is $0.5T$.   (a) Torques about A: $(0.5T)(2\ \text{m}) = (300\ \text{N})(1\ \text{m}) + (100\ \text{N})(1\ \text{m}) + (100\ \text{N})(2\ \text{m})$; $T = 600$ N. (b) From $\Sigma F_x = 0$, $H = T\cos 30° = 520$ N; from $\Sigma F_y = 0$, $V + 0.5T = 200$ N + 300 N; $V = 200$ N.

5-B40 The maximum possible frictional force is $\mu_s mg$, proportional to the mass of the casting. The required force is ma, also proportional to the mass of the casting. Note the implicit use of the principle of equivalence (p. 70) according to which inertial mass is proportional to gravitational mass.

5-C2 $\mu_s(mg\cos\theta) = mg\sin\theta$; $\mu_s = \sin\theta/\cos\theta = \tan\theta$.

5-C3   As in Prob. 5-C2, the block is in equilibrium and the same analysis shows that $\mu_k = \tan\theta$ for a block sliding downhill at constant speed.

5-C4   Here θ is the angle with the *vertical*; the normal force at the ground is W, and the torque condition (about the bottom) gives $P(L\cos\theta) = W(L/2)\sin\theta$. Thus $H = P = W\sin\theta/2\cos\theta$ and $\mu_s = H/V = \sin\theta/2\cos\theta = \frac{1}{2}\tan\theta$. Limiting cases: $\mu_s \to 0$ as $\theta \to 0$ (ruler almost vertical); $\mu_s \to \infty$ as $\theta \to 90°$ (a nearly horizontal ruler would require a large frictional force if the wall is perfectly smooth).

5-C5 $(8\cos 30°\text{ lb})(4\text{ ft}) + (8\sin 30°\text{ lb})(4\text{ ft}) = 43.7\text{ lb·ft}$.

5-C6   The weight is most advantageously placed at the table edge, midway between two legs, at a distance R from the center. The lever arm of the added weight is $R - R\sqrt{2}/2$; the lever arm for the table's weight is $R\sqrt{2}/2$. Then $R(1 - \sqrt{2}/2)(W) = (R\sqrt{2}/2)(20\text{ N})$; $W = 200(\sqrt{2} + 1)\text{ N} = 483\text{ N}$.

5-C7   (a) 20 lb;   (b) front legs, 31 lb each; back legs, 19 lb each;   (c) 31.6 lb, downward and forward, 79° below the horizontal.   [The desk is in dynamic equilibrium, since its acceleration is 0. (a) $N_1 + N_2 = 100$ lb; total frictional force is $f_1 + f_2 = (0.20)(N_1 + N_2) = 0.20(100\text{ lb}) = 20$ lb. The condition for horizontal equilibrium gives $F - 20\text{ lb} = 0$; $F = 20$ lb.   (b) We apply the torque condition about a horizontal axis on the floor, passing through the front legs (all forces in lb, lever arms in inches): $F(30) + N_1(50) = 100(25)$; we have found that $F = 20$ lb, hence $N_1 = 38$ lb, i.e., 19 lb on each front leg. Similarly, using an axis through the rear legs gives $N_2 = 62$ lb, i.e., 31 lb on each rear leg. *Check:* the sum of vertical forces on all four legs is 100 lb.   (c) $f_2 = \mu_s N_2 = (0.20)(62\text{ lb}) = 12.40$ lb, i.e., 6.20 lb of friction on each front leg. The vector sum of $\frac{1}{2}f_2$ and $\frac{1}{2}N_2$ is $\sqrt{(6.20)^2+(31)^2} = 31.6$ lb, upward and to the rear at 79° above the horizontal. By Newton's third law, the force of a rear leg on the floor is 31.6 lb, downward and forward, 79° below the horizontal.]

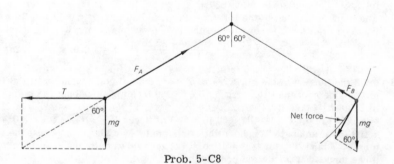

Prob. 5-C8

5-C8   In position A, $\dfrac{mg}{F_A} = \cos 60°$, whence $F_A = \dfrac{mg}{\cos 60°}$. In position B, the ball is not in equilibrium; the net force must be tangent to the arc of the circular path. $\dfrac{F_B}{mg} = \cos 60°$, whence $F_B = mg\cos 60°$. The ratio of the two

forces is $\dfrac{F_A}{F_B} = \dfrac{\dfrac{mg}{\cos 60°}}{mg\cos 60°} = \dfrac{1}{\cos^2 60°} = 4$. [See also Prob. 5-B9 and Prob. 8-C5.]

5-C9 The force diagram shows that $\mathbf{W'} + \mathbf{C} + \mathbf{T} = 0$. The law of sines is useful here [remember that $\sin(180° - 21°)$ $= \sin 21°$]: $C/\sin(180° - 21°) = T/\sin 15° = (200\text{ lb})/\sin 6°$; $C = 686$ lb, $T = 495$ lb. These forces are much greater than the man's weight.

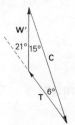

5-C10 First find the acceleration: $a = v^2/2s = (7\text{ m/s})^2/2(6\text{ m})$ $= 4.08\text{ m/s}^2$. $mg\sin\theta - \mu_k mg\cos\theta = ma$; the mass cancels out. $(9.8\text{ m/s}^2)\sin 30° - \mu_k(9.8\text{ m/s}^2)\cos 30° = 4.08\text{ m/s}^2$; $\mu_k = 0.096$.

5-C11 The angle of repose is found from $\tan\theta = \mu_s = 0.35$; $\theta = 19.3°$. After the block starts to move, the force of friction is $\mu_k F_n = 0.15(mg\cos 19.3°)$. The acceleration is found from $mg\sin 19.3°$ $- 0.15(mg\cos 19.3°) = ma$; $a = (9.8\text{ m/s}^2)$ $\cdot(\sin 19.3° - 0.15\cos 19.3°) = 1.85\text{ m/s}^2$. $s = \frac{1}{2}at^2 = \frac{1}{2}(1.85\text{ m/s}^2)(1.5\text{ s})^2 = 2.08\text{ m}$.

Prob. 5-C9
(Not drawn to scale.)

5-C12 The boy can climb until the angle of repose is exceeded. $\tan\theta = \mu_s = 0.51$; $\theta = 27.0°$; $OA = (10\text{ m})\cos 27.0° = 8.91\text{ m}$. Hence $AB = 1.09\text{ m}$.

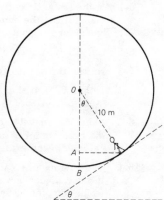

5-C13 Use W/g for the mass m. $W(0.05)$ $= \left(\dfrac{W}{32\text{ ft/s}^2}\right)a$; $a = 1.6\text{ ft/s}^2$. $t = \sqrt{2s/a}$ $= \sqrt{2(20\text{ ft})/(1.6\text{ ft/s}^2)} = 5\text{ s}$.

5-C14 $\tan\theta_2 = T_1/T_2 = 0.5$; $\theta_2 = 27°$, hence $\theta_1 = 63°$. We have $T_1^2 + T_2^2 = 100$ lb, also $T_2 = 2T_1$. Solve simultaneously to obtain $T_1 = 44.7$ lb in the rope that is $63°$ from the vertical, and $T_2 = 89.4$ lb in the rope that is $27°$ from the vertical.

Problem 5-C12

5-C15 (a) $x_{\text{c.m.}} = \dfrac{(3\text{ kg})(0) + (5\text{ kg})(8\text{ m})}{8\text{ kg}} = +5\text{ m}$.

(b) Body A receives acceleration $(-6\text{ N})/(3\text{ kg}) = -2\text{ m/s}^2$, and its displacement is $\frac{1}{2}(-2\text{ m/s}^2)(4\text{ s})^2 = -16\text{ m}$. Similarly, body B's acceleration is $+1\text{ m/s}^2$ and its displacement is $\frac{1}{2}(1\text{ m/s}^2)(4\text{ s})^2 = +8\text{ m}$; its new position is at $x = 8\text{ m} + 8\text{ m} = +16\text{ m}$, east of the origin. The new c.m.

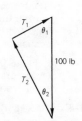

is at $\dfrac{(3\text{ kg})(-16\text{ m}) + (5\text{ kg})(+16\text{ m})}{8\text{ kg}} = +4\text{ m}$. ($c$) The

c.m. has moved 1 m to the left. (d) From $s_{\text{c.m.}}$ $= \frac{1}{2}a_{\text{c.m.}}t^2$, $a_{\text{c.m.}} = 2s_{\text{c.m.}}/t^2 = 2(1\text{ m})/(4\text{ s})^2 = \frac{1}{8}\text{ m/s}^2$. ($e$) Check: $\Sigma F/\Sigma m = (-6\text{ N} + 5\text{ N})/(8\text{ kg}) = -\frac{1}{8}\text{ m/s}^2$. The acceleration of the c.m. is the same as if the net force were applied at the c.m.

Problem 5-C14

5-C16 The cubes have weights in proportion $2:1:1$. Using Eq. 5-6, we obtain

$$x_{\text{c.g.}} = \frac{2(1\text{ cm}) + 1(3\text{ cm}) + 1(3\text{ cm})}{4} = +2.0\text{ cm}. \text{ Similarly,}$$

$$y_{\text{c.g.}} = \frac{2(1\text{ cm}) + 1(1\text{ cm}) + 1(3\text{ cm})}{4} = +1.5\text{ cm};$$

$$z_{\text{c.g}} = \frac{2(-1\text{ cm}) + 1(-1\text{ cm}) + 1(-1\text{ cm})}{4} = -1.0\text{ cm}.$$

5-C17   If the mass of a solid disk is M, the mass of the hole is $-\frac{1}{4}M$.
$$x_{c.m.} = \frac{M(0) + (-\frac{1}{4}M)(\frac{1}{2}R)}{M - \frac{1}{4}M} = -\frac{1}{6}R.$$

Chapter 6   Conservation of Momentum and Energy

Questions

6-1   In the inelastic collision between the apple and the earth, the system (earth + apple) has the same momentum (but almost zero velocity) that the apple had before impact.

6-2   No. The water recoils and no net momentum is created.

6-3   He can throw the bag of uranium ore away from himself.

6-4   Inelastic. The ship gains momentum; most of the KE of the plane is "lost" (see start of Sec. 6-11).

6-5   Yes. The rocket's velocity relative to the earth can always be increased by the reaction force of the exhaust gases, no matter how large or small the velocity of the exhaust gases relative to the rocket.

6 6-6   The bumpmobile can actually move along the floor in apparent violation of the law of conservation of momentum. If the man lifts the mallet slowly to the left, the reaction force tends to push the plank to the right. However, if the floor is rough enough, the plank remains fixed relative to the earth, and the very massive earth-plank system recoils (invisibly). Now, when the mallet is let fall, during impact the force on the plank is greater than friction can sustain, and the mallet's momentum is shared between the plank and the mallet; the plank starts to move and eventually comes to rest because of friction.

6-7   (a) From the chemical PE in the battery;   (b) from the KE of the car. See the discussion of back torque and regenerative braking on p. 505. The car slows down (imperceptibly) in case (b).

6-8   Solar energy is nuclear energy (see p. 750). Muscular energy comes from metabolism of foodstuffs grown with the help of solar energy. Waterfalls derive their energy from the raising of clouds of water by solar energy. Nonsolar sources are (a) nuclear energy, e.g., in a reactor;   (b) the heat of volcanoes and geysers;   (c) tidal energy (see answer to Ques. 6-11).

6-9   The satellite's gravitational PE and its KE have both come from the chemical PE of the fuel. As the satellite spirals in, its energy is eventually transformed into thermal energy.

6-10   No; for a circular orbit the gravitational force is always perpendicular to the displacement along the orbit. The earth's orbit is, in fact, an ellipse and some work is done on the earth or by the earth during various parts of the orbit. This causes the earth to speed up and slow down (Kepler's law of areas, p. 69), but the net work on the earth is zero around any closed path in the gravitational field of the sun.

6-11   The gravitational pull of the moon maintains a high tide on earth as a bulge, more or less beneath the moon. As the earth turns, any given point on the coast passes beneath the moon, and the water rises, then falls. Except at a very few tidal-energy installations, the PE of the raised water is dissipated as heat when the outgoing tide strikes the rocks and the beach. Tidal energy thus comes from the earth's KE; if the earth were not turning, there would be no rise and fall of tides. The earth is losing KE and slowing down because of this "tidal friction." Tides in the earth's crust and in the atmosphere also contribute to the dissipation of the earth's KE. The same process has acted more significantly on the moon to slow its rotation down, so that now the same side of the moon always faces us; there is a permanent "high tide" on the moon's surface (at the center of the visible side), as well as a permanent high tide opposite the earth (see Fig. 8-28). No further up-and-down motion occurs on the moon, and no further slowing down will take place. In due time, the earth will present always the same face to the moon, and the day and the month will have the same length (estimated to be about 60 times the length of the present day).

6-12   The watt is not a unit of work.

6-13   1 kWh = (1000 J/s)(3600 s) = 3.6×10^6 J.

6-14   The speeds are the same but the velocities (vectors) are different.

6-15   Yes, within the limits of precision of the best analytical balance (conservation of mass, and proportionality between gravitational mass and inertial mass). The mass equivalent of the radiant energy that has escaped is too small to be detected. The flash bulb must cool off to avoid problems with convection currents in the air and unequal expansion of the arms of the balance; one must also assume that the bulb's volume has not changed, so the buoyancy of the air remains unaltered.

6-16   In calculating torque, the force is multiplied by a lever arm that is perpendicular to the force (cross product); in calculating work, the force is multiplied by a displacement component that is parallel to the force (dot product).

6-17   Since the momentum mv is constant, the increase of m is accompanied by a decrease of v. The car slows down.

Multiple Choice

6-18 (*a*);   6-19 (*c*);   6-20 (*b*);   6-21 (*c*);   6-22 (*b*);   6-23 (*c*).

Problems

6-A1   (110 kg)(2 m/s) = 220 kg·m/s.
6-A2   (0.06 kg)(80 m/s) = 4.8 kg·m/s.
6-A3   Truck: momentum = $(10 \times 10^3$ kg)(1 m/s) = 10^4 kg·m/s; KE = $\frac{1}{2}(10^4$ kg) ·(1 m/s)^2 = 5×10^3 J. Bullet: momentum = (0.025 kg)(10^3 m/s) = 25 kg·m/s; KE = $\frac{1}{2}(0.025$ kg)(10^3 m/s)^2 = 1.25×10^4 J. The momentum of the truck is 400 times that of the bullet; the KE of the bullet is 2.5 times that of the truck.

6-A4 $\Delta p/\Delta t = (4.8 \text{ kg·m/s})/(2 \times 10^{-4} \text{ s}) = 2.4 \times 10^4 \text{ kg·m/s}^2$. The forces on the ball and on the club are equal and opposite, each of magnitude 2.4×10^4 N.

6-A5   Since mass is proportional to weight, the law of conservation of momentum becomes $(0.01 \text{ lb})(1000 \text{ ft/s}) - (5 \text{ lb})v$; $v = 2$ ft/s.

6-A6 $(0.01 \text{ lb})(1000 \text{ ft/s}) = (100 \text{ lb})v$; $v = 0.1$ ft/s.

6-A7 $(3000 \text{ kg})(10 \text{ m/s}) = (20\,000 \text{ kg})v$; $v = 1.5$ m/s.

6-A8 $(10 \text{ kg})(2 \text{ m/s}) = (80 \text{ kg})v$; $v = 0.25$ m/s.

6-A9   Initial PE $= mgh$. Since there is no loss of KE during an elastic impact, the final PE must be the same as the initial PE, hence h is the same as the original height.   [The same result is obtained by a rather tortuous repeated use of $v^2 = v_0^2 + 2gh$.]

6-A10   (a) $W = (0.6 \text{ m})(30 \text{ N}) = 18$ J;   (b) $W = (0.6 \text{ m})(150 \text{ N}) = 90$ J.

6-A11 $(0.75 \text{ cm})(30\,000 \text{ dyn}) = 2.25 \times 10^4$ erg.

6-A12   The c.g. is raised 3 m; $W = (3 \text{ m})(200 \text{ N}) = 600$ J.

6-A13 $0.01(5 \times 10^6 \text{ kg})(9.8 \text{ N/kg})(10^3 \text{ m}) = 4.9 \times 10^8$ J.

6-A14 $(25 \times 10^3 \text{ J})/(400 \text{ N}) = 62.5$ m.

6-A15   The c.g. is raised 0.14 m; $W = (0.14 \text{ m})(600 \text{ N}) = 84$ J. The increase in PE comes from chemical PE released in the muscles.

6-A16   (a) $(6.2 \text{ N} + 18.2 \text{ N})/2 = 12.2$ N;   (b) $(1.5 \text{ m})(12.2 \text{ N}) = 18.3$ J.

6-A17 $\frac{1}{2}(5 \text{ kg})(4 \text{ m/s})^2 = 40$ J.

6-A18   Use W/g for mass: $\text{KE} = \frac{1}{2}\left(\dfrac{8 \times 2000 \text{ lb}}{32 \text{ ft/s}^2}\right)(24 \text{ ft/s})^2 = 1.44 \times 10^5$ ft·lb. The angle of the hill is unimportant.

6-A19 $\frac{1}{2}(1.67 \times 10^{-27} \text{ kg})(3 \times 10^2 \text{ m/s})^2 = 7.52 \times 10^{-23}$ J.

6-A20 $\frac{1}{2}(800 \text{ kg})(3.5 \text{ m/s})^2 = 4900$ J.

6-A21   Use W/g for mass; $\frac{1}{2}\left(\dfrac{128 \text{ lb}}{32 \text{ ft/s}^2}\right)v^2 = 1800$ ft·lb; $v = 30$ ft/s.

6-A22 $330 \text{ J} = (60 \text{ N})s$; $s = 5.5$ m.

6-A23 $125 \text{ erg} = F(2 \times 10^{-1} \text{ cm})$; $F = 625$ dyn.

6-A24 $m = W/g = (24.5 \text{ dyn})/(980 \text{ cm/s}^2) = 0.025$ g. From $\text{KE} = \frac{1}{2}mv^2$, $125 \text{ erg} = \frac{1}{2}(0.025 \text{ g})v^2$; $v = 100$ cm/s.

6-B1 $F = \Delta p/\Delta t = (90\,000 \text{ kg·m/s} - 30\,000 \text{ kg·m/s})/(120 \text{ s}) = 500$ N. The force was exerted by the water.

6-B2 $F = \Delta p/\Delta t = (0.1 \text{ kg})(65 \text{ m/s})/(0.001 \text{ s}) = 6500$ N, westward.

6-B3 $F = \Delta p/\Delta t = \left(\dfrac{16 \text{ lb}}{32 \text{ ft/s}^2}\right)(18 \text{ ft/s}) / (1.25 \text{ s}) = 7.2$ lb.

6-B4 $\Delta t = \Delta p/F = (1200 \text{ kg})(2 \text{ m/s})/(400 \text{ N}) = 6$ s.

6-B5   (a) $\Delta p/\Delta t = (900 \text{ kg})(25 \text{ m/s})/(60 \text{ s}) = 375$ kg·m/s.   (b) -375 N; (c) $+375$ N.

6-B6   Using $d = 1.293 \text{ kg/m}^3$, the mass of 100 m³ of air is found to be 129.3 kg. $F = (129.3 \text{ kg})(20 \text{ m/s})/(60 \text{ s}) = 43.1$ N.

6-B7 $(80 \text{ kg})(6 \text{ m/s}) + (100 \text{ kg})(-3 \text{ m/s}) = (180 \text{ kg})v$; $v = +1$ m/s, in direction of the fullback's motion.

6-B8   (a) $(0.03 \text{ kg})(200 \text{ m/s}) = (5.03 \text{ kg})v$; $v = 1.193$ m/s.   (b) Time in the air $t = \sqrt{2s/g} = \sqrt{2(10 \text{ m})/(9.8 \text{ m/s}^2)} = 1.428$ s. Range $R = (1.193 \text{ m/s})(1.428 \text{ s}) = 1.70$ m.

6-B9 $(0.05 \text{ kg})v = (20.05 \text{ kg})(8 \text{ m})/(0.40 \text{ s})$; $v = 8020$ m/s.

6-B10   The total momentum is 0 after the swimmers dive off the raft. $0 = (80 \text{ kg}) \cdot (4 \text{ m/s}) - (50 \text{ kg})(4 \text{ m/s}) - (200 \text{ kg})v$; $v = 0.6$ m/s, in the direction of the 50-kg diver's motion.

6-B11 The height of the c.g. cannot change (no external force); hence the toes (and the outstretched fingertips) are raised by 3 cm.

6-B12 $KE = W = Fs = mas = m\left(\dfrac{v^2 - v_0{}^2}{2s}\right)s = \frac{1}{2}mv^2 - \frac{1}{2}mv_0{}^2$.

6-B13 The c.g. has been raised from 2 cm to 20 cm above the table top. The gain in PE is $mgh = (200\ N)(0.18\ m) = 36\ J$. The same result is obtained by considering separately the increase of each book's PE.

6-B14 $\frac{1}{2}(0.0026\ kg)(320\ m/s)^2 = F(0.08\ m)$; $F = 1664\ N = 1.66\ kN$.

6-B15 The work done on the arrow was $(400\ N)(0.08\ m) = 320\ J$.   (a) 320 J $= \frac{1}{2}(0.1\ kg)v^2$; $v = 80\ m/s$.   (b) $320\ J = (0.1\ kg)(9.8\ m/s^2)h$; $h = 327\ m$.   (c) $320\ J = F(0.3\ m)$; $F = 1067\ N$.

6-B16 Initial PE $= (70\ kg)(9.8\ N/kg)(50\sin30°\ m) = 17\ 150\ J$. Final KE $= \frac{1}{2}(70\ kg)$ $\cdot(10\ m/s)^2 = 3500\ J$. $(17\ 150\ J - 3500\ J) = 13.65\ kJ$ transformed into thermal energy.

6-B17 Final KE $= \frac{1}{2}(60\ kg)(8\ m/s)^2 = 1920\ J$. The work done to overcome friction was $3200\ J - 1920\ J = 1280\ J$.

6-B18 Initial KE + initial PE = final KE; $\frac{1}{2}mv^2 + m(9.8\ m/s^2)(1\ m) = \frac{1}{2}m(6\ m/s)^2$; $v = 4.05\ m/s$.   [In applying the energy principle, we can ignore the rotational KE of the rolling ball because the ball retains this rotational KE throughout the motion.]

6-B19 Initial KE + initial PE = final KE; use mgh for gravitational PE. $\frac{1}{2}m(30\ ft/s)^2 + m(32\ ft/s^2)(25\ ft) = \frac{1}{2}mv^2$; $v = 50\ ft/s$.   [The energy principle shows that the same speed would be reached for a stone thrown at any angle. The result for this problem can be checked using the methods developed in Chap. 3 for projectile motion.]

6-B20 $\frac{1}{2}(1\ kg)(10\ m/s)^2 - (2.5\ N)(15\ m) = \frac{1}{2}(1\ kg)v^2$; $v = 5\ m/s$.

6-B21 $\frac{1}{2}(30\ kg)(4\ m/s)^2 - (9\ N)(20\ m) = \frac{1}{2}(30\ kg)v^2$; $v = 2\ m/s$.

6-B22 (a) $(3000\ kg)(9.8\ m/s^2)(33\ m - 10\ m) = \frac{1}{2}(3000\ kg)v^2$; $v = 21.2\ m/s$. (b) $(3000\ kg)(9.8\ m/s^2)(33\ m - 15\ m) = \frac{1}{2}(3000\ kg)v^2$; $v = 18.8\ m/s$.

6-B23 Final KE = gain from motor − loss to friction + gain from PE (A to B) − loss to PE (B to C): $\frac{1}{2}(200\ kg)(40\ m/s)^2 = 250 \times 10^3\ J - 100 \times 10^3\ J$ $+ (200\ kg)(9.8\ m/s^2)(10\ m) - (200\ kg)(9.8\ m/s^2)(h - 2\ m)$; $h = 6.90\ m$.

6-B24 (a) Loss of PE $= (50\ kg)(9.8\ m/s^2)(2\ m) = 980\ J$;   (b) work against friction $= (120\ N)(5\ m) = 600\ J$;   (c) final KE = initial KE + loss of PE − work against friction: $\frac{1}{2}(50\ kg)v^2 = \frac{1}{2}(50\ kg)(3\ m/s)^2 + 980\ J - 600\ J$; $v = 4.92\ m/s$.

6-B25 Use the energy principle to find the speed with which the ball reaches the bottom of the chute: $(2\ kg)(9.8\ m/s^2)(1.5\ m) = \frac{1}{2}(2\ kg)v_1{}^2$; $v_1 = 5.42\ m/s$. Now an inelastic collision takes place; use the law of conservation of momentum to find the velocity v_2 of the combined mass just after impact: $(2\ kg)(5.42\ m/s) = (5\ kg)v_2$; $v_2 = 2.17\ m/s$. Finally, use the energy principle to find how far the system coasts on the rough surface: $\frac{1}{2}(5\ kg)$ $\cdot(2.17\ m/s)^2 = 0.4(5\ kg)(9.8\ m/s^2)D$; $D = 0.60\ m$.   [It would be incorrect to equate the initial PE to the work against friction; some mechanical energy is necessarily lost during the inelastic collision, as discussed on p. 127.]

6-B26 (a) KE = loss of PE $= (49 \times 10^3\ dyn)(20 \times 10^2\ cm) = 9.8 \times 10^7\ erg = 9.8\ J$. (b) $(9.7 \times 10^7\ erg) = F(30\ cm)$; $F = 3.27 \times 10^6\ dyn = 32.7\ N$.

6-B27 The boy's c.g. is raised by $(5\ m - 5\cos30°\ m) = 0.670\ m$; PE $= (400\ N)$ $\cdot(0.670\ m) = 268\ J$.

6-B28 At the highest point of each swing, the boy's c.g. is 12 ft above the lowest point. Using mg for W, we have $\frac{1}{2}mv^2 = mgh = m(32\ ft/s^2)(12\ ft)$; $v = 27.7$ ft/s.

6-B29 The 3 kg mass has lost PE and the 2 kg mass has gained PE. Equate the net loss of PE to the gain of KE of the system: $(3 \text{ kg})(9.8 \text{ m/s}^2)(0.5 \text{ m})$ $- (2 \text{ kg})(9.8 \text{ m/s}^2)(0.5 \text{ m}) = \frac{1}{2}(5 \text{ kg})v^2$; $v = 1.40 \text{ m/s}$. The answer can be checked by finding the acceleration, as an Atwood's machine problem.

6-B30 $\frac{1}{2}mv^2 = (\mu_s mg)D$; $D = v^2/2\mu_s g$. Since it is assumed that the car is not skidding, at the point of contact the tire is instantaneously at rest relative to the road. Hence μ_s is used.

6-B31 The c.g. of the chain has fallen 60 cm. Use the energy principle: $\frac{1}{2}mv^2$ $= m(9.8 \text{ m/s}^2)(0.60 \text{ m})$; $v = 3.43 \text{ m/s}$.

6-B32 $\text{eff} = \dfrac{\text{work out}}{\text{work in}} = \dfrac{60 \text{ J}}{(4 \text{ N})(20 \text{ N})} = 0.75.$

6-B33 $\text{eff} = \dfrac{\text{work out}}{\text{work in}} = \dfrac{400 \text{ J} - 60 \text{ J}}{400 \text{ J}} = 0.85.$

6-B34 $\text{eff} = W_{\text{out}}/W_{\text{in}}$; $W_{\text{in}} = W_{\text{out}}/\text{eff} = (1200 \text{ J})/0.80 = 1500 \text{ J}.$

6-B35 The 1 hp motor uses energy at the rate of 746 W. In 10 min, the battery must supply $(100 \text{ W} + 746 \text{ W})(600 \text{ s}) = 508 \text{ kJ}.$

6-B36 $P = fv = (800 \text{ N})(25 \text{ m/s}) = 200 \times 10^3 \text{ W} = 200 \text{ kW}.$

6-B37 $\text{Power in} = \dfrac{\text{power out}}{\text{eff}} = (0.5 \text{ hp})\left(\dfrac{746 \text{ W}}{1 \text{ hp}}\right)\Big/0.85 = 439 \text{ W}.$

6-B38 $3(0.70)(0.3 \text{ hp})\left(\dfrac{550 \text{ ft·lb/s}}{1 \text{ hp}}\right)t = (800 \text{ lb})(110 \text{ ft})$; $t = 254 \text{ s}.$

6-B39 (a) Use W/g for mass; $\text{KE} = \frac{1}{2}\left(\dfrac{50 \times 2000 \text{ lb}}{32 \text{ ft/s}^2}\right)(6000 \text{ ft/s})^2 = 5.63 \times 10^{10} \text{ ft·lb}$

(b) $P = \dfrac{W}{t} = \left(\dfrac{5.63 \times 10^{10} \text{ ft·lb}}{60 \text{ s}}\right)\left(\dfrac{1 \text{ hp}}{550 \text{ ft·lb/s}}\right) = 1.70 \times 10^6 \text{ hp}.$ [For an exact solution, the change in mass (as fuel is consumed) would be considered. With the simplifying assumptions of constant acceleration and constant mass, one finds that the rocket rose 1.8×10^5 ft in 1 min and the work against gravity (the PE) is about 1.8×10^{10} ft·lb, certainly not negligible.]

6-B40 (a) $(230 \text{ hp})\left(\dfrac{0.746 \text{ kW}}{1 \text{ hp}}\right) = 172 \text{ kW}$;   (b) $W = Pt = (172 \times 10^3 \text{ J/s})(1.206$ $\times 10^5 \text{ s}) = 2.07 \times 10^{10} \text{ J}$;   (c) $P = fv$; $f = P/v = (1.72 \times 10^5 \text{ J/s})/(50 \text{ m/s})$ $= 3.43 \times 10^3 \text{ N}.$ In part (b), we assume constant power. In part (c), this assumption is not made, since we are given the instantaneous power and speed.

6-B41 A human power output of 1 hp (746 W) is not unusual for a few seconds, but the dray horse can deliver this power for an extended period of time. See Reference 7 at the end of the chapter.

6-B42 $(2.5 \text{ mi/h})\left(\dfrac{88 \text{ ft/s}}{60 \text{ mi/h}}\right) = \dfrac{11}{3} \text{ ft/s}$; $P = fv = (150 \text{ lb})(11/3 \text{ ft/s}) = 550 \text{ ft·lb/s}.$

6-B43 (a) $W = mgh = (15\,000 \text{ N})(10 \text{ m}) = 150 \text{ kJ}$;   (b) the energy supplied to the motor is $(150 \text{ kJ})/0.60 = 250 \text{ kJ}$.   (c) At 10 kW, the time required is found from $P = W/t$; $t = W/P = (150 \text{ kJ})/(10 \text{ kJ/s}) = 15 \text{ s}.$

6-B44 $P = W/t = (2 \times 10^6 \text{ kg})(9.8 \text{ m/s}^2)(40 \text{ m})/(10 \times 3600 \text{ s}) = 21.8 \text{ kW}.$

6-B46 KE before impact = initial PE = 24 ft·lb. After impact, the KE is $\frac{1}{2}\left(\dfrac{16 \text{ lb}}{32 \text{ ft/s}^2}\right)(6 \text{ ft/s})^2 = 9 \text{ ft·lb}.$ The loss of KE during the inelastic impact is 15 ft·lb.

6-B47 (a) $(3 \text{ kg})(8 \text{ m/s}) + (1 \text{ kg})(4 \text{ m/s}) = (4 \text{ kg})v$; $v = 7 \text{ m/s}$, westward.
(b) Total KE before impact: $\frac{1}{2}(3 \text{ kg})(8 \text{ m/s})^2 + \frac{1}{2}(1 \text{ kg})(4 \text{ m/s})^2 = 104 \text{ J}$; total KE after impact: $\frac{1}{2}(4 \text{ kg})(7 \text{ m/s})^2 = 98 \text{ J}$. The loss of KE is 6 J.

6-B48 (a) In the elastic collision, both momentum and KE are conserved. Let v_1 be the final velocity of the neutron and v_2 be that of the oxygen nucleus. Momentum: $(1)v_0 = (1)v_1 + (16)v_2$; KE: $(1)v_0^2 = (1)v_1^2 + (16)v_2^2$. Solving simultaneously gives $v_2 = \frac{2}{17}v_0$.   (b) The fraction of the KE that is transferred to the oxygen nucleus is $\dfrac{16(\frac{2}{17}v_0)^2}{1(v_0)^2} = \dfrac{64}{289}$.

6-B49 Let eastward be the + direction. (a) $(3\text{ kg})(2\text{ m/s}) + (1\text{ kg})(-2\text{ m/s}) = (4\text{ kg})v$; $v = +1$ m/s, eastward.   (b) During collision, the KE of the system changes from 8 J to 2 J, a loss of 6 J.

6-B50 In the elastic collision, both momentum and KE are conserved. Let x and y be the final (eastward) velocities of the 3 kg and 1 kg balls, respectively. Using masses in kg and velocities in m/s, the simultaneous equations are $3(2) + 1(-2) = 3x + 1y$; $3(2)^2 + 1(-2)^2 = 3x^2 + 1y^2$. Algebraically, there are two solutions: (1) $x = 2$, $y = -2$, or (2) $x = 0$, $y = 4$. The first solution is *possible*, but it represents no collision at all (x and y are the same as before the collision). Hence the desired solution is $x = 0$, $y = 4$ m/s. The heavy ball stops dead and the small ball rebounds with twice its initial speed.

6-C1 From conservation of momentum, $v_A/v_B = m_B/m_A$. Then
$$\frac{\text{KE}_A}{\text{KE}_B} = \frac{\frac{1}{2}m_A v_A^2}{\frac{1}{2}m_B v_B^2} = \frac{m_A}{m_B}\left(\frac{m_B}{m_A}\right)^2 = \frac{m_B}{m_A}.$$

6-C2 (a) By the energy principle, $mgh = \frac{1}{2}mV^2$; $V = \sqrt{2gh} = \sqrt{2(9.8\text{ m/s}^2)(0.07\text{ m})}$ $= 1.17$ m/s.   (b) $(0.006\text{ kg})v = (4.006\text{ kg})(1.17\text{ m/s})$; $v = 782$ m/s. The length of the string does not enter into the problem.

6-C3 The c.g. is now at the center of the stretched-out paper, instead of at the top of the plane. As discussed by Freeman (Reference 9), throughout the action the paper is making inelastic impacts at points along the plane, accounting for the loss of mechanical energy.

6-C4 (a) The horizontal component of momentum must become 0; $(80\text{ kg})(20\text{ m/s})$ $\cdot \cos 60° - m(100\text{ m/s}) = 0$; $m = 8$ kg.   (b) New mass is 72 kg; the astronaut's vertical momentum is unaltered by the horizontal thrust, hence $(72\text{ kg})v = (80\text{ kg})(20\text{ m/s})\sin 60°$; $v = 19.2$ m/s.   [It is instructive to note that some of the PE of compressed gas has been transformed into KE; the astronaut's KE has increased from 16 kJ to 53.3 kJ. A similar increase in KE can be pointed out in the case of the trapped uranium prospector (Question 6-3 on p. 131).]

6-C5 621 N, downward to right, 15° from vertical.   [Horizontal momentum change per second decreases from 1200 kg·m/s² to 1039 kg·m/s²; hence $F_x = -161$ N. Vertical momentum change per second increases from 0 to 600 kg·m/s²; hence $F_y = +600$ N. Resultant force exerted *by the roof* to cause these changes is $\sqrt{(-161\text{ N})^2 + (600\text{ N})^2} = 621$ N, upward to left, 15° from vertical. Force of water *on roof* is the opposite of this.]

6-C6 Time to reach P is found from H $= \frac{1}{2}gt^2$; $t = \sqrt{2H/g}$; $R = AC$ $= (2\sqrt{2H/g})v_{0x}$. At point P, **v** is horizontal, of magnitude v_{0x}. After the explosion, the horizontal momentum is all in one fragment, and conservation of momentum gives $v_{0x}{}'$ $= 2v_{0x}$. The remaining time in the air is $\sqrt{2H/g}$; and $BD = (2v_{0x})(\sqrt{2H/g})$. Thus $BD = R$, and $AD = \frac{1}{2}R + R = \frac{3}{2}R$.

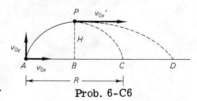

Prob. 6-C6

6-C7 Let V be the struck ball's velocity; express masses in kg and velocities in m/s. Conservation of momentum gives $3v_0 = 3(-\frac{1}{4}v_0) + mV$. Conservation of KE gives $3v_0^2 = 3(-\frac{1}{4}v_0)^2 + mV^2$. Solve simultaneously for V and m, obtaining $V = +\frac{3}{4}v_0$ and $m = 5$ kg.   [If Sec. 6-13 is studied, the velocity of the struck ball can be found from the fact that the relative velocity of separation equals the relative velocity of approach; $v_0 - 0 = V - (-\frac{1}{4}v_0)$; $V = \frac{3}{4}v_0$.]

6-C8 Methods similar to those used for Prob. 6-C7 give $M = m(n + 1)/(n - 1)$.

6-C9 About $\frac{2}{3}$.

6-C10 If velocities are in m/s, conservation of momentum gives $2m + 0 = mV_1 + mV_2$; partially elastic impact gives $V_2 - V_1 = (2 - 0)(0.8)$. Thus $V_1 = 0.2$ m/s, $V_2 = 1.8$ m/s. After collision, the balls are moving in the same direction with a relative velocity of separation of 1.6 m/s.

6-C11 Initial KE $= \frac{1}{2}m(2)^2 + 0 = 2m$ units. Final KE $= \frac{1}{2}m(0.2)^2 + \frac{1}{2}m(1.8)^2 = 1.64m$ units. The fractional loss of KE is $0.36/2 = 18\%$.

6-C12 At impact, the ball's speed is $\sqrt{2gh}$. It rebounds with speed $v' = e\sqrt{2gh}$, and reaches a height $h' = v'^2/2g = e^2(2gh)/2g = e^2h$. Thus $e = \sqrt{h'/h}$ $= \sqrt{(81 \text{ cm})/(100 \text{ cm})} = 0.9$.

6-C13 Use $v^2 = v_0^2 + 2as$ to find that the second body's initial speed, just after impact, is 2.8 m/s. Conservation of momentum then gives $v' = -0.2$ m/s for the velocity of the first body just after impact. Finally, the coefficient of restitution is given by $e = \dfrac{2.8 - (-0.2)}{4.0 - 0} = 0.75$.

6-C14 The c.g. of the ball falls 72 in., and if of maximum liveness the c.g. rebounds to a height that is 44 in. above its lowest point.
$$e = \frac{\text{velocity of separation}}{\text{velocity of approach}} = \sqrt{\frac{2g(3\frac{2}{3}\text{ft})}{2g(6\text{ ft})}} = \sqrt{\frac{11}{18}} = 0.782.$$

6-C15 With masses in kg and velocities in m/s, let V_1 and V_2 be the velocities of the 3 kg and 1 kg balls after impact.   (a) Conservation of momentum gives $3(2) + 1(-2) = 3V_1 + 1V_2$; partially elastic impact gives $0.8[2 - (-2)] = V_2 - V_1$. Solving simultaneously gives $V_1 = 0.2$ m/s, $V_2 = 3.4$ m/s.   (b) Straightforward calculation of total KE gives values 8 J (before impact) and 5.84 J (after impact); loss of KE is 2.16 J.

6-C16 The lower ball is projected upward at a speed $\sqrt{2gh}$. After a time t, the balls collide at height h_1 above the ground, at a point which is h_2 below the top of the tower. (This point is more than halfway up the tower.) Let v_1 and V_1 be the velocities of the upper ball before and after collision; similarly, v_2 and V_2 refer to the lower ball. Choose the positive direction to be upward. First we prove that the balls have equal speeds when they collide. The upper ball has fallen $h_1 = v_1^2/2g$; the lower ball has risen $h_2 = (2gh - v_2^2)/2g$. Substitute into $h_1 + h_2 = h$ and simplify, obtaining $v_1^2 = v_2^2$. The velocities are equal and opposite; thus, we write $v_2 = v$

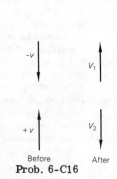

Prob. 6-C16

and $v_1 = -v$, where v is the magnitude of these equal and opposite velocities. To calculate v, note that in time t, the rising ball loses as much speed as the falling one gains; $v = gt$. Since the speeds are equal at the time of impact, $\sqrt{2gh} - gt = gt$; thus $\sqrt{2gh} - v = v$, whence $v = \sqrt{gh/2}$. Now we are ready to apply the equations for an inelastic impact. The total momentum both before and after impact is 0, hence the final velocities are equal and opposite, each of magnitude V. The relative velocity of separation is $2V$. From $e = (2V)/(2v)$ we obtain $V = ev$. The loss of KE of the top ball during collision is $\Delta \text{KE} = \frac{1}{2}mv^2 - \frac{1}{2}m(ev)^2 = \frac{1}{2}mv^2(1 - e^2)$. This means that when this ball reaches its highest point, its PE is less than at the start by this same amount. Thus, $mg\Delta h = \frac{1}{2}mv^2(1 - e^2)$. Substitute the value of v from above, and solve for Δh, obtaining $\Delta h = \frac{1}{4}(1 - e^2)h$. The new height h' is $h - \Delta h$, or $(3 + e^2)(h/4)$. In the limit, as $e \to 1$ (perfectly elastic collision), the equations show that $\Delta h \to 0$ and $h' \to h$.

6-C17 The weight of 38 liters of water is 38(9.8) = 372.4 N; total load is 392.4 N.
(a) IMA = (25 cm)/(5 cm) = 5;   (b) AMA = 0.80(IMA) = 4;   (c) F
= (load)/AMA = (392.4 N)/4 = 98.1 N.

6-C18 (a) IMA = (60 cm)/(1 cm) = 60;   (b) eff $= \dfrac{\text{work out}}{\text{work in}} = \dfrac{(1000\ \text{N})(0.80\ \text{m})}{1600\ \text{J}} = 50\%$;
(c) AMA = (IMA)(eff) = 30;   (d) F = load /AMA = (1000 N)/30 = 33.3 N.

6-C19 (a) IMA = (4.00 m)/(0.20 m) = 20;   (b) AMA = (800 N)/(100 N) = 8;
(c) eff = AMA/IMA = 8/20 = 40%.

6-C20 IMA $= \dfrac{\text{input distance}}{\text{output distance}} = \dfrac{1.2\ \text{in.}}{9.0\ \text{in.}} = 0.133$. Alternatively, assuming 100%
efficiency, IMA = AMA $= \dfrac{\text{output force}}{\text{input force}} = \dfrac{10\ \text{lb}}{75\ \text{lb}} = 0.133$. Considered as a
machine, the advantage is less than 1; the function is to magnify distance, rather than to magnify force.

Chapter 7   Relativity

Questions

7-1 (a) 2 s;   (b) 12 m behind the car;   (c) straight up and down;   (d) a parabola.

7-2 Because it is moving in a circle of greater radius, the ball has an eastward velocity relative to a point directly beneath the point of release. The eastward displacement can be considered to be the result of a Coriolis force. This displacement is very small (given by $\frac{1}{3}\omega g t^3$, where ω is 2π rad/day), and is only about 2 mm for a fall of 19.6 m (a 6-story building). This would be very difficult to observe.

7-3 There is a magnet in the suitcase; the bus went around a curve toward the right.

7-4 The inertial forces $-m\mathbf{a}$ may be considered to act at the center of mass of each brick or beam of the building.

7-5 3×10^8 m/s; 3×10^8 m/s.

7-6   Yes. Einstein's postulate of the constancy of the speed of light is, in a sense, redundant, although of great historical importance.

7-7   Does the student accept logical consequences of experimental observations? The twin is, in actual fact, "really" younger by all physical and biological criteria.

7-8   No; momentum is mv, and can increase without limit as m increases. In the extreme relativistic limit, momentum $\approx mc$ (see Sec. 31-8).

7-9   True.

7-10   Yes, the energy E radiated as light and heat carries away an unobservably small amount of mass given by E/c^2. In Ques. 6-15 this was not considered.

7-11   Yes; since KE is $mc^2 - m_0 c^2$ and m increases without limit, there is no limit to the KE of a particle. See Table 31-1 for an illustration of this.

7-12   The special theory of relativity.

Multiple Choice

7-13 (a);   **7-14** (c);   **7-15** (c);   **7-16** (a);   **7-17** (c);   **7-18** (b).

Problems

7-A1   (1 ft)/(0.5 ft/s) = 2 s.

7-A2 $x' = 5$ ft; $x = 22$ ft.

7-A3 $m = m_0/\sqrt{1 - (v^2/c^2)} = m_0/\sqrt{1 - (0.8)^2} = 1.67 m_0$.

7-A4 $2m_0 = \dfrac{m_0}{\sqrt{1 - v^2/c^2}}$; $\sqrt{1 - v^2/c^2} = \frac{1}{2}$; $v = 0.866c = 2.60 \times 10^8$ m/s.

7-A5 $\Delta E = (\Delta m)c^2 = (20 \times 10^{-6} \text{ kg})(3 \times 10^8 \text{ m/s})^2 = 1.8 \times 10^{12}$ J = 1.8 TJ.
$\Delta E = mgh$; $h = \Delta E/mg = (1.8 \times 10^{12} \text{ J})/(4 \times 10^9 \text{ kg})(9.8 \text{ m/s}^2) = 45.9$ m.

7-B1   Use the conversion factor in the Appendix (p. 803) to find velocities in m/s. (a) Relative to the floor, the girl's velocity is 2.5 ft/s, or 0.762 m/s; KE $= \frac{1}{2}(30 \text{ kg})(0.762 \text{ m/s})^2 = 8.71$ J.   (b) Relative to the suitcase, $v = 0.5$ ft/s = 0.152 m/s; KE $= \frac{1}{2}(30 \text{ kg})(0.152 \text{ m/s})^2 = 0.35$ J.

7-B2   (a) net $F = ma = (50 \text{ kg})(2 \text{ m/s}^2) = 100$ N (downward).   (b) As in Fig. 7-5, net $F = mg - P$; $P = mg -$ net $F = (50 \text{ kg})(9.8 \text{ m/s}^2) - 100$ N = 390 N.

7-B3   Let W' be the apparent weight and W the true weight ($= mg$). $W' - W = ma$; $a = \dfrac{W' - W}{W/g} = \dfrac{W' - W}{W}g = \dfrac{700 \text{ N} - 600 \text{ N}}{600 \text{ N}}(9.8 \text{ m/s}^2) = \frac{1}{6}g = 1.63$ m/s^2.

7-B4   The acceleration is $(v - v_0)/t = (2 \text{ m/s} - 16 \text{ m/s})/(3.5 \text{ s}) = -4$ m/s^2 (eastward). $F' = -ma = -(100 \text{ kg})(-4 \text{ m/s}^2) = +400$ N (westward).

7-B5   (a) $(6.5 \times 10^9 \text{ kg})(9.8 \text{ m/s}^2) = 6.37 \times 10^{10}$ N.   (b) $(6.37 \times 10^{10} \text{ N})(37 \text{ m}) = 2.36 \times 10^{12}$ J.   (c) $\Delta m = \Delta E/c^2 = (2.36 \times 10^{12} \text{ J})/(3 \times 10^{10} \text{ m/s})^2 = 2.62 \times 10^{-5}$ kg. This is about 26 mg of mass; the mass came from the decrease of the mass of the workmen that accompanied the loss of chemical PE in their muscles.

7-B6 The increase in mass can be attributed to the rocket's KE. For $v \ll c$, KE $\approx \frac{1}{2}mv^2$. Hence $\frac{1}{2}(10^6$ kg$)v^2 \approx (2 \times 10^{-3}$ kg$)(3 \times 10^8$ m/s$)^2$; $v = 1.90 \times 10^4$ m/s. Alternatively, use the binomial theorem and the equation for relativistic mass. $m = \dfrac{10^6 \text{ kg}}{\sqrt{1 - v^2/c^2}} = 10^6$ kg $+ 2 \times 10^{-3}$ kg. To solve for v, note that for small x, $(1 + x)^n \approx 1 + nx$, so $(1 + x)^{1/2} \approx 1 + \frac{1}{2}x$. Hence $\sqrt{1 - v^2/c^2}$ $= \dfrac{10^6}{10^6 + 2 \times 10^{-3}} = \dfrac{10^6}{10^6(1 + 2 \times 10^{-9})} \approx 1 - 2 \times 10^{-9}$. Thus $1 - v^2/c^2 = 1 - 4 \times 10^{-9}$; $v^2/c^2 = 4 \times 10^{-9}$; $v = \sqrt{4 \times 10^{-9}}\,(3 \times 10^8$ m/s$) = 1.90 \times 10^4$ m/s.

7-B7 The time dilation factor is

$$\frac{1}{\sqrt{1 - v^2/c^2}} = \frac{1}{\sqrt{1 - \left(\dfrac{1.5 \times 10^8}{3 \times 10^8}\right)^2}} = 1.15$$

(a) The duration in the earth frame is 1.15 days. (b) The stay-at-home twin's heart beats 115 000 times; he is older than his twin. See Reference 4 at the end of the chapter.

7-C1 The truck's weight is $(4 \times 10^3$ kg$)(9.8$ m/s$^2) = 39.2$ kN. (a) If there is no acceleration, each axle bears half the truck's weight, i.e., 19.6 kN. (b) $-ma = -(4000$ kg$)(-5$ m/s$^2) = +20$ kN. This inertial force acts in a forward direction, with a lever arm 1 m (height of the c.m. above the road). Torques about axis at B: $(39.2$ kN$)(2$ m$) + (20$ kN$)(1$ m$) = F_1(4$ m$)$; $F_1 = 24.6$ kN. Torques about axis at A: $F_2(4$ m$) + (20$ kN$)(1$ m$) = (39.2$ kN$)(2$ m$)$; $F_2 = 14.6$ kN. *Check*: $F_1 + F_2 = 24.6$ kN $+ 14.6$ kN $= 39.2$ kN, equal to the weight of the loaded truck.

7-C2 (a) The inertial force $-ma$ acts in a backward direction at the c.m. of the book; the book tends to topple backward. (b) The torque of the inertial force, which has lever arm 11 cm, balances the torque of the weight, which has lever arm 3 cm: $(ma)(11$ cm$) = mg(3$ cm$)$; $a = \frac{3}{11}g = 2.67$ m/s^2.

7-C3 (a) In the laboratory frame, $t = (3 \times 10^3$ m$)/(3 \times 10^8$ m/s$) = 10$ μs. (b) In the electron's frame, the length contraction, $\sqrt{1 - v^2/c^2}$, is the same as the mass ratio $m_0/m = 10^{-4}$. The apparent length is $10^{-4}(3 \times 10^3$ m$) = 0.3$ m. (c) $t_0 = t\sqrt{1 - v^2/c^2} = t(10^{-4}) = (10^{-5}$ s$)(10^{-4}) = 10^{-9}$ s $= 1$ ns.

7-C4 $m/m_0 = 3$; hence $mc^2/m_0c^2 = 3$, and the total energy is $mc^2 = 3m_0c^2$. Subtract the rest energy m_0c^2 to obtain KE $= 2m_0c^2 = 2(1.67 \times 10^{-27}$ kg$)(3 \times 10^8$ m/s$)^2 = 3.01 \times 10^{-10}$ J.

7-C5 (a) $1/\sqrt{1 - v^2/c^2} \approx 1 + \frac{1}{2}v^2/c^2 = 1 + \frac{1}{2}(7.8 \times 10^3$ m/s$)^2/(3 \times 10^8$ m/s$)^2 = 1 + 3.38 \times 10^{-10}$. (b) $\Delta t = (3.38 \times 10^{-10})t = (3.38 \times 10^{-10})(10 \times 8.64 \times 10^4$ s$) = 2.92 \times 10^{-4}$ s ≈ 300 μs.

7-C6 It is convenient to let $v^2/c^2 = x$, a small dimensionless quantity. Then KE $= m_0c^2(1 - x)^{-\frac{1}{2}} - m_0c^2 = m_0c^2[1 + (-\frac{1}{2})(-x) + (-\frac{1}{2})(-\frac{3}{2})(-x)^2/2! + \cdots] - m_0c^2 = m_0c^2(\frac{1}{2}x + \frac{3}{8}x^2 + \cdots) = \frac{1}{2}m_0c^2\dfrac{v^2}{c^2} + \frac{3}{8}m_0c^2\dfrac{v^4}{c^4} + \cdots$, or KE $= \frac{1}{2}m_0v^2\left(1 + \frac{3}{4}\dfrac{v^2}{c^2} + \cdots\right)$. As $v^2/c^2 \to 0$, this reduces to the classical formula for KE.

7-C7 (a) $\dfrac{m_0}{\sqrt{1 - \dfrac{v^2}{c^2}}} = \dfrac{9.11 \times 10^{-31} \text{ kg}}{\sqrt{1 - \left(\dfrac{2.4}{3.0}\right)^2}} = 15.18 \times 10^{-31}$ kg. (b) $\Delta m = (15.18 - 9.11)$ $\times 10^{-31}$ kg $= 6.07 \times 10^{-31}$ kg

(c) KE $= (\Delta m)c^2 = (6.07 \times 10^{-31}$ kg$)(3 \times 10^8$ m/s$)^2 = 5.46 \times 10^{-14}$ J.

(d) $\frac{1}{2}m_0 v^2$ gives 2.62×10^{-14} J; $\frac{1}{2}mv^2$ gives 4.37×10^{-14} J. Both of these values are incorrect; Eq. 7-8 *must* be used to find the KE of a relativistic particle.

7-C8   Use v_x = rocket relative to earth; $v_x{}'$ = rocket relative to ship; v = ship relative to earth. Eq. 7-16 then gives

$$v_x = \frac{(2 \times 10^8) + (2 \times 10^8)}{1 + \left(\dfrac{2 \times 10^8}{9 \times 10^{16}}\right)(2 \times 10^8)} = \frac{4 \times 10^8}{1 + \frac{4}{9}} = \frac{36}{13} \times 10^8 = 2.77 \times 10^8 \text{ m/s}.$$

As expected, this relativistic velocity is less than c.

7-C9   To carry out the proof, let $a = 1 - x$ and $b = 1 - y$, where x and y are positive fractions. Then $a + b = 2 - (x + y)$; $1 + ab = 1 + (1 - x)(1 - y) = 2 - (x + y) + xy$. Therefore, $a + b < 1 + ab$.

7-C10   (a) Relative to the ship, $m = \dfrac{m_0}{\sqrt{1 - \left(\dfrac{2 \times 10^8}{3 \times 10^8}\right)^2}} = 1.342\,m_0$. KE $= (m - m_0)c^2$

$= 0.342\,m_0 c^2 = 0.342(10^3$ kg$)(3 \times 10^8$ m/s$)^2 = 3.07 \times 10^{19}$ J.   (b) Relative to the earth, the velocity is 2.77×10^8 m/s;

$$m = \frac{m_0}{\sqrt{1 - \left(\dfrac{2.77 \times 10^8}{3 \times 10^8}\right)^2}} = 2.60\,m_0$$

KE $= (m - m_0)c^2 = 1.60\,m_0 c^2 = 1.60(10^3$ kg$)(3 \times 10^8$ m/s$)^2 = 14.4 \times 10^{19}$ J.

(c) $\frac{1}{2}m_0 v^2 = \frac{1}{2}(10^3$ kg$)(2.77 \times 10^8$ m/s$)^2 = 2.84 \times 10^{19}$ J. The latter quantity has no physical significance.

Chapter 8   Rotation

Questions

8-1   The blade now points straight down.

8-2   The velocity (a vector) is not constant; the penny is not in equilibrium.

8-3   Yes, as in uniform circular motion.

8-4   The centripetal force is supplied by the cohesive forces (short-range electric forces) between aluminum atoms.

8-5   The seat pushes upward on the pilot, with a force greater than his weight.

8-6   Molecules of air push the bird toward the left.

8-7   As viewed by an outside observer, there is no such thing as centrifugal force. The earth *is* falling toward the sun, with an acceleration v^2/r.

8-8   The reaction torque due to the blades acting on the body of the fan occurs only during the angular acceleration of the blades.

8-9   Yes, because v is much less than c.

8-10   No, on a frictionless surface, there is no way of obtaining centripetal force. Exception: a curved path would be possible if the game were played on a merry-go-round, where inertial forces arise because of the acceleration of the frame of reference. But even then the path would be a straight line as viewed by an outside observer who is in an inertial frame of reference.

8-11 He now rotates in the opposite direction.

8-12 The earth's angular momentum is such that the surface moves toward the east. The force of the sprinter on the earth pushes the earth toward the west, thus increasing the length of the day (the angular momentum of the earth decreases by an amount numerically equal to that of the sprinter). When the worker ascends, the length of the day increases ($I\omega$ remains constant, with I increasing and ω decreasing). All these changes are un-observable because of the very large angular momentum of the earth.

Multiple Choice

8-13 (*b*);   8-14 (*b*);   8-15 (*c*);   8-16 (*a*);   8-17 (*b*);   8-18 (*b*).

Problems

8-A1 (*a*) 3.14 rad;   (*b*) 1.05 rad;   (*c*) 1.57 rad;   (*d*) 0.87 rad;   (*e*) 1.88 rad.

8-A2 (*a*) 69°;   (*b*) 19°;   (*c*) 30°;   (*d*) 180°;   (*e*) 360°.

8-A3 $v = r\omega = (1 \text{ m})(3 \text{ rad/s}) = 3 \text{ m/s}$.

8-A4 $\omega = 45 \dfrac{\text{rev}}{\text{min}} \left(\dfrac{2\pi \text{ rad}}{1 \text{ rev}}\right)\left(\dfrac{1 \text{ min}}{60 \text{ s}}\right) = 4.71 \text{ rad/s}$.

8-A5 $s = r\theta = (\tfrac{1}{2} \text{ ft})\left(33\tfrac{1}{3} \dfrac{\text{rev}}{\text{min}}\right)\left(\dfrac{2\pi \text{ rad}}{1 \text{ rev}}\right)(3 \text{ min}) = 314 \text{ ft}$.

8-A6 (*a*) $\theta = (2160 \text{ mi})/(240\,000 \text{ mi}) = 0.0090 \text{ rad}$;   (*b*) $0.0090 \text{ rad} \left(\dfrac{360°}{2\pi \text{ rad}}\right)$ $= 0.52°$.   [A full moon is only half as large as the little fingernail held at arm's length; the larger apparent size of a rising moon is an optical illusion.]

8-A7 (2 in.)/(120 in.) = $\tfrac{1}{60}$ rad.

8-A8 (*a*) $(2\pi r)/(120 \text{ s}) = 200 \text{ m/s}$; $r = 3820 \text{ m} = 3.82 \text{ km}$;   (*b*) $a = v^2/r$ $= (200 \text{ m/s})^2/(3820 \text{ m}) = 10.5 \text{ m/s}^2$.

8-A9 (*a*) $\omega = (2\pi \text{ rad})/(86\,164 \text{ s}) = 7.29 \times 10^{-5} \text{ rad/s}$.   [The earth turns on its axis in a sidereal day, which is about 3 min, 56 s shorter than the mean solar day of 24 h or 86 400 s. See any astronomy textbook. However, this fine point does not affect the answer, to 3 significant figures.]   (*b*) $a = r\omega^2$ $= (6.37 \times 10^6 \text{ m})(7.29 \times 10^{-5} \text{ rad/s})^2 = 3.39 \text{ cm/s}^2$.

8-A10 $a = v^2/r = (15 \text{ m/s})^2/(50 \text{ m}) = 4.50 \text{ m/s}^2$.

8-A11 (*a*) $\omega = (2\pi \text{ rad})/(3600 \text{ s}) = 1.745 \times 10^{-3} \text{ rad/s}$;   (*b*) $a = r\omega^2 = (25 \text{ cm})$ $\cdot (1.745 \times 10^{-3} \text{ rad/s})^2 = 7.62 \times 10^{-5} \text{ cm/s}^2$.

8-A12 $I = MR^2 = (2 \text{ kg})(0.30 \text{ m})^2 = 0.18 \text{ kg·m}^2$.

8-A13 $P = \tau\omega$ where P is power in watts, τ is the torque in N·m, and ω is the angular velocity in rad/s.

8-A14 $I = MR^2 = (15 \text{ kg})(8 \text{ m})^2 = 960 \text{ kg·m}^2$.

8-A15 $I\omega = (15 \text{ kg·m}^2)(6\pi \text{ rad/s}) = 283 \text{ kg·m}^2/\text{s}$.

8-A16 $[ML^2T^{-1}]$; $[ML^2T^{-2}]$.

8-A17 365 days; the orbit's radius is the same as that of the earth's orbit, and by Kepler's third law the periods are the same.

8-B1 $\omega^2 = \omega_0{}^2 + 2\alpha\theta$; $\alpha = \omega^2/2\theta = \left(\dfrac{33\frac{1}{3}\ \text{rev}}{60\ \text{s}}\right)^2 \Big/ 2(\frac{1}{4}\ \text{rev}) = 0.617\ \text{rev/s}^2$;

$\left(0.617\ \dfrac{\text{rev}}{\text{s}^2}\right)\left(\dfrac{2\pi\ \text{rad}}{1\ \text{rev}}\right) = 3.88\ \text{rad/s}^2.$

8-B2 (a) $\alpha = (\omega - \omega_0)/t = (250\ \text{rev/min} - 1750\ \text{rev/min})/(0.5\ \text{min}) = -3000$ rev/min^2;   (b) $\theta = \omega_0 t + \frac{1}{2}\alpha t^2 = (1750\ \text{rev/min})(0.5\ \text{min}) + \frac{1}{2}(-3000$ rev/min$^2)(0.5\ \text{min})^2 = 500\ \text{rev}.$ [Check: The average velocity is $\frac{1}{2}(250 + 1750) = 1000\ \text{rev/min}$. Then $\theta = \omega_{\text{av}}t = (1000\ \text{rev/min})(0.5\ \text{min})$ $= 500\ \text{rev}.$]

8-B3 (a) $\alpha = (\omega - \omega_0)t = (0.6\ \text{rev/s})/(30\ \text{s}) = 0.02\ \text{rev/s}^2.$ (b) $\theta = \frac{1}{2}\alpha t^2$ $= \frac{1}{2}(0.02\ \text{rev/s}^2)(30\ \text{s})^2 = 9\ \text{rev}.$

8-B4 $\omega^2 = \omega_0{}^2 + 2\alpha\theta$; $\theta = \omega^2/2\alpha = (60\ \text{rad/s})^2/2(15\ \text{rad/s}^2) = 120\ \text{rad}.$

8-B5 The angular speed is $\left(45\ \dfrac{\text{rev}}{\text{min}}\right)\left(\dfrac{2\pi\ \text{rad}}{1\ \text{rev}}\right)\left(\dfrac{1\ \text{min}}{60\ \text{s}}\right) = \frac{3}{2}\pi\ \text{rad/s}.$

$F = ma = mr\omega^2 = (0.5\ \text{g})(6\ \text{cm})(\frac{3}{2}\pi\ \text{rad/s})^2 = 66.6\ \text{dyn}.$

8-B6 The force of friction, $\mu_s mg$, supplies the centripetal force mv^2/r: $\mu_s m(9.8\ \text{m/s}^2) = m(20\ \text{m/s})^2/(60\ \text{m})$; $\mu_s = 0.68.$

8-B7 As in Prob. 8-B6, $\mu_s mg = mv^2/R$; $v = \sqrt{\mu_s Rg}$. The safe speed is independent of the mass of the car.

8-B8 $F = \left(\dfrac{W}{g}\right)\left(\dfrac{v^2}{r}\right) = \left(\dfrac{3200\ \text{lb}}{32\ \text{ft/s}^2}\right)\left(\dfrac{(70\ \text{ft/s})^2}{200\ \text{ft}}\right) = 2450\ \text{lb}.$

8-B9 $F = mv^2/r = (800\ \text{kg})(24\ \text{m/s})^2/(60\ \text{m}) = 7680\ \text{N}.$

8-B10 The angular speed is $\left(9 \times 10^4\ \dfrac{\text{rev}}{\text{min}}\right)\left(\dfrac{2\pi\ \text{rad}}{1\ \text{min}}\right)\left(\dfrac{1\ \text{min}}{60\ \text{s}}\right) = 9425\ \text{rad/s}.$

Field $= F/m = a = r\omega^2 = (0.0375\ \text{m})(9425\ \text{rad/s})^2 = 3.33 \times 10^6\ \text{m/s}^2$ $= (3.4 \times 10^5)g.$

8-B11 $a = r\omega^2$; $\omega = \sqrt{a/r} = \sqrt{(3 \times 10^5)(9.8\ \text{m/s}^2)/(0.1\ \text{m})} = 5422\ \text{rad/s} = 5.18 \times 10^4$ rev/min.

8-B12 $a = v^2/r = (3\ \text{m/s})^2/(5\ \text{m}) = 1.80\ \text{m/s}^2.$ From net $F = ma$, we have $T - (50\ \text{kg})(9.8\ \text{m/s}^2) = (50\ \text{kg})(1.80\ \text{m/s}^2)$; $T = 580\ \text{N}.$

8-B13 (a) $a = g = r\omega^2$; $\omega = \sqrt{g/r} = \sqrt{(9.8\ \text{m/s}^2)/(20\ \text{m})} = 0.700\ \text{rad/s}.$ (b) At the bottom, the acceleration is $+g$ (upward); net $F = ma$; if P is the upward push of the seat cushion, then $P - (100\ \text{kg})(9.8\ \text{m/s}^2) = (100\ \text{kg})(+9.8\ \text{m/s}^2)$; $P = 1960\ \text{N}.$ The apparent weight is twice the true weight.   [Alternatively, from the point of view of the passenger who is in an accelerated frame of reference, the inertial force $-ma$ at the lowest point is directed opposite to a and is thus downward; the total force in this frame is therefore $mg + mg = 2mg.$]

8-B14 (a) $9800\ \text{N} - F = (1000\ \text{kg})(15\ \text{m/s})^2/(40\ \text{m})$; $F = 4175\ \text{N}.$ (b) At 20 m/s, a calculation similar to (a) gives $F = -200\ \text{N}.$ The weight is insufficient, and an attractive (downward) force of 200 N would be needed to prevent the car from becoming airborne.

8-B15 (a) $P - (80\ \text{kg})(9.8\ \text{m/s}^2) = (80\ \text{kg})(300\ \text{m/s})^2/(1200\ \text{m})$; $P = 6780\ \text{N}.$
(b) 6.78 N; the pilot may black out if the blood supply to the brain is insufficient.

8-B16 On the level stretch, $v^2 = 2gh = 2(9.8\ \text{m/s}^2)(20\ \text{m}) = 392\ \text{m}^2/\text{s}^2.$ During the turn, $F = mv^2/r = (50\ \text{kg})(392\ \text{m}^2/\text{s}^2)/(25\ \text{m}) = 784\ \text{N}.$

8-B17 The angular speed is 2.827 rad/s.   (a) Inward force $= mr\omega^2 = (70 \text{ kg})$ $\cdot(2.5 \text{ m})(2.287 \text{ rad/s})^2 = 1399 \text{ N } (\approx 1400 \text{ N})$.   (b) When the floor is removed, the wall now supplies an additional vertically upward frictional force of $70(9.8) \text{ N} = 686 \text{ N}$. A coefficient of static friction of $(686 \text{ N})/$ $(1399 \text{ N}) = 0.49$ would be sufficient to give rise to this force; the rider has no need to worry.

8-B18 $\tan\theta = v^2/rg = (8 \text{ m/s})^2/(16 \text{ m})(9.8 \text{ m/s}^2)$; $\theta = 22°$.

8-B19 $\tan\theta = v^2/rg = (25 \text{ m/s})^2/(200 \text{ m})(9.8 \text{ m/s}^2)$; $\theta = 18°$.

8-B20 $\tan\theta = \dfrac{v^2}{rg} = \dfrac{\left[\left(55\,\dfrac{\text{mi}}{\text{h}}\right)\left(\dfrac{88 \text{ ft/s}}{60 \text{ mi/h}}\right)\right]^2}{(100 \text{ ft})(32 \text{ ft/s}^2)}$; $\theta = 12°$.

8-B21 $v^2 = rg\tan\theta = (60 \text{ m})(9.8 \text{ m/s}^2)\tan 25°$; $v = 16.6 \text{ m/s}$.

8-B22 $I = \frac{1}{3}ML^2 = \frac{1}{3}(4 \text{ kg})(5 \text{ m})^2 = 33.3 \text{ kg·m}^2$.

8-B23 $I = (3 \text{ kg})(0.6 \text{ m})^2 + (5 \text{ kg})(0.1 \text{ m})^2 = 1.13 \text{ kg·m}^2$.

8-B24 $I = \frac{1}{2}MR^2 = \frac{1}{2}(100 \text{ kg})(1.2 \text{ m})^2 = 72 \text{ kg·m}^2$. Now apply Newton's second law: $\alpha = \tau/I = (80 \text{ N})(1.2 \text{ m})/(72 \text{ kg·m}^2) = 1.333 \text{ rad/s}^2$. $\omega = \omega_0 + \alpha t = (1.333 \text{ rad/s}^2)$ $\cdot(3 \text{ s}) = 4.00 \text{ rad/s}$.   [Check: Angular impulse = change in momentum; $\tau\,\Delta t = \Delta(I\omega)$; $(80 \text{ N})(1.2 \text{ m})(3 \text{ s}) = (72 \text{ kg·m}^2)\omega$; $\omega = 4.00 \text{ rad/s}$.]

8-B25 $\alpha = \tau/I = (180 \text{ N})(5 \text{ m})/(2000 \text{ kg·m}^2) = 0.45 \text{ rad/s}^2$. $t = \sqrt{2\theta/\alpha}$ $= \sqrt{2(\frac{1}{2}\pi \text{ rad})/(0.45 \text{ rad/s}^2)} = 2.64 \text{ s}$.

8-B26 $I = \frac{1}{12}ML^2 = \frac{1}{12}(0.6 \text{ kg})(0.7 \text{ m})^2 = 0.0245 \text{ kg·m}^2$. $\text{KE} = \frac{1}{2}I\omega^2 = \frac{1}{2}(0.0245 \text{ kg·m}^2)$ $\cdot(6\pi \text{ rad/s})^2 = 4.35 \text{ J}$. The light rubber ball might have a noticeable effect because of its placement at a large radius of rotation.

8-B27 (a) $I_1 = (2 \text{ kg})(1 \text{ m})^2 + (2 \text{ kg})(1 \text{ m})^2 + 1 \text{ kg·m}^2 = 5 \text{ kg·m}^2$; $I_1\omega_1 = (5 \text{ kg·m}^2)$ $\cdot(10 \text{ rad/s}) = 50 \text{ kg·m/s}$.   (b) The new moment of inertia is $I_2 = (2 \text{ kg})$ $\cdot(0.3 \text{ m})^2 + (2 \text{ kg})(0.3 \text{ m})^2 + 1 \text{ kg·m}^2 = 1.36 \text{ kg·m}^2$. By the law of conservation of angular momentum, $I_2\omega_2 = I_1\omega_1$; $\omega_2 = (5/1.36)(10 \text{ rad/s}) = 36.8 \text{ rad/s}$. The man speeds up.   (c) Using $\text{KE} = \frac{1}{2}I\omega^2$ gives $\text{KE}_1 = 250 \text{ J}$; $\text{KE}_2 = 919 \text{ J}$. [There has been no change of gravitational PE; the increased KE came from the decrease of muscular PE as the man pulls the objects inward against the centrifugal force (an inertial force arising because of the rotation of his frame of reference).]

8-B28 KE of truck $= \frac{1}{2}(10^4 \text{ kg})(30 \text{ m/s})^2 = 4.5 \times 10^6 \text{ J}$; amount stored is 50% of this or $2.25 \times 10^6 \text{ J}$.   (a) For the flywheel, $I = \frac{1}{2}MR^2 = \frac{1}{2}(16 \text{ kg})(0.5 \text{ m})^2$ $= 2 \text{ kg·m}^2$. Energy stored $= \frac{1}{2}I\omega^2$; $2.25 \times 10^6 \text{ J} = \frac{1}{2}(2 \text{ kg·m}^2)\omega^2$; $\omega = 1500$ rad/s $= 14\,300$ rev/min.   (b) Although the rotational speed found in part (a) is large, the device is quite safe; the energy stored is only about $\frac{1}{6}$ the safe amount.

8-B29 (a) To find the KE, ω must be expressed in rad/s; 1800 rev/min $= 188.5$ rad/s. $\text{KE} = \frac{1}{2}I\omega^2 = \frac{1}{2}[\frac{1}{2}(10 \text{ kg})(0.12 \text{ m})^2](188.5 \text{ rad/s})^2 = 1280 \text{ J}$. (b) The force of friction is $0.8(10 \text{ N}) = 8 \text{ N}$.

$\alpha = \dfrac{\tau}{I} = \dfrac{(-8 \text{ N})(0.12 \text{ m})}{\frac{1}{2}(10 \text{ kg})(0.12 \text{ m})^2} = -13.33 \text{ rad/s}^2$.

$\omega = \omega_0 + \alpha t = 188.5 \text{ rad/s} + (-13.33 \text{ rad/s}^2)(6 \text{ s}) = 108.5 \text{ rad/s} = 1036$ rev/min.   [As a check, $\Delta\omega$ can be found from angular impulse: $\tau\,\Delta t$ $= I\,\Delta\omega$; $(-8 \text{ N})(0.12 \text{ m})(6 \text{ s}) = (0.072 \text{ kg·m}^2)(\Delta\omega)$; $\Delta\omega = -80 \text{ rad/s}$, leading to $\omega = 108.5 \text{ rad/s}$ as before.]

8-B30 $v^2 = 2g(23 \text{ m} - 15 \text{ m})$; $F = \dfrac{mv^2}{r} = \dfrac{Wv^2}{gr} = \dfrac{W(16 \text{ m})(g)}{(g)(7.5 \text{ m})} = \frac{32}{15}W$. The push of the rails is then found from $P + W = \frac{32}{15}W$; $P = \frac{17}{15}W$.

8-B31 (a) $mr\omega^2 = \dfrac{GM_E m}{r^2}$; $\omega = \sqrt{\dfrac{GM_E}{r^3}}$; $T = \dfrac{2\pi}{\omega} = 2\pi\sqrt{\dfrac{r^3}{GM_E}}$.

(b) $2\pi\sqrt{\dfrac{(7 \times 10^6 \text{ m})^3}{(5.98 \times 10^{24} \text{ kg})(6.67 \times 10^{-11} \text{ N·m}^2/\text{kg}^2}} = 5827 \text{ s} = 97.1 \text{ min.}$

8-B32 From Kepler's third law, $(8 \text{ y})^2/(1 \text{ y})^2 = R^3/(1 \text{ a.u.})^3$; $R = 4$ a.u.

8-B33 The areas of the sectors are equal, according to Kepler's law of areas. $v_B\,\Delta t/\approx av_A\,\Delta t$; the equation becomes increasingly valid as $\Delta t \to 0$.

8-B34 (a) $\dfrac{mv^2}{r} = \dfrac{GMm}{r^2}$; $v = \sqrt{\dfrac{GM}{r}} = \sqrt{\dfrac{(6.61 \times 10^{-11} \text{ N·m}^2/\text{kg}^2)(5.98 \times 10^{24} \text{ kg})}{6.38 \times 10^6 \text{ m}}}$

$= 7907 \text{ m/s} = 7.91 \text{ km/s}.$ (b) $T = 2\pi r/v = 2\pi(6.38 \times 10^6 \text{ m})/(7.91 \times 10^3 \text{ m/s})$
$= 5070 \text{ s} = 84.5 \text{ min.}$

8-B35 (a) If R is the radius of the earth's orbit, and M is the mass of the sun, Eq. 8-16 gives

$M = \dfrac{4\pi^2}{G}\left(\dfrac{r^3}{T^2}\right) = \dfrac{4\pi^2(1.50 \times 10^{11} \text{ m})^3}{(6.67 \times 10^{-11} \text{ N·m}^2/\text{kg}^2)(365.3 \times 24 \times 3600 \text{ s})^2} = 2.01 \times 10^{30} \text{ kg.}$

(b) The volume of the sun is $\frac{4}{3}\pi(6.95 \times 10^8 \text{ m})^3 = 1.406 \times 10^{27} \text{ m}^3$. The density is $(2.01 \times 10^{30} \text{ kg})/(1.406 \times 10^{27} \text{ m}^3) = 1426 \text{ kg/m}^3$; the specific gravity is 1.43.   [The specific gravity of the sun is greater than that of water. The sun is a "dense gas" and emits a continuous blackbody spectrum (see first paragraph of second column of p. 673).]

8-B36 The ratio of the sun's force to the earth's force is about 2.1, both at the time of a new moon and at the time of a full moon.   [The earth-moon system should be thought of as a double planet, with both components in orbit around the sun. Since the net force is always toward the sun, the moon's orbit is everywhere concave toward the sun, as is the earth's orbit. The curvatures of both orbits vary in such a way that the moon's orbit relative to the earth is an ellipse.]

8-B37 (a) From the fact that gravitational force varies as $1/r^2$, $a = (9.8 \text{ m/s}^2)/(60^2) = 2.72 \times 10^{-3} \text{ m/s}^2$.   (b) $a = 4\pi^2(60R_E)/T^2 = 4\pi^2(60 \times 6.38 \times 10^6 \text{ m})/(27.3 \times 86\,400 \text{ s})^2 = 2.72 \times 10^{-3} \text{ m/s}^2$.

8-C1 During the elastic collision of two equal pucks, the tethered puck receives all the momentum of the moving one, which stops dead (see p. 127-28). The tethered puck makes one revolution in $2\pi(5 \text{ m})/(6.28 \text{ m/s}) = 5 \text{ s}$, then it hits the other puck and gives it a speed of 6.28 m/s. During the next 3 s, this puck moves $(6.28 \text{ m/s})(3 \text{ s}) = 18.8 \text{ m.}$

8-C2 $x_{\text{c.m.}} = \dfrac{(3.0 \text{ kg})(20 \text{ cm}) + (5.0 \text{ kg})(70 \text{ cm})}{8.0 \text{ kg}} = 51.25 \text{ cm.}$ About an axis through this point, $I_{\text{c.m.}} = (3.0 \text{ kg})(0.3125 \text{ m})^2 + (5.0 \text{ kg})(0.1875 \text{ m})^2 = 0.46875 \text{ kg·m}^2$. [This is, indeed, less than I about the other axes mentioned in other problems already solved (Example 11-2, Prob. 8-B23): About $x = 0$, $I = 2.57$ kg·m^2; about $x = 50$ cm, $I = 0.47000$ kg·m^2; about $x = 80$ cm, $I = 1.13$ kg·m^2; about $x = 100$ cm, $I = 2.37$ kg·m^2.]

8-C3 (a) $I = \frac{1}{3}ML^2 = \frac{1}{3}(800 \text{ kg})(1.5 \text{ m})^2 = 600 \text{ kg·m}^2$;   (b) $\theta = \frac{1}{2}\alpha t^2 = \frac{1}{2}(\tau/I)t^2$
$= \frac{1}{2}(100 \text{ N})(1.5 \text{ m})(2 \text{ s})^2/(600 \text{ kg·m}^2) = 0.500 \text{ rad.}$

8-C4 PE of vertical ladder becomes KE as it strikes the ground: $Mg(L/2)$
$= \frac{1}{2}(\frac{1}{3}ML^2)\omega^2$; $\omega = \sqrt{3g/L}$, and hence $v = r\omega = L\sqrt{3g/L} = \sqrt{3gL}$.

8-C5 Before the thread is burned, the upward component of T equals the weight; $T\cos 60° = mg$; $T = 2mg$. After the thread is burned, the ball falls $r/2$ to reach the lowest point; the energy principle gives $\frac{1}{2}mv^2 = mg(r/2)$; $v^2 = rg$. At the lowest point, the ball has an upward (centripetal) acceleration. $T - mg = mv^2/r$; $T = mv^2/r + mg = m(rg)/r + mg = 2mg$.

8-C6   The proof in effect uses the saggital theorem (p. 792). $(DB)^2 = (AD)$
$\cdot (2r - AD)$; neglect AD in comparison to $2r$. Thus $CB \approx AD \approx (DB)^2/2r$
$\approx (AB)^2/2r = (vt)^2/2r = \frac{1}{2}(v^2/r)t^2$. The result is in the form $s = \frac{1}{2}at^2$, as
for a falling body.

8-C7   We carry calculations to four figures to avoid rounding errors.
(a) $\frac{1}{2}mv^2 = mgh$; $v = \sqrt{2gh} = \sqrt{2(9.8 \text{ m/s}^2)(2.0 \text{ m})} = 6.261$ m/s.
(b) $\omega = v/r = (6.261 \text{ m/s})/(3.0 \text{ m}) = 2.087$ rad/s.   (c) $I_2\omega_2 = I_1\omega_1$;
$(50 \text{ kg})(2.9 \text{ m})^2\omega_2 = (50 \text{ kg})(3.0 \text{ m})^2(2.087 \text{ rad/sec})$; $\omega_2 = 2.233$ rad/s.
KE2$= \frac{1}{2}I_2\omega_2^2 = \frac{1}{2}(50 \text{ kg})(2.9 \text{ m})^2(2.333 \text{ rad/s})^2 = 1049$ J.   (d) 1049 J
$= (50 \text{ kg})(9.8 \text{ m/s}^2)h_2$; $h_2 = 2.14$ m.   [The original KE was 980 J,
so he gained 69 J of KE; this is accounted for by the work done
(by his muscles) against an inertial force $-ma$ (centrifugal force), which
is of magnitude $mr\omega^2 = (50 \text{ kg})(2.95 \text{ m})(2.16 \text{ rad/s})^2 = 688$ N (using average
values for r and ω). Work $= Fs = (688 \text{ N})(0.1 \text{ M}) \approx 69$ J, which checks with
the calculated increase in KE given by 1049 J $- 980$ J.]

8-C8 1.04×10^{23} kg.   [From Table 8-1, $I_{\text{Venus}} = \frac{2}{5}MR^2 = \frac{2}{5}(6 \times 10^{24} \text{ kg})$
$\cdot (36 \times 10^{12} \text{ m}^2) = 86.4 \times 10^{36}$ kg·m^2. If the original ω for Venus was same
as earth's, $\omega = 2\pi \text{ rad}/86.4 \times 10^3$ s. Then original $I\omega$ for Venus was 2π
$\times 10^{33}$ kg·m^2/s (the final $I\omega$ is negligible). Equate this to mrv for the small
planet using as r the radius of the tangent path as it struck Venus (i.e.,
6×10^6 m). The result is about $\frac{1}{60}$ the mass of Venus. See Singer, *Science*,
170, 1196 (1970); French, *Science*, 173, 169 (1971); and Singer's reply to
French, *Science*, 173, 171 (1971).]

8-C9 $I = \frac{1}{2}mr^2 = \frac{1}{2}(10 \text{ kg})(0.1 \text{ m})^2 = 0.05$ kg·m^2. Loss of PE = gain of KE; both the
cylinder and the tomatoes gain KE. Use v/r for ω.

$$(20 \text{ kg})(9.8 \text{ m/s}^2)(6 \text{ m}) = \frac{1}{2}(20 \text{ kg})v^2 + \frac{1}{2}(0.05 \text{ kg·m}^2)\left(\frac{v}{(0.1 \text{ m})^2}\right)^2;$$

$v = 9.70$ m/s.   [The energy principle gives v but cannot give the acceleration or the time. See Prob. 8-C16, where the same system is treated as
an Atwood's machine to find the time of fall.]

8-C10 Use the moment of inertia of a solid sphere from the table on p. 183.
(a) $mgH = \frac{1}{2}(\frac{2}{5}MR^2)(v^2/R^2) + \frac{1}{2}Mv^2$; $v = \sqrt{10gH/7}$.   (b) If the sphere (or
any other object) slides down the plane, $MgH = \frac{1}{2}Mv^2$; $v = \sqrt{2gH}$.
[The rolling sphere takes longer to reach the bottom, and is moving more
slowly.]

8-C11 A to B.

8-C12 Upward; no.   [The flywheel is rotating oppositely to the direction of
the flywheel of the racing car discussed on p. 201.]

8-C13 $\Delta\theta = (AB)/(I\omega) = \tau \, \Delta t/I\omega$; hence $\Omega = \Delta\theta/\Delta t = \tau/I\omega$.

8-C14 $\Omega = \dfrac{\tau}{I\omega} = \dfrac{(10 \text{ kg})(9.8 \text{ m/s}^2)(0.25 \text{ m})}{(10 \text{ kg})(0.35 \text{ m})^2(31.4 \text{ rad/s})} = 0.637$ rad/s.   [The wheel
precesses once around in 9.9 s.]

8-C15 (a) Observed $\Omega = \dfrac{2\pi \text{ rad}}{26\,000 \text{ y}}\left(\dfrac{1 \text{ y}}{3.16 \times 10^7 \text{ s}}\right) = 7.7 \times 10^{-12}$ rad/s. Also, the

spin angular velocity ω of the earth is $\dfrac{2\pi \text{ rad}}{86\,400 \text{ s}} = 7.3 \times 10^{-5}$ rad/s.
(b) $\frac{2}{5}(6 \times 10^{24} \text{ kg})(6.4 \times 10^6 \text{ m})^2 \approx 1 \times 10^{38}$ kg·m^2.   (c) $m \approx (10 \times 10^3 \text{ m})$
$\cdot (6 \times 10^6 \text{ m})^2(3 \times 10^3 \text{ kg/m}^3) \approx 1 \times 10^{21}$ kg.
(d) $F_1 = \dfrac{(6.67 \times 10^{-11} \text{ N·m}^2/\text{kg}^2)(10^{21} \text{ kg})(7.3 \times 10^{22} \text{ kg})}{(3.84 \times 10^8 \text{ m})^2} = 3.30 \times 10^{16}$ N;
similarly, $F_2 = 3.10 \times 10^{16}$ N.   (e) net torque $= (F_1 - F_2)$(lever arm)
$= (0.20 \times 10^{16} \text{ N})(3 \times 10^6 \text{ m}) = 6 \times 10^{21}$ N·m

(f) Calculated $\Omega = \dfrac{\tau}{I\omega} = \dfrac{6 \times 10^{21} \text{ N·m}}{(1 \times 10^{38} \text{ kg·m}^2)(7.3 \times 10^{-5} \text{ rad/s})} \approx 8 \times 10^{-13} \text{ rad/s}$.

(g) The predicted precessional rate is about $\frac{1}{10}$ the observed rate found in part (a). The earth has a dense core (p. 70); so I is less than for a uniform sphere. This would make Ω larger. Also, the sun's torque would increase τ and make Ω larger.

8-C16   (a) As in Sec. 8-11 we set up Newton's second law for the cylinder and for the tomatoes. The cylinder's moment of inertia is $\frac{1}{2}mr^2 = \frac{1}{2}(10 \text{ kg})(0.1 \text{ m})^2 = 0.05 \text{ kg·m}^2$.

(cylinder)   net $\tau = I\alpha$; $T(0.1 \text{ m}) = (0.05 \text{ kg·m}^2)\left(\dfrac{a}{0.1 \text{ m}}\right)$

(tomatoes)   net $F = ma$; $196 \text{ N} - T = (20 \text{ kg})a$

Solving simultaneously gives $a = 7.84 \text{ m/s}^2$.   (b) $t = \sqrt{2s/a}$ $= \sqrt{2(6 \text{ m})/(7.84 \text{ m/s}^2)} = 1.237 \text{ s}$.   (c) $v = at = (7.84 \text{ m/s}^2)(1.237 \text{ s})$ $= 9.70 \text{ m/s}$. The final velocity checks with the value found in Prob. 8-C9 using the energy principle.

Chapter 9   Elasticity and Vibration

Questions

9-1   The telephone dial does not follow Hooke's law; it is constructed to "wind up" only slightly when turned through an angle.

9-2   Yes.

9-3   (a) Stretch modulus; the wood fibers along the bottom surface of the board are stretched, and those along the top surface are compressed;   (b) shear modulus; the length of wire in the coil doesn't change, but its shape (pitch of the helix) does.   (c) bulk modulus;   (d) shear modulus;   (e) shear modulus.

9-4   The weight of the bones is small compared with the other forces.

9-5   Acceleration is zero at the positions of zero displacement, where the speed is a maximum.

9-6   No. SHM is the projection of *uniform* circular motion.

9-7   The gravity field may be less above a salt dome; a spring balance is stretched less at such a location.

9-8   A pendulum bob is nowhere in equilibrium, since it still has centripetal acceleration at the center of its swing. See also Ques. 9-5.

9-9   At higher altitude, g is less and the period is greater. The clock will lose time.

9-10   Since $\sin\theta$ is less than θ (in radians), the restoring torque is too small, and the pendulum picks up speed too slowly. The exact formula for the period of a pendulum gives a result slightly greater than $2\pi\sqrt{l/g}$.

9-11 The vibration of an air column in a flute is SHM; a heartbeat is a relaxation oscillation.

Multiple Choice

9-12 (b);   9-13 (c);   9-14 (a);   9-15 (c);   9-16 (b);   9-17 (a).

Problems

9-A1   Strain = $\Delta L/L$ = (3 cm)/(30 cm) $\approx$ 0.1. The answer is approximate, since it is not clear whether the initial or final length should be used for L.

9-A2 $\left(\dfrac{(20\ \text{kg})(9.8\ \text{m/s}^2)}{0.01\ \text{cm}^2}\right)\left(\dfrac{10^2\ \text{cm}}{1\ \text{m}}\right)^2$ = 1.96 $\times$ 10^8 N/m^2.   The length is unimportant.

9-A3   Strain = (0.04 m)/(80 m) = 5 $\times$ 10^{-4}.

9-A4 $k = \Delta F/\Delta s$; $\Delta s = \Delta F/k$ = (60 N $-$ 20 N)/(200 N/m) = 0.2 m = 20 cm. New length is approximately 70 cm.

9-A5   The stretch is $\frac{1}{16}$ in. = $\frac{1}{192}$ ft. $k = \Delta F/\Delta s$ = ($\frac{1}{16}$ lb)/($\frac{1}{192}$ ft) = 12 lb/ft.

9-A6 $T = 1/\nu$ = 1/(250 s^{-1}) = 0.004 s.

9-A7 $T = \frac{1}{4}$ s; time for 200 vibrations is 50 s.

9-A8 (a) 7.5 cm; (b) 0.

9-A9 (a) 6 cm; (b) 6 cm.

9-A10 (a) $\nu = 1/T$ = 1/(2.5 s) = 0.4 vib/s; (b) (0.4 vib/s)(50 s) = 20 vib.

9-A11 (a) [T]; (b) [T^{-1}]; (c) [MT^{-2}] or [FL^{-1}].

9-A12 $T = 2\pi\sqrt{\dfrac{1\ \text{kg}}{16\ \text{N/m}}}$ = $\dfrac{\pi}{2}$ s = 1.57 s.

9-A13 $T = 2$ s $= 2\pi\sqrt{\dfrac{l}{9.8\ \text{m/s}^2}}$; l = (9.8)/π^2 = 0.993 m.

9-A14 $T = 2\pi\sqrt{\dfrac{40\ \text{m}}{9.8\ \text{m/s}^2}}$ = 12.7 s.

9-B1 $\Delta L = \dfrac{\Delta F L}{EA}$ = $\dfrac{(4000\ \text{N})(10\ \text{m})}{(20\times 10^{10}\ \text{N/m}^2)(40)(5\times 10^{-6}\ \text{m}^2)}$ = 10^{-3} m = 1.0 mm.

9-B2 $A = \dfrac{\Delta F L}{E\,\Delta L}$ = $\dfrac{(1800\ \text{N})(0.15\ \text{m})}{(2\times 10^{10}\ \text{N/m}^2)(0.5\times 10^{-3}\ \text{m})}$ = 2.7 $\times$ 10^{-5} m^2 = 27 mm^2.

9-B3 $E = \dfrac{\Delta F L}{A\,\Delta L}$ = $\dfrac{(0.8\ \text{kg})(9.8\ \text{N/kg})(25.1\times 10^{-2}\ \text{m})}{(6.5\times 10^{-3}\ \text{m})(13\times 10^{-3}\ \text{m})(0.19\times 10^{-2}\ \text{m})}$ = 1.2 $\times$ 10^7 N/m^2.

9-B4 $A = \dfrac{\Delta F L}{E\,\Delta L}$ = $\dfrac{(16\times 10^3\ \text{N})(25\ \text{m})}{(20\times 10^{10}\ \text{N/m}^2)(5\times 10^{-3}\ \text{m})}$ = 4 $\times$ 10^{-4} m^2 = 4.0 cm^2.

9-B5   Strain = $\dfrac{\text{stress}}{E}$ = $\dfrac{5\times 10^8\ \text{N/m}^2}{20\times 10^{10}\ \text{N/m}^2}$ = 0.0025   [This steel wire can be stretched only $\frac{1}{4}$ percent before it breaks.]

9-B6   See the answer to Prob. 9-B5; a 1% stretch would require a stress of 20 $\times$ 10^8 N/m^2, which is 4 times the ultimate tensile strength.

9-B7 $E = (20\times 10^{10}\ \text{N/m}^2)\left(\dfrac{1.45\times 10^{-4}\ \text{lb/in.}^2}{1\ \text{N/m}^2}\right)$ = 29 $\times$ 10^6 lb/in.^{2}.

   $\Delta L = \dfrac{\Delta F L}{EA}$ = $\dfrac{(2\times 10^4\ \text{lb})(10\ \text{ft})}{(29\times 10^6\ \text{lb/in.}^2)(\pi)(4\ \text{in.})^2}$ $\left(\dfrac{12\ \text{in.}}{1\ \text{ft}}\right)$ = 0.00165 in.

9-B8   Centripetal force is $mr\omega^2$; if U is the ultimate tensile strength (a stress), $U = F/A = mr\omega^2/A$. Hence,

$$\omega = \sqrt{\frac{UA}{mr}} = \sqrt{\frac{(4.8 \times 10^7 \text{ N/m}^2)(10^{-6} \text{ m}^2)}{(10 \text{ kg})(0.3 \text{ m})}} = 4.00 \text{ rad/s.}$$

9-B9   Shearing stress = $\dfrac{6000 \text{ N}}{\pi(0.015 \text{ m})^2} = 8.49 \times 10^6 \text{ N/m}^2$. Quite safe, by a factor of almost 10.

9-B10   Shearing stress = $(1.2 \text{ N})/(4 \times 10^{-4} \text{ m}^2) = 3000 \text{ N/m}^2$. Shearing strain = $(2.0 \text{ mm})/(80 \text{ mm}) = 0.025$. Shear modulus = stress/strain = $1.2 \times 10^5 \text{ N/m}^2$.

9-B11 $B = \dfrac{\Delta P}{\Delta V/V} = \dfrac{(8.8 - 1.0) \times 10^5 \text{ N/m}^2}{(2 \text{ cm}^3)/(4000 \text{ cm}^3)} = 1.6 \times 10^9 \text{ N/m}^2$.

9-B12 $P = B(\Delta V/V) = (11 \times 10^{10} \text{ N/m}^2)(0.01) = 1.1 \times 10^9 \text{ N/m}^2$.

9-B13 $V = M/d = (1580 \text{ kg})/(7860 \text{ kg/m}^3) = 0.201 \text{ m}^3$. $\Delta V = V\Delta P/B = (0.201 \text{ m}^3)$ $\cdot (1.8 \times 10^6 \text{ N/m}^2)/(9.0 \times 10^{10} \text{ N/m}^2) = 4.02 \times 10^{-6} \text{ m}^3 = 4.02 \text{ cm}^3$.

9-B14   Volume (at surface) = $(160 \text{ g})/(3.51 \text{ g/cm}^3) = 45.6 \text{ cm}^3$.

$$\Delta V = \frac{V\Delta P}{B} = \frac{(45.6 \text{ cm}^3)(1.5 \times 10^{10} \text{ N/m}^2)}{62 \times 10^{10} \text{ N/m}^2} = 1.1 \text{ cm}^3$$

The original volume (at high pressure) was less than the volume at the surface, hence subtract ΔV: $V_0 = 45.6 \text{ cm}^3 - 1.1 \text{ cm}^3 = 44.5 \text{ cm}^3$.

9-B15   From $T = 2\pi\sqrt{m/k}$, $k = 4\pi^2 m/T^2 = 4\pi^2 m\nu^2 = 4\pi^2(2 \text{ kg})(2 \text{ s}^{-1})^2 = 316 \text{ N/m}$. Then $F = ks = (316 \text{ N/m})(1.5 \text{ m}) = 474 \text{ N}$.

9-B16 $v_0 = 2\pi A/T = 2\pi\nu A = 2\pi(2 \text{ s}^{-1})(7.5 \text{ cm}) = 94.2 \text{ cm/s}$.

9-B17   (a) $v_0 = 2\pi\nu A = 2\pi(200 \text{ s}^{-1})(10^{-3} \text{ m}) = 1.26 \text{ m/s}$;   (b) $a_0 = v_0^2/A$ = $(1.26 \text{ m/s})^2/(10^{-3} \text{ m}) = 1.58 \times 10^3 \text{ m/s}^2$.

9-B18   (a) $v_0 = 2\pi A/T = 2\pi(0.20 \text{ m})/(2 \text{ s}) = 0.628 \text{ m/s}$;   (b) $k = 4\pi^2 m/T^2 =$ $4\pi^2(1 \text{ kg})/(2 \text{ s})^2 = 9.87 \text{ N/m}$;   (c) $\Delta s = \Delta F/k = (1.0 \text{ kg})(9.8 \text{ N/kg})/(9.87 \text{ N/m})$ = 0.993 m.

9-B19   (a) Time required = $\frac{1}{4}T = \frac{1}{4}\left[2\pi\sqrt{(0.2 \text{ kg})/(20 \text{ N/m})}\right] = 0.157 \text{ s}$;   (b) $v_0 =$ $2\pi A/T = 2\pi(0.1 \text{ m})/4(0.157 \text{ s}) = 1.00 \text{ m/s}$.   [Note that it would be wrong to use the equations of uniformly accelerated motion to find the velocity at the midpoint; a is not constant during SHM. The energy principle can also give the maximum velocity. Using $\frac{1}{2}kA^2$ for the initial PE, we have $\frac{1}{2}kA^2$ = $\frac{1}{2}mv_0^2$; $\frac{1}{2}(20 \text{ N/m})(0.1 \text{ m})^2 = \frac{1}{2}(0.2 \text{ kg})v_0^2$; whence $v_0 = 1.00 \text{ m/s}$.]

9-B20   Force constant is $k = (100 \text{ kg})(9.8 \text{ N/kg})/(0.08 \text{ m}) = 12\,250 \text{ N/m}$. Now T = $2\pi\sqrt{m/k} = 2\pi\sqrt{(400 \text{ kg})/(12\,250 \text{ N/m})} = 1.135 \text{ s/vib}$. In 5 s, the raft makes $(5 \text{ s})/(1.135 \text{ s/vib}) = 4.40 \text{ vib}$.

9-B21   The force constant is 16 lb/in. or 192 lb/ft.

$$T = 2\pi\sqrt{\frac{W/g}{k}} = 2\pi\sqrt{\frac{(8 \text{ lb})/(32 \text{ ft/s}^2)}{192 \text{ lb/ft}}} = 0.227 \text{ s.}$$

9-B22 $T = 2\pi\sqrt{m/k} = 2\pi\sqrt{(4 \text{ kg})/(100 \text{ N/m})} = 0.4\pi$. Equation 9-5 gives

$$y = A\sin\left(\frac{2\pi t}{T}\right) = -2\sin\left(\frac{2\pi t}{0.4\pi}\right) \text{ or } y = -2\sin 5t.$$

[The $-$ sign is used because the body is moving *downward* at $t = 0$.]

9-B23   In Example 9-6, the total energy is 11.3 J. Hence KE = $11.3 \text{ J} - 7.2 \text{ J} = 4.1 \text{ J}$.

9-B24   PE = $\frac{1}{2}kx^2 = \frac{1}{2}(1000 \text{ N/m})(0.05 \text{ m})^2 = 1.25 \text{ J}$.

9-B25   First find the force constant: $k = 4\pi^2 m/T^2 = 4\pi^2(20 \text{ kg})/(0.5 \text{ s})^2 = 3158 \text{ N/m}$. It is most convenient to calculate the maximum PE (the KE is 0 at this point): $\frac{1}{2}kA^2 = \frac{1}{2}(3158 \text{ N/m})(0.02 \text{ m})^2 = 0.632 \text{ J}$.

9-B26   Here $T = 3.14 \text{ s} = \pi \text{ s}$. (a) $k = 4\pi^2 m/T^2 = 4\pi^2(5 \text{ kg})/(\pi \text{ s})^2 = 20 \text{ N/m}$; (b) $\text{PE}_{max} = \frac{1}{2}kA^2 = \frac{1}{2}(20 \text{ N/m})(2 \text{ m})^2 = 40 \text{ J}$;   (c) $v_0 = 2\pi A/T = 2\pi(2 \text{ m})/(\pi \text{ s})$ = 4 m/s, hence $\text{KE}_{max} = \frac{1}{2}mv_0^2 = \frac{1}{2}(5 \text{ kg})(4 \text{ m/s})^2 = 40 \text{ J}$.

9-B27   Force constant $k = (20 \text{ N})/(0.01 \text{ m}) = 2000 \text{ N/m}$. (a) PE $= \frac{1}{2}kA^2$
$= \frac{1}{2}(2000 \text{ N/m})(0.20 \text{ m})^2 = 40$ J (the mass of the stone does not enter into
the calculation so far); (b) PE becomes KE: $40 \text{ J} = \frac{1}{2}(0.05 \text{ kg})v^2$;
$v = 40 \text{ m/s}$.

9-B28   Let x be the mass of the platform. Since T^2 is proportional to the total
mass (k remains the same), we have $5^2 = C(50 + x)$; $10^2 = C(350 + x)$.
Solving simultaneously gives $x = 50$ g and $C = \frac{1}{4}$ unit. Finally, with the
unknown load, $15^2 = \frac{1}{4}(m + 50)$; $m = 850$ g.

9-B29 $\left(\dfrac{T'}{T}\right)^2 = \dfrac{m'}{m}$; $\left(\dfrac{T'}{0.1 \text{ s}}\right)^2 = \dfrac{16 \text{ kg}}{1 \text{ kg}}$; $T' = 0.4$ s.   [The fact that the value
of g has changed is of no consequence; we are measuring mass, not weight.]

9-B30 $a_0 = \dfrac{v_0^2}{A} = \dfrac{(2\pi\nu A)^2}{A} = 4\pi^2\nu^2 A$. Thus the amplitude is
$A = \dfrac{a_0}{4\pi^2\nu^2} = \dfrac{(10)(9.8 \text{ m/s}^2)}{4\pi^2(20 \text{ s}^{-1})^2} = 6.21 \times 10^{-3} \text{ m} = 6.21 \text{ mm}$.

9-B31 (a) The package becomes a freely falling body if the downward acceleration
of the platform is $\geq g$; this first occurs (as amplitude is increased) at the
top of the motion. (b) $a_0 = \dfrac{v_0^2}{A} = \dfrac{1}{A}\left(\dfrac{2\pi A}{T}\right)^2 = \dfrac{4\pi^2 A}{T^2}$. From $g = 4\pi^2 A/T^2$
we find $A = gT^2/4\pi^2 = (9.8 \text{ m/s}^2)(0.2 \text{ s})^2/4\pi^2 = 9.93 \times 10^{-3} \text{ m} = 9.93 \text{ mm}$.

9-B32   KE $= \frac{1}{2}mv_0^2 = \frac{1}{2}m(2\pi A/T)^2 = 2\pi^2 A^2/T^2$.

9-B33 $T = (2.0 \text{ s})\sqrt{6} = 4.90$ s.

9-B34   The time to fall $\frac{1}{4}$ ft is $\sqrt{2h/g} = \sqrt{2(\frac{1}{4} \text{ ft})/(32 \text{ ft/s}^2)} = \frac{1}{8}$ s. The period is
twice this, or $\frac{1}{4}$ s. The frequency is 4 vib/s.

9-C1 $F - 1000(9.8) \text{ N} = (1000 \text{ kg})(2.20 \text{ m/s}^2)$; $F = 1.2 \times 10^4$ N. Stress $= F/A$;
$A = F/\text{stress} = (1.2 \times 10^4 \text{ N})/(1.2 \times 10^8 \text{ N/m}^2) = 10^{-4} \text{ m}^2$. From $\frac{1}{4}\pi D^2 = 10^{-4}$
m^2 we find $D = 1.13 \times 10^{-2} \text{ m} = 1.13$ cm.

9-C2 (a) From $E = \dfrac{\Delta F/A}{\Delta L/L}$ we have $k = \dfrac{\Delta F}{\Delta L} = \dfrac{EA}{L} = \dfrac{(20 \times 10^{10} \text{ N/m}^2)(0.5 \times 10^{-6} \text{ m}^2)}{30 \text{ m}}$
$= 3.33 \times 10^3 \text{ N/m}$. (b) $T = 2\pi\sqrt{m/k}$; $\nu = (1/2\pi)\sqrt{k/m} = (1/2\pi)$
$\cdot \sqrt{(3.33 \times 10^3 \text{ N/m})/(10 \text{ kg})} = 2.91$ vib/s.

9-C3   From $E = \dfrac{\Delta F/A}{\Delta L/L}$ we have $k = \dfrac{\Delta F}{\Delta L} = \dfrac{EA}{L}$ or $k = \pi r^2 E/L$.

9-C4 $E = \dfrac{\Delta F/A}{\Delta L/L} = \dfrac{L}{A}\left(\dfrac{\Delta F}{\Delta L}\right) = Lk/A = Lk/\pi r^2$. Since $k = 4\pi^2 m/T^2$, we obtain E
$= 4\pi m L/r^2 T^2$.

9-C5   From $E = \dfrac{\Delta F/A}{\Delta L/L}$, $k = \dfrac{\Delta F}{\Delta L} = \dfrac{EA}{L}$. Now $T = 2\pi\sqrt{\dfrac{m}{k}}$ becomes $T = 2\pi\sqrt{\dfrac{mL}{EA}}$,
whence $A = \dfrac{4\pi^2 mL}{ET^2} = \dfrac{4\pi^2 mL\nu^2}{E}$. Using E for copper (Table 9-1), we obtain
$A = \dfrac{4\pi^2(10 \text{ kg})(10 \text{ m})(10 \text{ s}^{-1})^2}{10 \times 10^{10} \text{ N/m}^2} = 3.95 \times 10^{-6} \text{ m}^2 = 3.95 \text{ mm}^2$.

9-C6 (a) Use the reference circle to find that the reference
particle moves through 60°. The time required is
$\left(\dfrac{60°}{360°}\right)T = \frac{1}{6}(6 \text{ s}) = 1$ s. (b) $v = v_0 \sin 60°$
$= \dfrac{2\pi(10 \text{ cm})}{6 \text{ s}} \sin 60° = 9.07 \text{ cm/s}$.

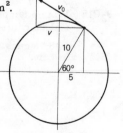

Prob. 9-C6

9-C7 $k = 4\pi^2 m/T^2 = 4\pi^2(2 \text{ kg})/(2 \text{ s})^2 = 19.7 \text{ N/m}$. The weight
of the load is $2(9.8) \text{ N} = 19.6$ N. At the extreme points,
the magnitude of the spring force (due to stretch) is
$\pm(19.7 \text{ N/m})(0.4 \text{ m}) = 7.9 \text{ N}$. (a) At the lowest

point, the total force in the spring is 19.6 N + 7.9 N
= 27.5 N;   (b) When passing through the midpoint
of its motion, the mass is in dynamic equilibrium,
net $F = 0$, and the spring force is 19.6 N;   (c) At
the highest point, the spring force is 19.6 N − 7.9 N
= 11.7 N.

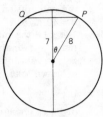

9-C8   2.01 h.   [The SHM of the water height has amplitude $\frac{1}{2}$(12 ft + 4 ft) = 8 ft; we want the time interval
during which $y \geq 7$ ft, to allow at most 1 ft of clear-
ance. The reference circle shows that the fraction of
12.5 h that is "clear" (corresponding to arc PQ) is
$2\theta/360°$. Since $\cos \theta = 7/8$, $\theta = 29°$, and $t = (58°/360°)$ Prob. 9-C8
× (12.5 h) = 2.01 h.]

9-C9   (a) The time for A to reach B is $\frac{1}{4} T$ for the SHM of a pendulum of length
8 ft: $\frac{1}{4}[2\pi\sqrt{(8 \text{ ft})/(32 \text{ ft/s}^2)}\ ]$ = 0.79 s. After collision, the time for B to
reach the floor is the time required to fall through 4 ft: $\sqrt{2s/g}$
= $\sqrt{2(4 \text{ ft})/(32 \text{ ft/s}^2)}$ = 0.50 s; total time is 0.79 s + 0.50 s = 1.29 s.
(b) To find the speed of A as it strikes B, use the energy principle (A falls
through a vertical distance 4 ft): $\frac{1}{2}mv^2 = mgh$; $v = \sqrt{2gh} = \sqrt{2(32 \text{ ft/s}^2)(4 \text{ ft})}$
= 16 ft/s. After the collision, ball B becomes a projectile. Let V_A and V_B
be the final velocities, just after collision. By the law of conservation of
momentum, $3m(16) + m(0) = 3mV_A + mV_B$. Also, since the collision is perfectly elastic, $V_B - V_A = 16$. Solving simultaneously gives $V_A = 8$ ft/s,
$V_B = 24$ ft/s. Range = $R = V_Bt = (24 \text{ ft/s})(0.5 \text{ s}) = 12$ ft.

9-C10 The final equilibrium point is 20 cm below the original free end of the
spring; the weight of the load has caused a stretch of 20 cm. The force
constant is $[m(9.8) \text{ N}]/(0.20 \text{ m}) = 49m$. $T = 2\pi\sqrt{\dfrac{m}{49m}} = 2\pi/7 = 0.898$ s.

9-C11 $I = 4(250 \text{ g})(10 \text{ cm})^2 = 10^5 \text{ g·cm}^2$. The torsion constant is $\tau/\theta = (2000 \text{ cm·dyn})/$
$(0.5 \text{ rad}) = 4 \times 10^3 \text{ cm·dyn}$. $T = 2\pi\sqrt{\dfrac{I}{\tau/\theta}} = 2\pi\sqrt{\dfrac{10^5 \text{ g·cm}^2}{4 \times 10^3 \text{ cm·dyn}}}$ = 31.4 s.
[The same result is obtained if all quantities are first converted to mks
units.]

9-C12 (a) $\tau/\theta = (3 \text{ N})(0.15 \text{ m})/(\pi/4 \text{ rad}) = 0.573$ N·m.   (b) $I = \frac{1}{2}MR^2 = \frac{1}{2}(8 \text{ kg})$
$\cdot(0.15 \text{ m})^2 = 0.090$ kg·m². Hence $T = 2\pi\sqrt{I/(\tau/\theta)} = 2\pi\sqrt{(0.090 \text{ kg·m}^2)}/$
$\sqrt{(0.573 \text{ N·m})}$ = 2.49 s; time for 40 vibrations is 40(2.49 s) = 99.6 s.

9-C13 $I = \frac{1}{3}ML^2$; $h = \frac{1}{2}L$; $T = 2\pi\sqrt{\dfrac{I}{mgh}} = 2\pi\sqrt{\dfrac{\frac{1}{3}mL^2}{mg(\frac{1}{2}L)}} = 2\pi\sqrt{\dfrac{2L}{3g}}$
$= 2\pi\sqrt{\dfrac{2(1 \text{ m})}{3(9.8 \text{ m/s}^2)}}$ = 1.64 s.

9-C14 $T = 2\pi\sqrt{\dfrac{I}{mgh}} = 2\pi\sqrt{\dfrac{ml^2}{mgl}} = 2\pi\sqrt{\dfrac{l}{g}}$.

9-C15 From Example 8-12, $I = 2.37$ kg·m² about the 100 cm end. Also, $x_{\text{c.m.}}$
= 51.25 cm (see the solution to Prob. 8-C2), so $h = (100.00 - 51.25)$ cm
= 48.75 cm. $T = 2\pi\sqrt{\dfrac{I}{mgh}} = 2\pi\sqrt{\dfrac{2.37 \text{ kg·m}^2}{(8 \text{ kg})(9.8 \text{ m/s}^2)(0.4875 \text{ m})}}$ = 1.56 s.

Chapter 10   Wave Motion

Questions

10-2   No; yes.

10-3   Yes; the density is increased wherever the pressure is greater than normal.

10-4   From $v_w = \sqrt{B/d}$, we expect speed to increase when the temperature rises. See p. 253, and pp. 378-79.

10-5   The bulk modulus.

10-6   No; perhaps a fish is biting. By its nature, a *wave* can only be visualized as a phenomenon extending over a region of space. The fisherman is observing a vibration, not a wave.

10-7   A wave of enthusiasm might be measured in noise level of a cheering crowd, or in rate of heartbeat of a person in a crowd. Wave velocity could be in m/s. Periodic waves of enthusiasm could be generated by a controlled news source in, say, Washington, D.C., which alternately flashes good news and bad news, carried westward by word of mouth. Such a wave would have a wavelength. A stationary wave of enthusiasm (with nodes and antinodes) could be discussed after Chap. 11 has been studied; rumor mills in Washington and in Hollywood could both affect the state of enthusiasm of a person at an intermediate location.

10-8   Yes. The transverse displacement of (say) a star in the flag is a somewhat periodic function of time, and the phase of disturbance moves out along the flag as it waves.

10-9   Not necessarily, if the elastic limit of the medium would be exceeded during the resultant disturbance.

10-10   A vibration occurs at a point; a wave is an interrelated set of vibrations whose phase differences remain in constant relation to each other.

10-11   A tape recorder in a moving car can be used to demonstrate the Doppler effect.

10-12   If there is no relative motion between observer and source,   (*a*) the wavelength is changed;   (*b*) the wave velocity is changed;   (*c*) the perceived frequency is not changed. The complete formula for the nonrelativistic Doppler effect is $\nu' = \nu \, \dfrac{v_w + v_{air} + v_{obs}}{v_w + v_{air} - v_{source}}$; this equation reduces to Eq. 10-5 or Eq. 10-6 if $v_{air} = 0$ and gives no frequency change if the observer and the source are both stationary. See also Ques. 10-18, where because of the motion of the cars there is an apparent wind v_{air} that in effect changes the wave velocity; molecules in a region of compression are carried toward the rear car by convection. In that situation, $v_{obs} = +\frac{1}{10} v_w$ and and $v_{source} = -\frac{1}{10} v_w$. The general formula shows that $\nu' = \nu$ in this case.

Multiple Choice

10-13 (*b*);   10-14 (*c*);   10-15 (*b*);   10-16 (*b*);   10-17 (*c*);   10-18 (*c*).

Problems

10-A1 v_w is proportional to $\sqrt{E}$; ratio is 2:1.

10-A2 v_w is proportional to $\sqrt{B}$; ratio is 1:2.

10-A3 $\sqrt{E/d} = \sqrt{(20 \times 10^{10}\text{ N/m}^2)/(7800\text{ kg/m}^3)} = 5060$ m/s   (answers rounded to 3 significant figures here and in following problems).

10-A4 $\sqrt{E/d} = \sqrt{(9.0 \times 10^{10}\text{ N/m}^2)/(8440\text{ kg/m}^3)} = 3270$ m/s.

10-A5 $\sqrt{B/d} = \sqrt{(0.20 \times 10^{10}\text{ N/m}^2)/(1000\text{ kg/m}^3)} = 1410$ m/s = 4640 ft/s.

10-A6 $\sqrt{B/d} = \sqrt{(2.5 \times 10^{10}\text{ N/m}^2)(13\ 600\text{ kg/m}^3)} = 1360$ m/s.

10-A7 $E = v_w^2 d = (4000\text{ m/s})^2(6.10\text{ kg})/(2.00 \times 10^{-3}\text{ m}^3) = 4.88 \times 10^{10}$ N/m^2.

10-A8 $t = 11.0$ s; $t = 11.6$ s; down.

10-A9 15 vib/min; to the right; $v_w = \lambda/T = (24\text{ m})/(4\text{ s}) = 6$ m/s.   [Part (b) of Fig. 10-7 shows that at $t = 3$ s, a particle at R' is rising (it will be a crest 1 s later, when $t = 4$ s). Therefore the crest at P' of part (a) is moving toward R'.]

10-A10 20 ft.

10-A11 $\nu = 1/T = 1/(0.004\text{ s}) = 250\text{ s}^{-1} = 250$ Hz.

10-A12 $\nu = v_w/\lambda = (340\text{ m/s})/(2\text{ m}) = 170$ times per second.

10-A13 $\lambda = v_w/\nu = (1080\text{ ft/s})/(120\text{ Hz}) = 9$ ft.

10-A14 $\lambda = v_w/\nu \approx (340\text{ m/s})(20\ 000\text{ Hz}) \approx 1.7 \times 10^{-3}$ m ≈ 17 mm.

10-A15 $\lambda = v_w/\nu = (340\text{ m/s})/(50\ 000\text{ Hz}) = 6.8 \times 10^{-3}$ m = 6.8 mm.

10-A16 $\lambda = v_w/\nu = (3 \times 10^8\text{ m/s})/(60 \times 10^6\text{ Hz}) = 5$ m.

10-A17 Beat frequency = $(413 - 408) = 5$ per second = 300 per minute.

10-A18 Since the observer is moving, λ is the same and v_w is altered (see Example 10-7 on p. 238). To have a 5% increase in ν, the observer's speed would be 5% of the speed of sound = $(0.05)(340\text{ m/s}) = 17$ m/s.

10-B1 The engine takes up the slack in each coupling in $\frac{6}{30}$ s = $\frac{1}{5}$ s; to stretch the entire train requires 20 s.

10-B2 Substitute kg·m/s^2 for N and simplify.

10-B3 Upward.

10-B4 $v_w = \lambda/T = (6\text{ m})/(0.004\text{ s}) = 1500$ m/s.   [The student may expect to get 340 m/s for this speed, but the container does not necessarily contain air at room temperature. The speed of sound in hydrogen gas (H$_2$) at 114°C is about 1500 m/s.]

10-B5 $T = \lambda/v_w = (3\text{ m})/(600\text{ m/s}) = 0.005$ s. The time required is half a period = 0.0025 s.

10-B6 $v_w = \sqrt{E/d} = \sqrt{(4.1 \times 10^{10}\text{ N/m}^2)/(1750\text{ kg/m}^3)} = 4840$ m/s; hence $\lambda = v_w/\nu$ = $(4840\text{ m/s})/(40 \times 10^3\text{ Hz}) = 0.121$ m.

10-B7 $v_w = \sqrt{E/d} = \sqrt{(7.0 \times 10^{10}\text{ N/m}^2)/(2700\text{ kg/m}^3)} = 5092$ m/s; $\nu = v_w/\lambda$ = $(5092\text{ m/s})/(0.25\text{ m}) = 20.4 \times 10^3$ Hz = 20.4 kHz.

10-B8 $2D = v_w t = (330\text{ m/s})(0.05\text{ s})$; $D = 8.25$ m.

10-B9 Distance = $v_w t = \sqrt{(20 \times 10^{10}\text{ N/m}^2)/(7800\text{ kg/m}^3)}$ (0.1 s) = 504 m.

10-B10 The distance from F to G is 1.5λ, hence $\lambda = (24\text{ m})/1.5 = 16$ m. $v_w = \lambda\nu$ = $(16\text{ m})(20\text{ min}^{-1}) = 320$ m/min = 5.33 m/s.

10-B11 $\nu_1 = (330\text{ m/s})/(5.5\text{ m}) = 60\text{ s}^{-1}$; $\nu_2 = (330\text{ m/s})/(6\text{ m}) = 55\text{ s}^{-1}$; $60 - 55 = 5$ beats/s.

10-B12 (a) $2040 - 2000 = 40$ beats/s;   (b) In $\frac{1}{40}$ s, each wave travels (340 m/s) $\cdot (\frac{1}{40}$ s) = 8.5 m; this is the separation of the regions of maximum resultant amplitude.   [In more detail, $\lambda_1 = 0.17$ m, $\lambda_2 = 0.166667$ m. In 8.5 m, there are $(8.5/0.17) = 50$ of the longer waves, and $(8.5/0.166667) = 51$ of the shorter waves. If pressure peaks coincide at $x = 0$, there will also be a coincidence at $x = +8.5$ m.]

10-B13 (a) $\lambda = c/\nu = (3 \times 10^8 \text{ m/s})/(91.9 \times 10^6 \text{ s}^{-1}) = 3.26 \text{ m}$; (b) $\Delta\nu = 0.002 \text{ MHz}$ $= 2000 \text{ beats/s}$.

10-B14 Use Eq. 10-5. (a) $\nu' = (1000 \text{ Hz})\left(\dfrac{340}{340 - 20}\right) = 1063 \text{ Hz}$; (b) ν' $= (1000 \text{ Hz})\left(\dfrac{340}{340 + 20}\right) = 944 \text{ Hz}$.

10-B15 Use Eq. 10-6. (a) $\nu' = (400 \text{ Hz})\left(\dfrac{340 + 30}{340}\right) = 435 \text{ Hz}$; (b) $\nu' = (400 \text{ Hz})$ $\left(\dfrac{340 - 30}{340}\right) = 365 \text{ Hz}$.

10-B16 $\nu' = (550 \text{ Hz})\left(\dfrac{340}{340 - 0.5}\right) = 550.8 \text{ Hz}$.

10-B17 (a) Observer moving: $1500 = (1000)\left(\dfrac{300 + v}{300}\right)$; $v = 150 \text{ m/s}$; (b) source moving: $1500 = (1000)\left(\dfrac{300}{300 - v}\right)$; $v = 100 \text{ m/s}$. [In the answer to Prob. 16-C20 it is calculated that the speed of sound is 300 m/s if the air temperature is $-49°$C.]

10-C1 (a) The train is between the observer and the cliff. Let x = distance of train from cliff and y = distance of train from observer. The observation of time lag yields $\dfrac{x + x + y}{340} - \dfrac{y}{340} = 3$; $x = \frac{3}{2}(340) = 510 \text{ m}$. (b) Let v be the speed of the train toward the observer. The reflected sound comes from a virtual source behind the cliff, moving away from the observer at speed v, and its apparent frequency is $\nu_1' = \nu(340)/(340 + v)$. Sound heard by the direct path is raised in frequency to $\nu_2' = \nu(340)/(340 - v)$. Then ν_1'/ν_2' $= 0.9$; solve for v, obtaining $v = 17.9 \text{ m/s}$. [If we suppose the observer to be between the cliff and the train, the frequency is changed by the same amount for both the direct and the reflected paths. This would make $\nu_1'/\nu_2' = 1$, contrary to the given data.]

10-C2 (a) Using $x = v/v_w$ as suggested in the hint, Eq. 10-6 becomes $\nu'/\nu = 1 + x$. Equation 10-5 becomes $\nu'/\nu = (1 - x)^{-1} = 1 + x + x^2 + x^3 + \cdots$. Thus Eqs. 10-5 and 10-6 agree to the first-order term x, differing only in higher order terms in x^2, x^3, $\cdots$. (b) Applying the binomial theorem to the relativistic Eq. 10-7 gives $\nu'/\nu = (1 + x)^{1/2}(1 + x)^{-1/2} = (1 + \frac{1}{2}x - \frac{1}{8}x^2 + \frac{1}{16}x^3 + \cdots)$ $\cdot(1 + \frac{1}{2}x + \frac{3}{8}x^2 + \frac{5}{16}x^3 + \cdots)$. Multiplying terms together reduces this to $(1 + x + \frac{1}{2}x^2 + \frac{1}{2}x^3 + \cdots)$. The relativistic formula thus reduces to $(1 + x)$ for small x. However, the neglected terms in x^2, x^3, $\cdots$ are different in the three cases.

10-C3 (a) $\lambda = (3 \times 10^8 \text{ m/s})/(2.5 \times 10^9 \text{ Hz}) = 1.2 \times 10^{-1} \text{ m} = 12 \text{ cm}$. (b) Source moves at $2v$: $\nu' = (2.5 \times 10^9)\left(\dfrac{3 \times 10^8}{3 \times 10^8 - 2v}\right)$. The beat frequency $\nu' - \nu$ is measured to be 1260 Hz. Hence $1260 = (2.5 \times 10^9)\left(\dfrac{3 \times 10^8}{3 \times 10^8 - 2v} - 1\right)$. Solving for v gives $v = 75.6 \text{ m/s}$.

10-C4 Let R be the radius of the earth, in km. (a) The S-wave travels along an arc that is $\frac{1}{6}(2\pi R) = \pi R/3$; $t = (\pi R/3)/(4.5 \text{ km/s}) = 0.2327R$. The P-wave travels along a chord of length R; $t = R/(7.8 \text{ km/s}) = 0.1282R$. The P-wave arrives first. (b) The difference in time of arrival is $(0.2327 - 0.1282)R$ $= (0.1045)(6.38 \times 10^3) = 667 \text{ s}$.

10-C5 For radar, use $(v/c) = \Delta\nu/\nu$. Here the relative speed is $2v$, twice the car's speed.

$$\frac{2v}{3 \times 10^8 \text{ m/s}} = \frac{2.05 \times 10^3 \text{ Hz}}{10.5 \times 10^9 \text{ Hz}}; \quad v = 29.3 \text{ m/s} = 65.5 \text{ mi/h}.$$

10-C6 The frequency of the laser beam was $(3 \times 10^8 \text{ m/s})/(10.59 \times 10^{-6} \text{ m}) = 2.833 \times 10^{13}$ Hz. Using $\Delta\nu/\nu = v/c$ gives $\Delta\nu = \nu(v/c) = (2.833 \times 10^{13} \text{ Hz})(30 \text{ m/s})/(3 \times 10^8 \text{ m/s}) = 2.83 \times 10^6$ Hz $= 2.83$ MHz.   [This frequency shift is observed by beating the reflected wave against a fraction of the transmitted wave; the beat frequency of 2.83 MHz is in the radio region of the e-m spectrum.]

10-C7 $\sqrt{\dfrac{1.01 \times 10^5 \text{ N/m}^2}{1.293 \text{ kg/m}^3}} = 279$ m/s.   [This result, essentially that obtained by Newton, is about 20% low. At any point, the temperature of the gas does not remain constant; local warming and cooling occurs during compression and rarefaction. The adiabatic bulk modulus γP must be used (see Eq. 16-19). The value of bulk modulus in Table 9-1 is measured under static conditions of constant temperature and is numerically equal to atmospheric pressure P.]

Chapter 11   Interference and Stationary Waves

Questions

11-1 Two waves, traveling in opposite directions, having the same wavelength and velocity, are needed to give stationary waves. The nodes will be of zero amplitude only if the interfering waves have equal amplitudes.

11-2 The ripples appear if the frequency of the dryer's rotation is in resonance with certain modes of vibration of the surface of the water.

11-3 After a guitar string is plucked, it may vibrate with an antinode at the center of the string. This is a result of constructive interference between a wave traveling down the string that meets a similar reflected wave coming back.

11-4 Yes, as in the top and next-to-bottom parts of Fig. 11-1.

11-5 The mass per unit length of a "low" string is increased by winding a heavy wire around the central steel wire that supports the tension. A solid wire of the necessary mass per unit length would be impossibly stiff.

11-6 Length, tension, and mass per unit length.

11-7 In general, harmonic overtones arise from bodies that have one-dimensional symmetry, such as strings or pipes. Bodies free to vibrate in two dimensions (plates, bars, bells, gongs, drumheads) satisfy differential equations in two dimensions, for which the characteristic frequencies are not simple multiples of the fundamental. If we classify bells, gongs, drums, etc. as "musical," the answer to the question is "no."

11-8 The intensity, frequency, and overtone structure are all different. These physical attributes are related to the sensations of loudness, pitch, and tone quality.

11-9 The odd harmonics predominate for the clarinet described in Table 11-1; this is similar to the overtone structure of a closed pipe. The French horn is more like an open pipe. See Reference 6 at the end of the chapter for a discussion of various musical instruments.

11-10 Resonance is desirable, even necessary, in a flute, where a pure tone is generated whose frequency depends on the length of the pipe. Resonance is not desirable in a piano, whose sounding board should respond more or less equally to many frequencies.

11-11 The vocal chords are the generator; the vocal cavities (from larynx to the mouth opening and the nose opening) make up the resonator. The soprano's overtone structure as well as pitch differ from those of a tenor.

11-12 They break step to avoid exciting the bridge in one of its natural modes of vibration—an undesirable resonance that might lead to the collapse of the bridge.

11-13 (a) The open A string is in resonance with one of the overtones of the lower (struck) string.   (b) The open A string's resonance is sharp enough (Fig. 11-10) so that there is negligible response to the overtones of a low A♭ or A#.   (c) Nothing happens; the upper A string has no subharmonics that could excite the lower string.

11-14 The long tone near the start of the sequence appears to have a large number of equally spaced overtones.

Multiple Choice

11-15 (a);   **11-16** (b);   **11-17** (a);   **11-18** (b);   **11-19** (b);   **11-20** (a).

Problems

11-A1 $v_w = \sqrt{F/(m/L)} = \sqrt{FL/m} = \sqrt{(25 \text{ N})(6 \text{ m})/(0.015 \text{ kg})} = 100 \text{ m/s}$.

11-A2 $v_w = \sqrt{\dfrac{FL}{W/g}} = \sqrt{\dfrac{FLg}{W}} = \sqrt{\dfrac{(9 \text{ lb})(40 \text{ ft})(32 \text{ ft/s}^2)}{5 \text{ lb}}} = 48 \text{ ft/s}$.

11-A3 $\lambda = v_w/\nu = (200 \text{ m/s})/(500 \text{ Hz}) = 0.4 \text{ m}$; $\frac{1}{2}\lambda = 0.2 \text{ m} = 20 \text{ cm}$.

11-A4 $\lambda = 2(0.3 \text{ m}) = 0.6 \text{ m}$. Thus, $v_w = \lambda\nu = (0.6 \text{ m})(60 \text{ Hz}) = 36 \text{ m/s}$.

11-A5 200 Hz; 400 Hz; 600 Hz.

11-A6 $v_w = \lambda\nu = (2 \times 0.75 \text{ m})(220 \text{ Hz}) = 330 \text{ m/s}$.

11-A7 $\nu = v_w/\lambda = (340 \text{ m/s})/(2 \times 0.85 \text{ m}) = 200 \text{ Hz}$.

11-A8 $\lambda = v_w/\nu = (340 \text{ m/s})/(200 \text{ Hz}) = 1.7 \text{ m}$; $L = \frac{1}{4}\lambda = 0.425 \text{ m}$.

11-A9 Fundamental frequency is $v_w/\lambda = (340 \text{ m/s})/(4 \times 0.17 \text{ m}) = 500 \text{ Hz}$. For this closed pipe, the next-to-lowest frequency is $3 \times 500 \text{ Hz} = 1500 \text{ Hz}$.

11-A10 (a) $\nu_1 = v_w/\lambda = (340 \text{ m/s})/(2 \times 1.7 \text{ m}) = 100 \text{ Hz}$;   (b) The new λ is 4×1.7 m; ν_1 for the closed pipe is 50 Hz.

11-A11 220 Hz; 440 Hz; 660 Hz.

11-A12 200 Hz; 400 Hz; 600 Hz.

11-A13 200 Hz; 600 Hz; 1000 Hz.

11-A14 $2 \times 2 \times 2 \times 192 \text{ Hz} = 1536 \text{ Hz}$.

11-A15 About 100 Hz.

11-B2 (a) $v_w = \sqrt{F/(m/L)} = \sqrt{FL/m} = \sqrt{FL/\pi r^2 L d} = \sqrt{F/\pi r^2 d}$. (b) $\nu_n = (n/2L)v_w$
$= (n/2L)\sqrt{F/\pi r^2 d} = (n/2Lr)\sqrt{F/\pi d}$.

11-B3 The wave velocity on the rope is $(10 \text{ m})/(0.25 \text{ s}) = 40 \text{ m/s}$. From v_w
$= \sqrt{F/(m/L)}$, $F = v_w^2 m/L = (40 \text{ m/s})^2 (0.9 \text{ kg})/(10 \text{ m}) = 144 \text{ N}$.

11-B4 (a) $v_w = (400 \text{ m})/(5.00 \text{ s}) = 80 \text{ m/s}$. Mass per unit length is $(LAd)/L = Ad$
$= (6 \times 10^{-4} \text{ m}^2)(2700 \text{ kg/m}^3) = 1.62 \text{ kg/m}$. From $v_w = \sqrt{F/(m/L)}$ we have
$F = v_w^2(m/L) = (80 \text{ m/s})^2 (1.62 \text{ kg/m}) = 1.04 \times 10^4 \text{ N} = 10.4 \text{ kN}$. (b) From
$E = \dfrac{\Delta F/A}{\Delta L/L}$, $\Delta L = \dfrac{L \,\Delta F}{EA} = \dfrac{(200 \text{ m})(1.04 \times 10^4 \text{ N})}{(7.0 \times 10^{10} \text{ N/m}^2)(6 \times 10^{-4} \text{ m}^2)} = 4.95 \times 10^{-2} \text{ m}$
$= 4.95 \text{ cm}$.

11-B5 $5(\tfrac{1}{2}\lambda) = 50 \text{ cm}$, hence $\lambda = 20 \text{ cm}$. $v_w = \lambda\nu = (20 \text{ cm})(200 \text{ Hz}) = 4000 \text{ cm/s}$.
Finally, $F = v_w^2 m/L = (4000 \text{ cm/s})^2(50 \text{ g})/(50 \text{ cm}) = 16 \times 10^6 \text{ dyn} = 16 \text{ Mdyn}$.
[In mks units, this is 160 N.]

11-B6 (a) The string vibrates in two segments; $\lambda = L$ for this mode. (b) v_w
$= \sqrt{F/(m/L)} = \sqrt{FL/m} = \sqrt{(4 \text{ N})(1 \text{ m})/(4 \times 10^{-4} \text{ kg})} = 100 \text{ m/s}$. Then $\nu = v_w/\lambda$
$= (100 \text{ m/s})/(1 \text{ m}) = 100 \text{ Hz}$.

11-B7 $v_w = \lambda\nu = (0.60 \text{ m})(440 \text{ Hz}) = 264 \text{ m/s}$. From $v_w = \sqrt{F/(m/L)}$, $F = v_w^2 m/L$
$= (264 \text{ m/s})^2(2 \times 10^{-3} \text{ kg})/(0.30 \text{ m}) = 465 \text{ N}$.

11-B8 The original length of the vibrating portion of the string is $68 \text{ cm} - 20 \text{ cm}$
$= 48 \text{ cm}$. The wavelength must be increased, so the cellist should move her
finger away from the bridge, toward the nut. Since $\nu = v_w/2L$ for the fun-
damental, $\dfrac{\nu}{\nu'} = \dfrac{L'}{L}$; $\dfrac{449 \text{ Hz}}{440 \text{ Hz}} = \dfrac{L'}{48 \text{ cm}}$; $L' = 48.98 \text{ cm}$. The finger should be
moved 0.98 cm toward the nut.

11-B9 (a) The fundamental frequency is given by $\nu = \dfrac{1}{2L}\sqrt{\dfrac{F}{m/L}}$; $m = \dfrac{F}{4L\nu^2}$
$= \dfrac{(18 \text{ N})}{4(2 \text{ m})(150 \text{ Hz})^2} = 1.00 \times 10^{-4} \text{ kg} = 0.1 \text{ g}$. (b) Assuming the same driv-
ing frequency, as in a common laboratory experiment (Melde's experiment),
to vibrate in three segments λ is $\tfrac{1}{3}$ as large, hence $v_w (=\lambda\nu)$ is also $\tfrac{1}{3}$ as
large, and F is $\tfrac{1}{9}$ as large, i.e., 2 N.

11-B10 The wave velocity is $v_w = \sqrt{F/(m/L)} = \sqrt{(1080 \text{ N})/(3.00 \times 10^{-3} \text{ kg/m})} = 600 \text{ m/s}$.
Since two adjacent frequencies are in the ratio 5:4, the fundamental fre-
quency must be $\tfrac{1}{5}(600 \text{ Hz}) = \tfrac{1}{4}(480 \text{ Hz}) = 120 \text{ Hz}$. Thus, in the fundamental
mode, $\lambda = v_w/\nu = (600 \text{ m/s})/(120 \text{ Hz}) = 5.00 \text{ m}$, and $L = \tfrac{1}{2}\lambda = 2.50 \text{ m}$.

11-B11 Frequency is proportional to $\sqrt{F}$; $\dfrac{\nu'}{523 \text{ Hz}} = \sqrt{\dfrac{194 \text{ N}}{200 \text{ N}}}$; $\nu' = 515.1 \text{ Hz}$; $\nu - \nu'$
$\approx 8 \text{ beats/s}$.

11-B12 For a closed pipe, $\lambda_1 = 4L$ (Fig. 11-6). Hence $\nu_1 = v_w/\lambda_1 = (340 \text{ m/s})/(4 \times 0.85$
m$) = 100 \text{ Hz}$. Overtones have frequencies in the ratio 1:3:5:..., so the fre-
quencies are 100 Hz, 300 Hz, 500 Hz.

11-B13 (a) This series of frequencies can only be from an open pipe; for example,
the ratio $880{:}440 = 2{:}1$ is not possible in the series 1:3:5:7:... that applies to
a closed pipe. (b) Evidently the fundamental frequency is 220 Hz; $L = \tfrac{1}{2}\lambda$
$= \tfrac{1}{2}(340 \text{ m/s})/(220 \text{ Hz}) = 0.773 \text{ m}$.

11-B14 Since $v_w \propto \sqrt{T}$, and λ is fixed, ν is also $\propto \sqrt{T}$. Thus $\nu' = (740 \text{ Hz})\sqrt{(304 \text{ K})/(300 \text{ K})}$
$= 744.9 \text{ Hz}$; $\nu' - \nu \approx 5 \text{ beats/s}$.

11-B15 $\nu_1 = (340 \text{ m/s})/(2 \times 0.400 \text{ m}) = 425 \text{ Hz}$; $\nu_2 = (340 \text{ m/s})/(2 \times 0.403 \text{ m}) = 421.8 \text{ Hz}$;
$\nu_1 - \nu_2 = 3.2 \text{ beats/s}$.

11-B16 (a) $v_w = \lambda\nu = (4 \times 0.60 \text{ m})(200 \text{ Hz}) = 480 \text{ m/s}$.   (b) If $\nu = 210 \text{ Hz}$, v_w
= $(4 \times 0.60 \text{ m})(210 \text{ Hz}) = 504 \text{ m/s}$.   [Mating behavior on the planet depends
on the sharpness of the resonance curve (Fig. 11-10) of the intercranial cav-
ity.]

11-B17 (a) Node at the center, antinodes at the free ends; additional nodes in the
overtone modes, but always retaining the node at the center. Compare Fig.
11-6, which could represent half of a rod clamped at the center.   (b) As
for a closed pipe, natural frequencies are in the ratio 1:3:5:7:... .   (c) In
the fundamental mode, $L = \frac{1}{2}\lambda$ (an antinode at each end); $\lambda = 2(2.10 \text{ m}) = 4.20$
m. $v_w = \lambda\nu = (4.20 \text{ m})(1175 \text{ Hz}) = 4935 \text{ m/s}$.

11-B18 (a) In the fundamental mode, there is a node at each end and an antinode at
the center. In the first overtone, there are also nodes at the ends and an antinode at the center (where air is set into motion by the metal plate), and there
is an additional node–antinode pair on each side of the center. The first
overtone has a wavelength that is $\frac{1}{3}$ the wavelength of the fundamental, and
this mode has a frequency 3 times that of the fundamental.
(b) $L = \frac{1}{2}\lambda = \frac{1}{2}(v_w/\nu) = \frac{1}{2}(340 \text{ m/s})/(400 \text{ Hz}) = 0.425 \text{ m}$.

11-B19 (a) Node at the clamped center; antinode at each free end; $L = \frac{1}{2}\lambda$.   (b) v_w
= $\lambda\nu = 2L\nu = 2(0.70 \text{ m})(2440 \text{ Hz}) = 3416 \text{ m/s}$.   (c) $v_w = \sqrt{E/d}$; $E = v_w{}^2 d$
= $(3416 \text{ m/s})^2(8440 \text{ kg/m}^3) = 9.85 \times 10^{10} \text{ N/m}^2$.

11-B20 The fundamental frequency of the pipe is $v_w/\lambda = (340 \text{ m/s})/(4 \times 1.5 \text{ m}) = 56.67$
Hz; the first overtone has frequency $3 \times 56.67 \text{ Hz} = 170 \text{ Hz}$. The string's
frequency is also 170 Hz. For the string, $v_w = \sqrt{T/(m/L)} = \sqrt{(400 \text{ N})/(10^{-2} \text{ kg/m})}$
= 200 m/s. Hence for the string, $L = \frac{1}{2}\lambda = \frac{1}{2}(200 \text{ m/s})/(170 \text{ Hz}) = 0.588 \text{ m}$.

11-B21 Assuming that a "considerable noise" is 1 W/m^2, the acoustic power is
$(1 \text{ W/m}^2)(10 \text{ m} \times 2 \text{ m}) = 20 \text{ W}$. Even for an unrealistic 100% efficiency
for the conversion of acoustic power to electric power, this would be insuffi-
cient to operate a 40 W lamp at full brilliance.

11-B22 $10 \log (800/1) = 29 \text{ dB}$.

11-B23 $43 \text{ dB} = 10 \log R$; $R = 20\,000{:}1$.

11-B24 At threshold, intensity = 10^{-12} W/m^2. $60 \text{ dB} = 10 \log \left(\dfrac{I}{10^{-12} \text{ W/m}^2}\right)$; $I = 10^{-6}$
W/m^2, and $P = IA = (10^{-6} \text{ W/m}^2)(50 \times 10^{-4} \text{ m}^2) = 5 \times 10^{-9} \text{ W}$. The time for 10^{-6} J
to be accumulated is $t = (10^{-6} \text{ J})/(5 \times 10^{-9} \text{ W}) = 200 \text{ s}$.

11-B25 $\beta_2 = 10 \log I_2/I_0 = 10 \log I_2 - 10 \log I_0$. Similarly, $\beta_1 = 10 \log I_1 - 10 \log I_0$.
Subtracting cancels the reference intensity, giving $\beta_2 - \beta_1 = 10(\log I_2 - \log I_1)$,
or $\Delta\beta = 10 \log (I_2/I_1)$.

11-B26 $0.6 \text{ dB} = 10 \log (I_2/I_1)$; $\log (I_2/I_1) = 0.06$. A log table gives $I_2/I_1 = 1.148$, which
represents about a 15 percent increase in intensity. The ear is remarkably
insensitive to rather large fractional changes in intensity; the pitch discrim-
ination is better than 0.5 percent.   [Many pocket calculators can give
I_2/I_1 directly as $10^{0.06} = 1.148$.]

11-C1 The air column is a closed pipe, for which $L_1 = \frac{1}{4}\lambda$, $L_2 = \frac{3}{4}\lambda$, $L_3 = \frac{5}{4}\lambda$, etc.
Thus, since $\lambda = (340 \text{ m/s})/(512 \text{ Hz}) = 66.4 \text{ cm}$, the resonant lengths are 16.6
cm, 49.8 cm, 83.0 cm, etc.

11-C2 (a) $[T]^{-1} = [M]^X [L]^y [MLT^{-2}]^z$. For this equation to be dimensionally correct,
we must satisfy three equations. For $[M]$: $0 = x + z$; for $[L]$: $0 = y + z$; for
$[T]$: $-1 = -2z$. These equations yield $z = \frac{1}{2}$, $x = -\frac{1}{2}$, $y = -\frac{1}{2}$, hence $\nu = K\sqrt{\dfrac{F}{mL}}$.
(b) For the fundamental mode, $L = \frac{1}{2}\lambda$ and hence $\lambda = 2L$. Now

$$\nu = \frac{v_w}{\lambda} = \frac{1}{2L}\sqrt{\frac{F}{m/L}} = \frac{1}{2L}\sqrt{\frac{FL}{m}} = \frac{1}{2}\sqrt{\frac{F}{mL}}$$

This is of the same form as found in part (a), with the added information that the dimensionless constant K is $\frac{1}{2}$.

11-C3 Pipe: Fundamental $\lambda = 4(1.5\text{ m}) = 6\text{ m}$; fundamental $\nu = (340\text{ m/s})/(6\text{ m})$; frequency of first overtone of the closed pipe is 3 times the fundamental frequency $= 3(340\text{ m/s})/(6\text{ m}) = 170\text{ Hz}$. Wire: Fundamental $\lambda = 2(1.25\text{ m})$ $= 2.50\text{ m}$. When the wire vibrates in 5 segments (4th overtone), $L = \frac{5}{2}\lambda$; $\lambda = \frac{2}{5}L = 0.50\text{ m}$. Thus, $170\text{ Hz} = \dfrac{1}{0.50\text{ m}}\sqrt{\dfrac{F}{(0.04\text{ kg})/(1.25\text{ m})}}$; $F = 231\text{ N}$.

11-C4 The wavelength is the distance between successive condensations, which must be two round trips, or $4L$.

11-C5 Since $\nu = v_w/\lambda$, $\nu \propto v_w \propto \sqrt{F}$. We have $\nu_2/\nu_1 = \sqrt{F_2/F_1} = \sqrt{242/200} = 1.10$. The string was originally 5 Hz lower than the fork and now is 5 Hz above the fork. We have two equations: $\nu_2 - \nu_1 = 10$ and $\nu_2/\nu_1 = 1.10$. Solving simultaneously gives $\nu_2 = 110\text{ Hz}$, $\nu_1 = 100\text{ Hz}$. The frequency of the tuning fork is 105 Hz.

11-C6 For the wire, $v_w = \sqrt{F/(m/L)} = \sqrt{FL/m} = \sqrt{FL/ALd} = \sqrt{F/Ad}$. Thus $\sqrt{E/d}$ $= 100\sqrt{F/Ad}$. The density cancels out, and stress $= F/A = (10^{-4})E = (10^{-4})(20$ $\times 10^{10}\text{ N/m}^2) = 2 \times 10^7\text{ N/m}^2$. Yes, this stress is less than the ultimate tensile strength of steel (p. 205).

Chapter 12 Fluids

Questions

12-1 Diamond and iron.

12-2 The magnitude of the force would be the same.

12-3 The explanation can be given either in terms of equalization of pressure or in terms of changes in PE. For instance, a glass tube 1 m tall is filled with water and connected at the bottom to an empty vertical tube 1 m tall. When the stopcock between the tubes is opened, the water level becomes 50 cm in each tube. It is easy to calculate that the PE of the system has decreased: The center of gravity of the water is now only 25 cm above the bottom of the tubes. This energy viewpoint will be used in dealing with the flow of electric charge in Chap. 18.

12-4 Consider both the increased density of the sea water (greater buoyancy) and the possible change in volume of the submarine (less buoyancy).

12-5 A balloon rises until the density of the surrounding air exactly equals the density of the enclosed gas. Both densities depend on altitude. Usually the balloon is filled at ground-level pressure, and the volume increases as it rises to a region of lower external pressure (the effect of temperature change is less important). The density of the surrounding air decreases exponentially as a function of height above the ground.

12-6 The glass ball falls; by pumping out the bell jar, we remove more buoyancy from the object of greater volume.

12-7 The water level remains the same.

12-8 Yes; if the system remains in equilibrium, the spring must supply an additional upward force equal to the weight (in air) of the trout.

12-9 N/m^2, $lb/in.^2$, g/cm would not have the dimensions of force/length or energy/area.

12-10 The Magnus effect predicts that the Frisbee will veer to the boy's right (as in Fig. 12-12).

12-11 Figure 12-24 is purposely drawn ambiguously; we use the Magnus effect to find the answer to the question. The air on the near side (toward the observer) is moving faster than the air on the far side; pressure is less on the near side; hence the force on the ship is toward the observer.

12-12 Consider what happens when the water rises in the tube. If it has a hemispherical surface (as in Fig. 12-17) when it reaches the top rim of the tube, more water will be pulled up; this will flatten out the hemisphere and the net upward force will decrease. When equilibrium is reached, the hemispherical assumption of Fig. 12-17 is no longer fulfilled, so the calculated rise of 10 cm is meaningless.

12-13 Although surface tension tends to pull floating objects together, a more important factor is the increased speed of the water as it streams through the funnel formed by the bows of the two ships and the narrow gap between them. Apply Bernoulli's equation.

Multiple Choice

12-14 (c);   **12-15** (a);   **12-16** (b);   **12-17** (b);   **12-18** (a);   **12-19** (a).

Problems

12-A1 $P = (\frac{1}{12} \times 1000 \text{ kg})(9.8 \text{ N/kg})/(0.5 \times 10^{-4} \text{ m}^2) = 1.63 \times 10^6 \text{ N/m}^2 = 16.1 \text{ atm.}$

12-A2 $P = (11 \times 10^3 \text{ N})/(20 \text{ m})(5.5 \text{ m}) = 100 \text{ Pa} = 9.87 \times 10^{-4} \text{ atm.}$

12-A3 $F = PA = (1.013 \times 10^5 \text{ N/m}^2)(0.60 \text{ m})(1.50 \text{ m}) = 912 \text{ kN}$. The upward force on the underside is also 912 kN.

12-A4 4 atm; 3040 mm Hg; 3039 kPa; 190 torr; 14700 lb/in.^{2}.

12-A5 441 lb/in.^{2}; 0.696 lb/in.^{2}; 76 mm Hg; 7.6×10^{-8} torr.

12-A6 (a) $P = hdg = (-0.50 \text{ m})(1000 \text{ kg/m}^2)(9.8 \text{ N/kg}) = -4900 \text{ N/m}^2 = -37 \text{ torr}$; (b) 760 torr $-$ 37 torr $=$ 723 torr;   (c) $F = PA = (4900 \text{ N/m}^2)(\frac{1}{4}\pi)(0.025 \text{ m})^2 = 2.4 \text{ N}$.

12-A7 (a) Use the ratio of density of water and mercury. $(40 \text{ mm H}_2\text{O})(1.00/13.6) = 2.94 \text{ mm Hg} = 2.94 \text{ torr}$.   (b) $(2.94 \text{ torr})\left(\dfrac{1.013 \times 10^6 \text{ dyn/cm}^2}{760 \text{ torr}}\right) = 3920$ dyn/cm^2;   (c) $(2.94 \text{ torr})\left(\dfrac{1013 \text{ mbar}}{760 \text{ torr}}\right) = 3.92 \text{ mbar.}$

12-A8 $P = hdg = (0.10 \text{ m})(13600 \text{ kg/m}^2)(9.8 \text{ N/kg}) = 1.33 \times 10^4 \text{ N/m}^2$. Also, $(1.33 \times 10^4 \text{ N/m}^2)\left(\dfrac{14.7 \text{ lb/in.}^2}{1.013 \times 10^5 \text{ N/m}^2}\right) = 1.93 \text{ lb/in.}^2$

12-A9 $P = hdg = (2.00 \text{ m})(700 \text{ kg/m}^3)(9.8 \text{ N/kg}) = 1.37 \times 10^4 \text{ N/m}^2 = 13.7 \text{ kPa}.$
[The length of the tank is unimportant.]

12-A10 $d = P/hg = (7.40 \times 10^4 \text{ dyn/cm}^2)/(60 \text{ cm})(980 \text{ dyn/g}) = 1.26 \text{ g/cm}^3;$ the liquid is glycerin.

12-A11 Loss of weight = $(0.06 \text{ m}^3)(1000 \text{ kg/m}^3)(9.8 \text{ N/kg}) = 588 \text{ N}.$

12-A12 BF = $(15 \text{ cm}^3)(0.8 \text{ g/cm}^3)(980 \text{ dyn/g}) = 1.18 \times 10^4 \text{ dyn}.$

12-A13 Since the total volume remains constant, $1000(\frac{4}{3}\pi r_1{}^3) = \frac{4}{3}\pi r_2{}^3;$ $r_2/r_1 = 1000^{1/3}$ = 10. Each small droplet has $\frac{1}{10}$ the radius, and $\frac{1}{100}$ the surface area, of the large drop; the total surface area of 1000 small droplets is $1000(\frac{1}{100}) = 10$ times the surface area of the large drop. The ratio of surface energy is therefore 10:1; the droplets of a fog release energy when they coalesce to make raindrops.

12-B1 $P = F/A;$ $3000 \text{ N/m}^2 = (0.2 \text{ kg})(9.8 \text{ N/kg})/\pi r^2;$ $r = 0.0144 \text{ m} = 1.44 \text{ cm}.$

12-B2 (a) $P = hdg = (3 \text{ m})(1000 \text{ kg/m}^3)(9.8 \text{ N/kg}) = 2.94 \times 10^4 \text{ N/m}^2;$ $F = PA = (2.94 \times 10^4 \text{ N/m}^2)(8 \text{ m})(25 \text{ m}) = 5.88 \times 10^6 \text{ N}.$ [This force can also be evaluated as the total weight of water in the pool.] (b) Force on end wall = $P_{av}A = \frac{1}{2}(2.94 \times 10^4 \text{ N/m}^2)(8 \text{ m})(3 \text{ m}) = 3.53 \times 10^5 \text{ N}.$

12-B3 The pressure inside the submarine is balanced by the air pressure at sea level; the pressure to be overcome is simply that due to 100 m of sea water. $F = PA = hdgA = (100 \text{ m})(1025 \text{ kg/m}^3)(9.8 \text{ N/kg})(1.2 \text{ m})(0.5 \text{ m}) = 6.03 \times 10^5 \text{ N}.$

12-B4 (a) Due to the height difference of 160 cm, $\Delta P = hdg = (160 \text{ cm})(0.816 \text{ g/cm}^3) \times (980 \text{ dyn/g}) = 0.13 \times 10^6 \text{ dyn/cm}^2.$ Recalling that the experiment is done on a day when atmospheric pressure is 1000 mbar = $1.00 \times 10^6 \text{ dyn/cm}^2$, we use the total pressure to compute the force: $F = PA = (1.13 \times 10^6 \text{ dyn/cm}^2)(2 \text{ cm}^2)$ = $2.26 \times 10^6 \text{ dyn}.$ (b) $2.26 \times 10^6 \text{ dyn};$ the magnitude of the force does not depend on the orientation of the surface.

12-B5 Pressure at G' is the same as at G, which is at a level 130 cm below A. $\Delta P = hdg = (130 \text{ cm})(0.816 \text{ g/cm}^3)(980 \text{ dyn/g}) = 0.104 \times 10^6 \text{ dyn/cm}^2 = 104 \text{ mbar}.$ Total pressure at G' is 1000 mbar + 104 mbar = 1104 mbar.

12-B6 $\Delta P = (200 \text{ cm})(0.816 \text{ g/cm}^3)(980 \text{ dyn/g}) = 0.160 \times 10^6 \text{ dyn/cm}^2 = 160 \text{ mbar};$ total pressure is 1000 mbar + 160 mbar = 1160 mbar.

12-B7 $\Delta P = hdg = (2 \text{ m})(1100 \text{ kg/m}^3)(9.8 \text{ N/kg}) = 21\,560 \text{ Pa} = (21\,560 \text{ Pa})$
$\times \left(\dfrac{760 \text{ torr}}{1.013 \times 10^5 \text{ Pa}}\right) = 162 \text{ torr}.$

12-B8 (a) $\Delta P = hdg = (10 \text{ cm})(1.08 \text{ g/cm}^3)(980 \text{ dyn/g}) = 1.058 \times 10^4 \text{ dyn/cm}^2$
= $(1.058 \times 10^4 \text{ dyn/cm}^2)\left(\dfrac{760 \text{ torr}}{1.013 \times 10^6 \text{ dyn/cm}^2}\right) = 7.94 \text{ torr} = 7.94 \text{ mm Hg}.$

(b) $B = \dfrac{\Delta P}{\Delta V/V} = \dfrac{1.058 \times 10^4 \text{ dyn/cm}^2}{(100 \text{ cm}^3)/(250 \text{ cm}^3)}\left(\dfrac{1 \text{ N/m}^2}{10 \text{ dyn/cm}^2}\right) = 2.4 \times 10^3 \text{ N/m}^2.$ The bulk modulus is about 2 or $3 \times 10^3 \text{ N/m}^2$. [The organ is not solid, so the volume change is not solely due to the compression of the tissue. The answer to part (b) is approximate because here (on account of the large V) it makes a difference whether we use the initial volume or the final volume for V in $B = -\Delta P/(\Delta V/V)$.]

12-B9 $P = \dfrac{(8 \times 10^3 \text{ kg})(9.8 \text{ N/kg})}{\pi(0.10 \text{ m})^2}\left(\dfrac{1 \text{ atm}}{1.013 \times 10^5 \text{ N/m}^2}\right) = 24.6 \text{ atm}.$ The available pressure of 25 atm is just sufficient.

12-B10 $F = PA = (80 \text{ lb/in.}^2)(\pi)(10 \text{ in.})^2 = 25\,100 \text{ lb}.$ The radius of the small piston need not be known.

12-B11 (a) BF = weight of aluminum cube; if V' is the volume of the submerged portion, $V'(13.6 \text{ g/cm}^3)g = (3 \text{ cm})^3(2.70 \text{ g/cm}^3)g$; g cancels out and $V' = 5.36 \text{ cm}^3$. (b) Now the BF is due to the entire volume of the block; let m be the mass of the lead. $(3 \text{ cm})^3(13.6 \text{ g/cm}^3)g = [(3 \text{ cm})^3(2.70 \text{ g/cm}^3 + m]g$; $m = 294$ g of lead; volume of the lead is $(294 \text{ g})/(11.3 \text{ g/cm}^3) = 26.0 \text{ cm}^3$.   [It is shown by W. P. Reid in *Am. J. Phys.*, **31**, 565 (1963), that a long bar of square cross section floats in stable equilibrium with its top flat surface horizontal if the ratio of the density of block to density of liquid lies between 0 and 0.211. This condition is fulfilled for an aluminum block floating in mercury.]

12-B12 BF = weight of $(88 - 76)$ g of water; volume = 12 cm^3. $d = (88 \text{ g})/(12 \text{ cm}^3)$ = 7.33 g/cm^3; sp. grav. = 7.33.

12-B13 (a) $(3 \text{ g} - 2 \text{ g})/(0.8 \text{ g/cm}^3) = 1.25 \text{ cm}^3$;   (b) sp. grav. = $3/1.25 = 2.40$.

12-B14 $m = (1500/9.8) = 153.1$ kg. The loss of weight = BF = weight of 0.06 m^3 of water = $(0.06 \text{ m}^3)(1000 \text{ kg/m}^3)(9.8 \text{ N/kg}) = 588$ N. The fractional loss is $588/1500 = 0.392 = 39.2\%$.

12-B15 BF = $(145 - 65)(980 \text{ dyn})$ = weight of displaced water. The mass of this much water is $(145 - 65)$ g = 80 g, and thus the cork's volume is 80 cm^3. Density of cork = $(20 \text{ g})/(80 \text{ cm}^3) = 0.25 \text{ g/cm}^3$.

12-B16 The boy's volume is that of 30 kg of water; $V = (30 \text{ kg})/(1000 \text{ kg/m}^3) = 0.030 \text{ m}^3$.

12-B17 (a) The swimmer's volume is that of 84 kg of water; $V = (84 \text{ kg})/(1000 \text{ kg/m}^3)$ = 0.084 m^3.   (b) The water displaced by the legs has mass $(84 - 60)$ kg = 24 kg. The volume of the legs is 0.024 m^3, or 0.012 m^3 per leg.   (c) A nose has a volume of about 5 cm^3, or 5×10^{-6} m^3.

12-B18 Taking the density of gasoline to be 675 kg/m^3, we calculate the extra BF as the weight of the additional sea water displaced as the tanker sinks h into the water. $(1600 \text{ m}^3)(675 \text{ kg/m}^3)g = (800 \text{ m}^2)(h)(1025 \text{ kg/m}^3)g$; $h = 1.32$ m.

12-B19 $V(0.1785 \text{ kg/m}^3)(9.8 \text{ N/kg}) + 88 \text{ N} = V(1.293 \text{ kg/m}^3)(9.8 \text{ N/kg})$; $V = 8.06 \text{ m}^3$.

12-B20 The volume of the metal equals the volume of $(108.0 - 68.0) = 40.0$ g of water; $V = 40.0 \text{ cm}^3$. This same volume of olive oil has a mass $(108.0 - 71.2)$ = 36.8 g. Now calculate the specific gravities. For the metal, $108.0/40.0$ = 2.70 (it is aluminum!) and for the oil, $36.8/40.0 = 0.92$.

12-B21 By Archimedes' principle, $L^3 d'g = L^2 L_1 dg$, whence $L_1 = L(d'/d)$. Then $L_2 = L - L_1$ becomes $L_2 = L(d - d')/d$.

12-B22 Calculate the change in total surface area (considering both the inner and outer surfaces of the thin film): $\Delta A = 2(4\pi)(2^2 - 1^2) = 75.4 \text{ cm}^2$. The change in surface energy is $(75.4 \text{ cm}^2)(25 \text{ erg/cm}^2) = 1885$ erg.

12-B23 500 dyn = $(2 \times \text{circumference of ring})\gamma$; $\gamma = (500 \text{ dyn})/(2)(2\pi)(1.20 \text{ cm}) = 33.2$ dyn/cm.

12-B24 $F = 2(72 \text{ dyn/cm})(4 \text{ cm}) = 576$ dyn.

12-B25 $F = (0.8\pi \text{ cm})(20 \text{ dyn/cm}) = 50$ dyn, downward.

12-B26 Net forward force = $(10 \text{ cm})(73 \text{ dyn/cm}) - (10 \text{ cm})(0.40)(73 \text{ dyn/cm}) = 438$ dyn. The mass of the toy boat is $(800 \text{ cm}^3)(0.45 \text{ g/cm}^3) = 360$ g.   (a) Net force is toward the left.   (b) $a = (\text{net } F)/m = (438 \text{ dyn})/(360 \text{ g}) = 1.217 \text{ cm/s}^2$; $v = at = (1.217 \text{ cm/s}^2)(5 \text{ s}) \approx 6 \text{ cm/s}$.

12-B27 (a) Circumference on the pavement is 3π cm; $F = 2(3\pi \text{ cm})(72 \text{ dyn/cm})$ = 1360 dyn.   (b) $\Delta P = (1360 \text{ dyn})/\pi(1.5 \text{ cm})^2 = 192 \text{ dyn/cm}^2$.   (c) ΔP = $2(2\pi R)\gamma/\pi R^2 = 4\gamma/R$.   [Here $4\gamma/R = 4(72 \text{ dyn/cm})/(1.5 \text{ cm}) = 192$ dyn/cm, in agreement with part (b).]

12-B28 $h = 2\gamma/rdg = 2(72.8 \text{ dyn/cm})/(0.0005 \text{ cm})(1 \text{ g/cm}^3)(980 \text{ dyn/g}) = 297$ cm.

12-B29 $r = 2\gamma/dhg = 2(63 \text{ dyn/cm})/(1.26 \text{ g/cm}^3)(4 \text{ cm})(980 \text{ dyn/g}) = 0.0244$ cm. Diameter = $2r = 0.051$ cm.

12-B30 (a) Table 12-1 gives $90°$ for the angle of contact; $\mathbf{R}$ must be perpendicular to the liquid surface, i.e., vertically downward. (b) $C/A = \sqrt{2} = 1.41$.
(c) There would be no rise.

12-B31 (a) $\dfrac{2\gamma}{rdg} = 2r$, whence $r = \sqrt{\dfrac{\gamma}{dg}}$; diameter $= 2r = 2\sqrt{\dfrac{\gamma}{dg}}$.

(c) $2r = 2\sqrt{\dfrac{75.6 \text{ erg/cm}^2}{(1.00 \text{ g/cm}^3)(980 \text{ cm/s}^2)}} = 0.555 \text{ cm}$.

12-B32 (a) $(1.0 \text{ J/s})(70 \times 3.156 \times 10^7 \text{ s}) = 2.2 \times 10^9 \text{ J}$. (b) The mass of the Pyramid is found in Prob. 2-A8 to be 6.5×10^9 kg. The height it could be raised is
$h = \text{PE/weight} = (2.2 \times 10^9 \text{ J})/(6.5 \times 10^9 \text{ kg})(9.8 \text{ N/kg}) = 0.035 \text{ m}$.

12-B33 Since the level does not change, Bernoulli's equation becomes $\frac{1}{2}dv^2 + P = $ constant. Thus,

$$\frac{1}{2}(1000 \text{ kg/m}^3)(3 \text{ m/s})^2 + (1.00 \times 1.013 \times 10^5 \text{ N/m}^2)$$
$$= \frac{1}{2}(1000 \text{ kg/m}^2)v_2{}^2 + (0.8 \times 1.013 \times 10^5 \text{ N/m}^2)$$

This equation yields $v_2 = 7.04$ m/s. (b) For an "incompressible" fluid such as water, $vA = $ constant (see p. 285). Hence, $A_1/A_2 = v_2/v_1 = 7.04/3.00 = 2.35$.
(c) $D_1/D_2 = \sqrt{A_1/A_2} = 1.53$.

12-B34 $m = W/g$ for 1 ft^3 of sea water is $(64 \text{ lb})/(32 \text{ ft/s}^2) = 2.0 \text{ lb·s}^2/\text{ft}$, and the density is $m/V = 2.0 \text{ lb·s}^2/\text{ft}^4$. Now apply Bernoulli's equation:

$$\frac{1}{2}(2 \text{ lb·s}^2/\text{ft}^4)(10 \text{ ft/s})^2 + 4000 \text{ lb/ft}^2 = \frac{1}{2}(2 \text{ lb·s}^2/\text{ft}^4)v_2{}^2 + 3200 \text{ lb/ft}^2.$$

Solving for v_2 gives $v_2 = 30$ ft/s. [Note that the units in the big equation are consistent.]

12-B35 We assume that the boot is large enough so the velocity of the upper water surface is essentially zero. Then we have a projectile problem in which the initial horizontal velocity of a water drop leaving the hole is (by the energy principle) the same as that of a body that has fallen 36 cm, starting from rest. $v_2 = \sqrt{2gh} = \sqrt{2(980 \text{ cm/s}^2)(36 \text{ cm})} = 266$ cm/s. Each drop of ejected water is in the air for the time to fall 4 cm: $t = \sqrt{2s/g} = \sqrt{2(4 \text{ cm})/(980 \text{ cm/s}^2)} = 0.0904$ s. Range $= v_2 t = (266 \text{ cm/s})(0.0904 \text{ s}) = 24$ cm. [Solving the problem using symbols gives for the range $R = \sqrt{hh'}$, where h is the distance of the hole below the top water level and h' is the height of the hole above the floor. The value of g cancels out. The problem can also be solved as an application of Bernoulli's equation, as outlined on p. 287. This is scarcely surprising, since Bernoulli's equation is based on the energy principle (Sec. 12-10).]

12-B36 As in Case 2 on p. 287, Bernoulli's equation reduces to $v^2 = 2gh$.
(a) $v = \sqrt{2gh} = \sqrt{2(9.8 \text{ m/s}^2)(4.9 \text{ m})} = 9.8$ m/s. (b) By the energy principle, the KE of the stream of water becomes PE, and the water rises to a height of 4.9 m.

12-B37 (a) $\frac{1}{2}(1.0 \text{ kg/m}^3)(200 \text{ m/s})^2 + P_1 = \frac{1}{2}(1.0 \text{ kg/m}^3)(250 \text{ m/s})^2 + P_2$. This gives $\Delta P = P_1 - P_2 = 11\,250 \text{ N/m}^2$. The resultant force is $F = A(P_1 - P_2) = (20 \text{ m}^2) \times (11\,250 \text{ N/m}^2) = 2.25 \times 10^5 \text{ N} = 225 \text{ kN}$.

12-C1 (a) $\Delta V/V = \Delta P/B = (7.54 \times 10^7 \text{ N/m}^2)/(0.21 \times 10^{10} \text{ N/m}^2) = 0.036 = 3.6\%$.
(b) The specific gravity increases: $(1.03)(1 + 0.036) = 1.07$.

12-C2 Since the log floats with $\frac{4}{5}$ its volume submerged, its specific gravity is 0.8, and the volume of the log is $(200 \text{ kg})/(800 \text{ kg/m}^3) = 0.25 \text{ m}^3$. To find the volume V of the iron, use Archimedes' principle; equating downward forces to upward forces gives (in mks units)

$[200 \text{ kg} + V(7860 \text{ kg/m}^3)](9.8 \text{ N/kg}) = (0.25 \text{ m}^3 + V)(1000 \text{ kg/m}^3)(9.8 \text{ N/kg})$ whence $V = 0.00729 \text{ m}^3$. The mass of the iron is $(0.00729 \text{ m}^3)/(7860 \text{ kg/m}^3)$ = 57.3 kg.

12-C3   (a) The diver's apparent weight is $(0.08)(75 \text{ kg})g$; the true weight of the diver and iron is $(75 \text{ kg})g + V(7860 \text{ kg/m}^3)g$; the buoyant force is $[(75 \text{ kg})/(980 \text{ kg/m}^3) + V](1000 \text{ kg/m}^3)g$. Set up an equation for apparent weight = true weight − buoyant force, and solve for V (g cancels out). The result is that $V = 1.098 \times 10^{-3} \text{ m}^3 = 1098 \text{ cm}^3$.   (b) In air, the weight of iron is $mg = (7860 \text{ kg/m}^3) \times (1.098 \times 10^{-3} \text{ m}^3)(9.8 \text{ N/kg}) = 84.6 \text{ N}$.

12-C4   (a) The flow is turbulent, since for streamline flow the air resistance would be proportional to v, not v^2 (p. 288).   (b) If $f \propto v^2$, then power $P = fv \propto v^3$. (c) If time for a lap is t, the work done against air resistance during that lap is $Pt \propto (1/t^3)t \propto 1/t^2$. Work done by $A \propto 4 \times (1/70^2) = 8.163 \times 10^{-4}$ units; work done by $B \propto 1/60^2 + 1/70^2 + 1/80^2 + 1/70^2 = 8.422$ units. The difference is 0.259 units, or $0.259/8.29 \approx 3\%$.

12-C5   The volume of the brass weights is $(400 \text{ g})/(8.4 \text{ g/cm}^3) = 47.6 \text{ cm}^3$.   (a) BF on aluminum = $(150 \text{ cm}^3)(1.293 \times 10^{-3} \text{ g/cm}^3)(980 \text{ dyn/g}) = 190.07 \text{ dyn}$. (b) BF on brass = $(47.6 \text{ cm}^3)(1.293 \times 10^{-3} \text{ g/cm}^3)(980 \text{ dyn/g}) = 60.34 \text{ dyn}$. (c) The excess buoyancy is 129.73 dyn, which corresponds to an apparent mass change of $129.73/980 = 0.132 \text{ g}$. If the true mass is 400.000 g, the apparent weight of the block corresponds to a mass of $(400.000 - 0.132)$ = 399.868 g.

12-C6   (a) Power = (KE per beat)(beats per second) = $\frac{1}{2}(60 \times 10^{-6} \text{ m}^3)(1000 \text{ kg/m}^3) \times (1.87 \times 0.75 \text{ m/s})^2(\frac{72}{60} \text{ beats/s}) = 0.0708 \text{ W}$; total for two ventricles $\approx 0.14 \text{ W}$. (b) Compared with the resting heart, $\frac{1}{2}mv^2$ is $10 \times 10^2 = 1000$ times as much; $1000(0.14 \text{ W}) = 140 \text{ W}$.   (c) See part (b) of Example 12-15, where ΔV was 60 cm^3. Here $\Delta V = 600 \text{ cm}^3$ and the power is 10 times as much as in Example 12-15, i.e., about 10 W.

Chapter 13   Temperature and Expansion

Questions

13-1   Length (of a solid); volume; electrical resistivity; color (of a blackbody).

13-2   When heat from the hot filament was conducted down the metal support, the equal thermal expansions of metal and glass prevented a buildup of stress that might crack the glass.

13-3   There are 50 marks in 7 cm; the separation is $\frac{7}{50}$ cm, or 1.4 mm.

13-4   Suppose the thermometer is held bulb end down, then jerked downward, and suddenly stopped with an upward acceleration **a**. From an outsider's viewpoint, the inertia of the liquid keeps it moving toward the bulb; the frictional force of the inner surface of the capillary tube is insufficient to cause the liquid to accelerate upward at the same rate at which the thermometer is accelerating, so the liquid "shakes down" into the bulb. From an insider's viewpoint (accelerated frame of reference), the liquid experiences a fictitious inertial force $-m\mathbf{a}$, which is downward (into the bulb). Compare the discussion of a washing machine dryer on p. 179.

13-5 Large bulb; capillary of small bore.

13-6 To allow for expansion of the slabs in hot weather.

13-7 Either length can be used, without significant difference in the results.

13-8 The coefficient 0.00366 $(°C)^{-1}$ refers to an original volume at 0°C, not to an arbitrary original volume.

13-9 Since $P = hdg$, and d decreases, h becomes larger and the barometer reading increases; it indicates a pressure that is higher than the correct value. For precise work, the expansion of the scale (usually brass in the older instruments) must be allowed for.

13-10 The thermal conductivity of aluminum allows the temperature to rise throughout the metal of the cup at the same (rapid) rate, so no stress is developed by unequal expansion of different parts of the cup.

13-11 Larger. Think of a circle drawn on a solid metal plate. When the plate is heated, the diameter of the circle increases. If the circle is replaced by a hole and a close-fitting circular plug of the same material, both the plug and the hole become larger.

13-12 The metal cap expands before the glass bottle (with its low thermal conductivity) has time to expand. The maneuver must be carried out quickly.

Multiple Choice

13-13 (c);   **13-14** (a);   **13-15** (a);   **13-16** (c);   **13-17** (c);   **13-18** (a).

Problems

13-A1 36.0°C; 41.0°C.

13-A2 39.2°F.

13-A3 20°C; −15°C; −200°C; 37°C.

13-A4 −17.8°C; −40°C; 500°C; 25°C.

13-A5 68°F; 1112°F; −40°F; −459.4°F.

13-A6 86°F; 14°F; 10832°F; −108.4°F.

13-A7 The interval is $\frac{5}{9}(3.6°C) = 2.0°C$.

13-A8 $\frac{9}{5}(2\text{ mm}) = 3.6$ mm.

13-A9 $\Delta L = L\alpha\,\Delta t = (12\text{ m})[11 \times 10^{-6}\ (°C)^{-1}](50°C) = 0.0066\text{ m} = 6.6$ mm.

13-A10 $\alpha = \Delta L/L\,\Delta t = \dfrac{102.664\text{ cm} - 102.503\text{ cm}}{(102.58\text{ cm})(60°C)} = 26.2 \times 10^{-6}\ (°C)^{-1}$; the metal is aluminum.

13-A11 $\Delta L = (11\text{ m})[11 \times 10^{-6}\ (°C)^{-1}](95°C) = 0.0115\text{ m} = 1.15$ cm.

13-A12 (a) $\alpha = \frac{5}{9}[11 \times 10^{-6}\ (°C)^{-1}] = 6.1 \times 10^{-6}\ (°F)^{-1}$; (b) $(4200\text{ ft})[6.1 \times 10^{-6}\ (°F)^{-1}]$ $\times (125°F) = 3.2$ ft.

13-A13 $\beta = 3\alpha = 45 \times 10^{-6}\ (°C)^{-1}$.

13-A14 Using $\beta = 3\alpha$, we have $\Delta V = (400.00\text{ cm}^3)[60 \times 10^{-6}\ (°C)^{-1}](0°C - 25°C) = -0.60$ cm^3; $V = (400.00 - 0.60)\text{ cm}^3 = 399.40\text{ cm}^3$.

13-A15 $\Delta V = V\beta \Delta t = (5 \text{ gal})[960 \times 10^{-6} \ (°C)^{-1}](40°C) = 0.19 \text{ gal}; \quad V = (5 + 0.19) \text{ gal}$
$= 5.19 \text{ gal}.$

13-B1 68°F = 20°C = 80° on the original scale.

13-B2 If body temperature is taken to be 37°C, the 12°N difference corresponded to a difference of 37°C; the size of the degree was 1°C = (12/37)°N, and −15° was $(-15)(12/37) = -4.9°N$. Some disadvantages of Newton's temperature scale: body temperature is variable and hence unsuitable for a fixed point; the 12° range between the ice point and body temperature makes the size of the degree inconveniently large.

13-B3 Size of 1°R was (100/80) as large as 1°C. Thus 50°R = 50(100/80)°C = 62.5°C.

13-B4 Either of two equations can be used: $\frac{9}{5}C + 32 = 3C$ or $\frac{5}{9}(3C - 32) = C$. In either case, we find that 26.67°C = 80.00°F.

13-B5 $\Delta L = (4.10 \text{ cm})[11 \times 10^{-6} \ (°C)^{-1}](100°C) = 0.0045 \text{ cm}$. New diameter = (4.1030 − 0.0045) cm = 4.0985 cm. There is 0.0015 cm to spare when the cold rivet is inserted in the hole.

13-B6 Use the relative coefficient of expansion:
0.001 cm = $(5.00 \text{ cm})[(19 - 11) \times 10^{-6} \ (°C)^{-1}](t - 20°C); \ t = 45°C.$

13-B7 (a) $\Delta L = 0.542 \text{ cm} = (270 \text{ cm})[11 \times 10^{-6} \ (°C)^{-1}](t - 15°C); \ t = 197°C.$

(b) From $E = \dfrac{F/A}{\Delta L/L}, \ F = EA(\Delta L/L) = EA(\alpha \Delta t)$

$= (19 \times 10^{10} \text{ N/m}^2)(2.50 \times 10^{-4} \text{ m}^2)[11 \times 10^{-6} \ (°C)^{-1}](197°C - 15°C) = 9.5 \times 10^4 \text{ N}.$
[The large tension ensures a snug fit.]

13-B8 (a) $\Delta L/L = \alpha \Delta t = [11 \times 10^{-6} \ (°C)^{-1}](18°C) = 0.020\%.$ (b) The tape reads too low. (c) $(0.02\%)(1500 \text{ cm}) = 0.30 \text{ cm} = 3 \text{ mm low.}$

13-B9 0.020 cm = $(10 \text{ cm})[19 \times 10^{-6} \ (°C)^{-1}](t - 20°C); \ t = 125°C.$

13-B10 10.000 cm + $(10 \text{ cm})[19 \times 10^{-6} \ (°C)^{-1}]\Delta t = 10.020 \text{ cm} + (10 \text{ cm})[11 \times 10^{-6} \ (°C)^{-1}]$ $\times \Delta t$. This reduces to $(10 \text{ cm})[8 \times 10^{-6} \ (°C)^{-1}]\Delta t = 0.020 \text{ cm}$, as would be expected using the relative expansion coefficient. We obtain $\Delta t = 250°C$, and the final temperature is 270°C.

13-B11 Equate ΔL from cooling to ΔL from applying a force. $L\alpha \Delta t = FL/AE$; L cancels out and we obtain $F = \alpha AE \Delta t = [19 \times 10^{-6} \ (°C)^{-1}](2 \times 10^{-4} \text{ m}^2)(9 \times 10^{10} \text{ N/m}^2)$ $\times (170°C) = 58 \text{ kN.}$

13-B12 See remarks for Prob. 13-B11. $F = \alpha AE \Delta t = [11 \times 10^{-6} \ (°C)^{-1}](2 \times 10^{-6} \text{ m}^2)$ $\times (20 \times 10^{10} \text{ N/m}^2)(10°C) = 44 \text{ N.}$

13-B13 Use the coefficient of expansion for lead relative to aluminum:
$\Delta L = L\alpha_{rel} \Delta t = (60 \text{ cm})[3 \times 10^{-6} \ (°C)^{-1}](100°C) = 0.018 \text{ cm.}$

13-B14 For aluminum, $\beta = 77 \times 10^{-6} \ (°C)^{-1}$ from Table 13-1; this is consistent with $\beta = 3\alpha$. Use the relative coefficient of volume expansion:
$\Delta V = V\beta_{rel} \Delta t = (200 \text{ cm}^3)[(485 - 77) \times 10^{-6} \ (°C)^{-1}](105°C) = 8.57 \text{ cm}^3.$

13-B15 Use the relative coefficient of volume expansion. The overflow is
$\Delta V = V\beta \Delta t = (200 \text{ liters})[(900 - 33) \times 10^{-6} \ (°C)^{-1}](20°C) = 3.5 \text{ liters.}$
The amount remaining in the drum is (200.0 − 3.5) liters = 196.5 liters.

13-B16 Imagine that the block is heated and expands; calculate the pressure required to bring the block back to its original volume. From $B = \Delta P/(\Delta V/V), \ \Delta P = B \Delta V/V$. Using $\Delta V/V = \beta \Delta t$, we have
$\Delta P = B\beta \Delta t = (7.5 \times 10^{10} \text{ N/m}^2)[77 \times 10^{-6} \ (°C)^{-1}](10°C) = 5.78 \times 10^7 \text{ N/m}^2$
$= (5.78 \times 10^7 \text{ N/m}^2)\left(\dfrac{1 \text{ atm}}{1.013 \times 10^5 \text{ N/m}^2}\right) = 570 \text{ atm.}$

13-B17 $\beta_{rel} = (581 - 77) \times 10^{-6} \ (°C)^{-1} = 504 \times 10^{-6} \ (°C)^{-1}.$

13-B18 The relative β is $(182 - 1) \times 10^{-6}$ $(°C)^{-1}$. As in Prob. 3-B16,

$$\Delta P = B\,\beta\,\Delta t = (2.5 \times 10^{10}\text{ N/m}^2)[181 \times 10^{-6}\text{ }(°C)^{-1}](0.30°C)\left(\frac{1\text{ atm}}{1.013 \times 10^5\text{ N/m}^2}\right)$$

= 13.4 atm.   [The quartz container is assumed to be thick enough so its expansion due to pressure is negligible.]

13-B19 $[0.00366\text{ }(°C)^{-1}]\Delta t = 0.0366$; $\Delta t = 10°C$.

13-B20 $\dfrac{(450 - 400)\text{ cm}^3}{(100 - 20)°C} = \dfrac{(520 - 400)\text{ cm}^3}{\Delta t}$; $\Delta t = 192°C$.

The indicated temperature is $192°C + 20°C = 212°C$.

13-C1 (a) Since $T = 2\pi(L/g)^{1/2}$, the fractional change in T is $\frac{1}{2}$ the fractional change in L. When the temperature increases by $10°C$, $\Delta L/L = \alpha\,\Delta t = [19 \times 10^{-6}\text{ }(°C)^{-1}] \times (10°C) = 190 \times 10^{-6}$. Hence $\Delta T/T = 95 \times 10^{-6}$, and $\Delta T = (95 \times 10^{-6})(2.000\text{ s}) = 190 \times 10^{-6}$ s. The new period is $2.000\text{ s} + 0.00019\text{ s} = 2.00019$ s.   (b) The clock is ticking slower, and in 1 day makes $\frac{1}{2}(86\,400) = 43\,200$ swings. The loss in 1 day is $(43\,200)(190 \times 10^{-6}\text{ s}) = 8.2$ s.   [The problem can also be slugged out using the binomial theorem (stated in Prob. 10-C2 on p. 244).

$\dfrac{T'}{T} = \left[\dfrac{L(1 + \alpha t)}{L}\right]^{1/2}$; $T' = T(1 + \alpha t)^{1/2} \approx T + T(\frac{1}{2}\alpha t)$, which leads to $\Delta t = 190 \times 10^{-6}$ s as above.]

13-C2 We imagine the rods expanding to some new lengths due to temperature rise, then being squeezed back by a stress S to their original total length (but differently apportioned between the rods). Using lengths in m, α in $(°C)^{-1}$, and temperature in $°C$, we calculate the total thermal expansion to be $(0.40)(11 \times 10^{-6})(30) + (0.30)(19 \times 10^{-6})(30) = 0.0003030$ m.   (a) The stresses (F/A) in the two rods are equal, since they have the same F (Newton's third law), and the same A. Call this stress S. From $E = $ stress/strain, we have $\Delta L/L = $ stress/E, or $\Delta L = LS/E$. Thus, the total contraction due to stress is given by

$$0.0003030 = \frac{S(0.40)}{20 \times 10^{10}} + \frac{S(0.30)}{9 \times 10^{10}}; \quad S = 5.681 \times 10^7\text{ N/m}^2.$$

(b) For the steel rod, the thermal expansion is 0.0001320 m and the contraction due to stress is $\Delta L = (5.681 \times 10^7)(0.40)/(20 \times 10^{10}) = 0.0001136$ m; net expansion is $(0.0001320 - 0.0001136) = 1.84 \times 10^{-5}$ m $= 0.0184$ mm. Similarly, for the brass rod, the thermal expansion is 0.0001710 m and the contraction due to stress is $\Delta L = (5.681 \times 10^7)(0.30)/(9 \times 10^{10}) = 0.0001894$ m; net expansion is $(0.0001710 - 0.0001894) = -1.84 \times 10^{-5}$ m $= -0.0184$ mm. As a check, we see that the steel rod is 0.0184 mm longer than at the start, and the brass rod is 0.0184 mm shorter than at the start. The junction has moved 0.0184 mm from its old position.   [In this solution we assume the data to be exact, to avoid rounding errors that would be needlessly confusing.]

13-C3 The true weight of the block is $(100\text{ cm}^3)(2.699\text{ g/cm}^3)g$ dyn.   (a) At $20°C$, BF $= (100.0\text{ cm}^3)(1.248\text{ g/cm}^3)g = 124.8g$ dyn. Apparent weight $= (269.9 - 124.8)g = 145.1 \times 980$ dyn.   (b) At $80°C$, the block's volume is $100.0\text{ cm}^3 + (100\text{ cm}^3)[77 \times 10^{-6}\text{ }(°C)^{-1}](60°C) = 100.462\text{ cm}^3$. The specific gravity of glycerin is less: $1.248 - (1.248)[485 \times 10^{-6}\text{ }(°C)^{-1}](60°C) = 1.2117$. Now the BF is $(100.462\text{ cm}^3)(1.2117\text{ g/cm}^3)g = 121.7g$ dyn. The apparent weight is $(269.9 - 121.7)g = 148.2 \times 980$ dyn.

Chapter 14   Heat and Heat Transfer

Questions

14-1   Heat is quantity of thermal energy; temperature is proportional to thermal energy per molecule (See Sec. 16-1). In Chap. 13, temperature is considered to be the quantity that a thermometer measures.

14-2   (a) The temperature of the sun's surface is 6000°C.   (b) Body temperature of a whale is 36°C.   (c) The heat required to melt lead is 5.86 cal/g.   (d) The specific heat of copper is 0.093 cal/g·°C.

14-3   Watt and horsepower are not units of energy.

14-4   Assume that the buckets lose heat at the same rate. From $\Delta t = \Delta Q/mc$, we see that for a given ΔQ the temperature change Δt is more for the substance of smaller specific heat. Hence glycerin cools more rapidly. If one bucket is painted black, it becomes a more efficient radiator and will lose heat faster, other factors remaining the same.

14-5   It becomes random KE of the molecules of book and floor, i.e., thermal energy.

14-6   1000(80 + 100 + 540) = 7200 cal.

14-7   Radiation from the fireplace, followed by convection as the stone is carried, finally conduction to the feet.

14-8   The metal is a good conductor of heat away from the fingers.

14-9   Yes, but with negligible intensity.

14-10 No; it absorbs less than it radiates (first law of thermodynamics). This is an extension of the statement on p. 324, which assumes no source of heat inside the earth. See also the footnote on p. 709.

Multiple Choice

14-11 (a);   14-12 (b);   14-13 (a);   14-14 (b);   14-15 (c);   14-16 (c).

Problems

14-A1   (400 g)(1 cal/g·°C)(20°C) = 8000 cal.
14-A2   (400 lb)(1 Btu/lb·°F)(150°F) = 60 000 Btu.
14-A3   (800 J)$\left(\dfrac{1 \text{ cal}}{4.18 \text{ J}}\right)$ = 191 cal.
14-A4 $\left(1 \dfrac{\text{cal}}{\text{g·°C}}\right)\left(\dfrac{4.18 \text{ J}}{1 \text{ cal}}\right)\left(\dfrac{1 \text{ kJ}}{10^3 \text{ J}}\right)\left(\dfrac{10^3 \text{ g}}{1 \text{ kg}}\right) = 4.18 \dfrac{\text{kJ}}{\text{kg·°C}}$.
14-A5   (640 cal)/(100 g)(8°C) = 0.80 cal/g·°C.
14-A6   (1200 cal)/(500 g)(10°C) = 0.24 cal/g·°C.
14-A7   (100 lb)(0.195 Btu/lb·°F)(60°F) = 1170 Btu.

14-A8 $(2000 \text{ g})(0.0306) = 61.2$ g.   [Here the term specific heat is used in the precise "specific" sense, in relation to water; similar to the use of "specific" gravity, a dimensionless ratio.]

14-A9 $(200 \text{ g})(1 \text{ cal/g} \cdot {}^\circ\text{C})(80^\circ\text{C}) = 16\,000$ cal.

14-A10 $(2 \text{ kg})(1 \text{ cal/g} \cdot {}^\circ\text{C})(79^\circ\text{C}) = 158$ kcal.

14-A11 $(40 \text{ g})(80 \text{ cal/g}) + (40 \text{ g})(1 \text{ cal/g} \cdot {}^\circ\text{C})(20^\circ\text{C}) = 4000$ cal.

14-A12 $(1 \text{ kg})(0.0306 \text{ kcal/kg} \cdot {}^\circ\text{C})(327^\circ\text{C}) + (1 \text{ kg})(5.9 \text{ kcal/kg}) = 15.9$ kcal.

14-A13 $(1180 \text{ cal})/(20 \text{ g}) = 59$ cal/g.

14-A14 $(50 \text{ J})\left(\dfrac{1 \text{ cal}}{4.18 \text{ J}}\right) = m \left(6 \dfrac{\text{cal}}{\text{g}}\right);$ $m = 1.99$ g.

14-A15 $\lambda = c/\nu = (3 \times 10^8 \text{ m/s})/(85 \times 10^6 \text{ Hz}) = 3.53$ m.   [Most roof-top TV antennas are a few meters in size.]

14-A16 $\nu = c/\lambda = (3 \times 10^8 \text{ m/s})/(0.56 \times 10^{-10} \text{ m}) = 5.36 \times 10^{18}$ Hz.

14-A17 10^4 Å; 1 μm; 1000 nm.

14-A19 Figure 14-4 shows the frequency to be 10^{14} Hz; $\lambda = (3 \times 10^8 \text{ m/s})/(10^{14} \text{ Hz}) = 3 \times 10^{-6}$ m $= 3 \times 10^4$ Å.   [This is in the infrared region.]

Note: In problems 14-B1 through 14-B11, dealing with the method of mixtures, the following units are assumed: mass in g, c in cal/g·°C, t in °C. Only Prob. 14-B1 is given in this solutions manual with the units in their full glory.

14-B1 $(600 \text{ g})(0.0306 \text{ cal/g} \cdot {}^\circ\text{C})(100^\circ\text{C} - 30.6^\circ\text{C}) = [(120 \text{ g})(0.22 \text{ cal/g} \cdot {}^\circ\text{C}) + (200 \text{ g})c] \times (30.6^\circ\text{C} - 20^\circ\text{C})$ whence $c = 0.47$ cal/g·°C.

14-B2 $(340.1)(17.3) = 62.5(17) + 62.5(\Delta h_f);$ $\Delta h_f = 77.1$ cal/g.

14-B3 (a) To bring to a boiling temperature of 100°C, after a time T, $[340(0.22) + 300(1)](100 - 20) = (100 \text{ cal/s})T;$ $T = 299.8$ s = 5 min. The water begins to boil at 5:20 P.M.   (b) $300(540) = (100 \text{ cal/s})T;$ $T = 1620$ s = 27 min; the water is all gone at 5:47 P.M.   [All the water must boil away before the pan's temperature starts to rise above 100°C.]

14-B4 A preliminary calculation shows that the steam *can* give up 5400 cal, but the amount needed to bring all the water to a boil is only 1600 + 2000 = 3600 cal. Hence not all of the steam condenses. Let m be the mass of steam that condenses. $540m = 20(80) + 20(100);$ $m = 6.67$ g. The final result is: 26.67 g of water at 100°C, 3.33 g of steam at 100°C.

14-B5 A preliminary calculation shows that to reach 100°C would require 9600 cal, which is more than is available. We set up the equation on the assumption that the final temperature t is between 0°C and 100°C. $60(80) + 60t = 10(540) + 10(100 - t);$ $t = 22.9$°C. The final result is: 70 g of water at 22.9°C.

14-B6 A preliminary calculation shows that it would take more than the available 5400 cal to melt all the ice. Let m be the mass of ice that melts. $m(80) = 10(540) + 10(100 - 0);$ $m = 80$ g. The final result is: 10 g of ice, 90 g of water, all at 0°C.

14-B7 Heat absorbed by aluminum chunk = heat given out by water. $500(0.182) \times (39 - t_0) = [200(0.093) + 400(1)](90 - 39);$ $t_0 = -196$°C.   [The liquid air was freshly made; see answer to Ques. 15-13.]

14-B8 The mass of glycerin is $(200 \text{ cm}^3)(1.26 \text{ g/cm}^3) = 252$ g; the mass of copper is $(10 \text{ cm}^3)(8.93 \text{ g/cm}^3) = 89.3$ g. $[60 + 252(0.60)](t - 20) = (89.3)(0.093)(100 - t);$ $t = 23.0$°C.

14-B9 $m(540) + m(100 - 40) = 70(80) + 70(40);$ $m = 14$ g.

14-B10 Heat required to bring the system up to 0°C is $[(40)(0.50) + (100)(0.22)](35) = 1470$ cal. Heat required to melt the ice = $40(80) = 3200$ cal. This leaves

$7000 - 1470 - 3200 = 2330$ cal to raise the temperature of the system.
$[(40)(1) + (100)(0.22)]t = 2330; \ t = 37.6°C.$

14-B11 The mass of cold water in the cup is 146 g. $7(\Delta h_v) + 7(100 - 40)$
$= [146(1) + 100(0.22)](40 - 15); \ \Delta h_v = 540$ cal/g.

14-B12 (a) $(500 \text{ kg})\left(1 \dfrac{\text{kcal}}{\text{kg·°C}}\right)(2°C) = \left(400 \dfrac{\text{kcal}}{\text{h}}\right)T; \$ time $T = 2.5$ h. (b) The water
is cooled by 1°C, freezes, and then the ice is cooled to $-1°C$.
$(500 \text{ kg})\left(1 \dfrac{\text{kcal}}{\text{kg·°C}}\right)(2°C) + (100 \text{ kg})\left(1 \dfrac{\text{kcal}}{\text{kg·°C}}\right)(1°C) + (100 \text{ kg})\left(80 \dfrac{\text{kcal}}{\text{kg}}\right)$
$+ (100 \text{ kg})\left(0.50 \dfrac{\text{kcal}}{\text{kg·°C}}\right)(1°C) = 400\left(\dfrac{\text{kcal}}{\text{h}}\right)T; \ T = \dfrac{9150 \text{ kcal}}{400 \text{ kcal/h}} = 22.9$ h.

14-B13 Use the solar constant, 1.94 cal/cm²·min (p. 324); the efficiency is 10^{-3}.
$\left(1.94 \dfrac{\text{cal}}{\text{cm}^2\text{·min}}\right)(10^{-3})(\cos 60°)\left(\dfrac{60 \text{ min}}{1 \text{ h}}\right)\left(\dfrac{1 \text{ g}}{540 \text{ cal}}\right)(1 \text{ km})^2\left(\dfrac{10^5 \text{ cm}}{1 \text{ km}}\right)^2\left(\dfrac{1 \text{ kg}}{10^3 \text{ g}}\right)$
$= 1080$ kg/h.
[The 60° angle of the sun's rays introduces a factor $\cos \theta$ $(= 0.500)$, since the
projected area of 1 cm² is only 0.500 cm² as seen broadside to the sun's rays.
The magnitude of evaporation from lakes (more than a ton per hour in this
example) makes conservation methods important. One technique is to coat the
surface of the lake with a nonvolatile monomolecular layer that retards evaporation. See V. K. La Mer and T. W. Healy, "Evaporation of Water: Its Re-
tardation by Monolayers," *Science*, 148, 36-42 (1965).]

14-B14 Half of the KE of the hammer head remains in the tray as thermal energy.
The specific heat of silver is (0.056×4180) J/kg·°C. $\frac{1}{2}(0.45 \text{ kg})(10 \text{ m/s})^2(0.5)(30)$
$= (0.080 \text{ kg})(0.056 \times 4180 \text{ J/kg·°C})\Delta t; \ \Delta t = 18.0°C.$

14-B15 $W = \frac{1}{2}(10 \times 10^3 \text{ kg})\left[\left(80 \dfrac{\text{km}}{\text{h}}\right)\left(\dfrac{1 \text{ h}}{3600 \text{ s}}\right)\left(\dfrac{10^3 \text{ m}}{1 \text{ km}}\right)\right]^2\left(\dfrac{1 \text{ kcal}}{4180 \text{ J}}\right) = 591$ kcal.

14-B16 $W = \frac{1}{2}\left(\dfrac{1600 \text{ lb}}{32 \text{ ft}/s^2}\right)(16 \text{ ft/s})^2\left(\dfrac{1 \text{ Btu}}{778 \text{ ft·lb}}\right) = 8.23$ Btu. [The conversion of Btu to
ft·lb is given on p. 314, also in the Appendix, p. 803.]

14-B17 (a) Loss of KE = $\frac{1}{2}(0.02 \text{ kg})[(400 \text{ m/s})^2 - (300 \text{ m/s})^2] = 700$ J. (b) $(0.60)(700 \text{ J})$
$= (0.02 \text{ kg})(0.0306 \times 4180 \text{ J/kg·°C})\Delta t; \ \Delta t = 164°C.$ The bullet will remain well
below the melting point of lead (Table 14-2).

14-B18 Loss of PE = $(40 \text{ kg})(9.8 \text{ N/kg})(3 \sin 45° \text{ m}) = 832$ J; KE at bottom = $\frac{1}{2}(40 \text{ kg})$
$\times (2 \text{ m/s})^2 = 80$ J. The loss of mechanical energy is $(832 - 80)$ J = 752 J.

14-B19 Initial KE = $\frac{1}{2}(80 \text{ kg})(5 \text{ m/s})^2 = 1000$ J. Half of this remains in the ice; 500 J
$= 119.6$ cal $= m$ (80 cal/g); $m = 1.50$ g. [The 20 m distance is not involved
in this solution by the energy method. More details of the motion can be found,
but they are not needed. The acceleration is $-v^2/2s = -0.625$ m/s²; the force
of friction is 50 N; the coefficient of kinetic friction (μ_k) is 0.064.]

14-B20 To evaporate 1 g: $(1 \text{ g})\left(\dfrac{540 \text{ cal}}{1 \text{ g}}\right)\left(\dfrac{4.18 \text{ J}}{1 \text{ cal}}\right) = 2257$ J. To lift 1 g: $mgh = (10^{-3} \text{ kg})$
$\times (9.8 \text{ N/kg})(1.5 \times 10^3 \text{ m}) = 14.7$ J. The ratio is about 154:1. [The ratio
is actually about 160:1, somewhat higher than the calculated ratio, since
the latent heat of vaporization would be somewhat higher than 540 cal/g if
evaporation takes place at, say 30°C or 40°C instead of at 100°C.]

14-B21 $(70 \text{ kcal})\left(\dfrac{4180 \text{ J}}{1 \text{ kcal}}\right) = (10 \text{ kg})(9.8 \text{ N/kg})(0.8 \text{ m})(N \text{ times}); \ N = 3732$ times.
[Dieting is the most effective method of weight control.]

14-B22 $\left(90 \dfrac{\text{J}}{\text{s}}\right)\left(\dfrac{1 \text{ kcal}}{4180 \text{ J}}\right)\left(\dfrac{86\,400 \text{ s}}{1 \text{ day}}\right) = 1860$ kcal/day.

14-B23 The water equivalent of the cup is $(120 \text{ g})(0.20) = 40$ g; it contains 0.2 liter of water = 200 g.

$$\left(200 \frac{\text{J}}{\text{s}}\right)T = (200 \text{ g} + 40 \text{ g})\left(1 \frac{\text{cal}}{\text{g} \cdot {}^\circ\text{C}}\right)(75{}^\circ\text{C} - 20{}^\circ\text{C})\left(\frac{4.18 \text{ J}}{1 \text{ cal}}\right);$$

$T = 276$ s = 4.60 min.

14-B24 (a) $m\left(580 \frac{\text{cal}}{\text{g}}\right) = \frac{20 \times 10^3 \text{ cal}}{60 \text{ min}}(10 \text{ min})$; $m = 5.75$ g. The sweat, of specific gravity approximately 1.00, has volume 5.75 cm^3. The thickness x is found from the volume and area: $x = (5.75 \text{ cm}^3)/(10^4 \text{ cm}^2) = 5.75 \times 10^{-4}$ cm = 0.005 mm. (b) At skin temperature, water molecules have less KE than at 100${}^\circ$C; hence more energy must be supplied from the outside in order to separate the molecules and form a vapor. (c) Heat might also be lost by conduction (air molecules gain energy upon colliding with the skin) and by radiation.

14-B25 $\left(20 \frac{\text{J}}{\text{s}}\right)\left(\frac{1 \text{ cal}}{4.18 \text{ J}}\right)\left(\frac{3600 \text{ s}}{1 \text{ h}}\right) = m\left(580 \frac{\text{cal}}{\text{g}}\right)$; $m =$ about 30 g/h.

14-B26 No. [From Table 14-3, the heat of combustion of carbohydrates and proteins is about 17 MJ/kg. Energy available from 300 g of foodstuffs is $(0.3 \text{ kg}) \times (17 \times 10^6 \text{ J/kg}) = 5.1 \times 10^6$ J. The amount needed in 1 day is $(90 \text{ J/s})(86\,400 \text{ s}) = 7.8 \times 10^6$ J.]

14-B27 $m(0.0306 \text{ kcal/kg} \cdot {}^\circ\text{C})(4180 \text{ J/kcal})\Delta t = m(9.8 \text{ N/kg})(30 \text{ m})(60\%)$; the mass cancels out, and we find a temperature rise $\Delta t = 1.38{}^\circ$C.

14-B28 (a) The ice and pipe must be warmed up from $-20{}^\circ$C to $0{}^\circ$C, then the ice must be melted. Assume that the volume of ice is that of the water from which it froze (it is under pressure), and is $\frac{1}{4}\pi (1 \text{ cm})^2(500 \text{ cm}) = 393$ cm^3, of mass 393 g.

$$W = [(393 \text{ g})(0.5 \text{ cal/g} \cdot {}^\circ\text{C}) + 2000 \text{ g})(0.11 \text{ cal/g} \cdot {}^\circ\text{C})](20{}^\circ\text{C}) + (393 \text{ g})(80 \text{ cal/g})$$
$$= 3.98 \times 10^4 \text{ cal} = 39.8 \text{ kcal}.$$

(b) $(39.8 \text{ kcal})\left(\frac{4180 \text{ J}}{1 \text{ kcal}}\right) = \left(1500 \frac{\text{J}}{\text{s}}\right)(0.60)T$; $T = 185$ s, about 3 min.

14-B29 $m(8000 \text{ kcal/kg})(0.80) = (700 \text{ kg})(0.25 \text{ kcal/kg} \cdot {}^\circ\text{C})(25{}^\circ\text{C})$; $m = 0.68$ kg.

14-B30 The area of the wall is 30 m^2 = 30×10^4 cm^2. We use Eq. 14-3.

$$\frac{\Delta Q}{\Delta T} = \left(0.0015 \frac{\text{cal} \cdot \text{cm}}{\text{cm}^2 \cdot \text{s} \cdot {}^\circ\text{C}}\right)(30 \times 10^4 \text{ cm}^2)\left(\frac{86\,400 \text{ s}}{1 \text{ day}}\right)\left(\frac{30{}^\circ\text{C}}{20 \text{ cm}}\right) = 5.83 \times 10^7 \text{ cal/day}$$
$$= 58\,300 \text{ kcal/day}.$$

14-B31 (a) $\frac{\Delta Q}{\Delta T} = KA \frac{\Delta t}{d} = \left(0.002 \frac{\text{cal} \cdot \text{cm}}{\text{cm}^2 \cdot \text{s} \cdot {}^\circ\text{C}}\right)(1 \text{ cm}^2)\left(\frac{3{}^\circ\text{C}}{10^4 \text{ cm}}\right)\left(\frac{1 \text{ }\mu\text{cal}}{10^{-6} \text{ cal}}\right) = 0.6$ μcal/s.

(b) The surface area of the earth is found from its radius (Table 7 in the Appendix): $A = 4\pi R^2 = 4\pi(6.38 \times 10^8 \text{ cm})^2 = 5.12 \times 10^{18}$ cm^2.

Total power = $\left(0.6 \times 10^{-6} \frac{\text{cal}}{\text{s} \cdot \text{cm}^2}\right)\left(\frac{4.18 \text{ J}}{1 \text{ cal}}\right)(5.12 \times 10^{18} \text{ cm}^2)\left(\frac{86\,400 \text{ s}}{1 \text{ day}}\right) = 1.1 \times 10^{18}$ J/day.

14-B32 $\frac{\Delta Q}{\Delta T} = \frac{KA \Delta t}{d} = \left(0.0025 \frac{\text{cal} \cdot \text{cm}}{\text{cm}^2 \cdot \text{s} \cdot {}^\circ\text{C}}\right)[4\pi(20 \text{ cm})^2]\left(\frac{\Delta t}{0.5 \text{ cm}}\right) = \left(100 \frac{\text{J}}{\text{s}}\right)\left(\frac{1 \text{ cal}}{4.18 \text{ J}}\right)$; $\Delta t = 0.95{}^\circ$C.

14-B33 We take the effective surface area of the container to be that of six surfaces each 25 cm $\times$ 25 cm. In Eq. 14-3, the time T is to be found.

$$\left(9 \times 10^{-5} \frac{\text{cal} \cdot \text{cm}}{\text{cm}^2 \cdot \text{s} \cdot {}^\circ\text{C}}\right)(6 \times 625 \text{ cm}^2)\left(\frac{33{}^\circ\text{C}}{5 \text{ cm}}\right)T = (7500 \text{ g})\left(80 \frac{\text{cal}}{\text{g}}\right); \quad T = 2.69 \times 10^5 \text{ s}$$
$$= 74.8 \text{ h}.$$

14-B34 $m(9.8 \text{ N/kg})h = m(4180 \text{ J/kg·°C})(1°C)$; $h = 427$ m.

14-C1 Use T for time, t for temperature. From $\Delta Q = mc\,\Delta t$, $\dfrac{\Delta Q}{\Delta T} = mc\dfrac{\Delta t}{\Delta T}$. In time T_1 (= 1800 s), the heat that leaves the lead is $mc\left(\dfrac{\Delta t}{\Delta T}\right)T_1$. Equate this to $m(\Delta h_f)$; m cancels out and the latent heat of fusion of lead is $\Delta h_f = c\left(\dfrac{\Delta t}{\Delta T}\right)T_1$
$= \left(0.0306 \dfrac{\text{cal}}{\text{g·°C}}\right)\left(\dfrac{6.0°C}{60 \text{ s}}\right)(1800 \text{ s}) \approx 5.5$ cal/g.   [This compares favorably with the value in Table 14-2. We have assumed the specific heat near the melting point to be the same as the value listed in Table 14-1 for 20°C.]

14-C2 Let the diameter be D, with other symbols having their usual meaning. From $\Delta Q = mc\,\Delta t$, $\frac{1}{4}\pi D^2 Ldc\,\Delta t = \Delta Q$. But $\Delta L = L\alpha\,\Delta t$, hence $\Delta L = 4\alpha\,\Delta Q/\pi D^2 cd$. ($L$ has cancelled out). Substituting the given values yields
$$\Delta L = \frac{4[26 \times 10^{-6} \ (°C)^{-1}](4000 \text{ cal})}{\pi(0.50 \text{ cm})^2(0.22 \text{ cal/g·°C})(2.70 \text{ g/cm}^3)} = 0.89 \text{ cm}.$$

14-C3 The temperature rise must be sufficient to expand the rod as much as it was originally stretched by the force ΔF. From $E = \dfrac{\Delta F/A}{\Delta L/L}$, $\Delta L = L\Delta F/EA$; equating to $\Delta L = L\alpha\,\Delta t$ gives $\Delta t = \Delta F/E\alpha A$. Now use $\Delta Q = mc\,\Delta t = ALdc\,\Delta t$, whence $\Delta Q = ALdc\,\Delta F/E\alpha A$. The cross-sectional area cancels out (!) and the desired equation is $\Delta Q = Ldc\,\Delta F/E\alpha$. Substituting the given data yields
$$\Delta Q = \frac{(2 \text{ m})(7860 \text{ kg/m}^3)(0.11 \text{ kcal/kg·°C})(50 \text{ N})}{(12 \times 10^{10} \text{ N/m}^2)[11 \times 10^{-6} \ (°C)^{-1}]} = 0.066 \text{ kcal} = 66 \text{ cal}.$$

14-C4 (*a*) Power $= \tau\omega = (0.02 \text{ N·m})\left(\dfrac{300 \times 2\pi \text{ rad}}{60 \text{ s}}\right) = 0.628 \text{ W} = 0.150$ cal/s.

(*b*) From $\Delta Q = mc\,\Delta t$, $\left(\dfrac{0.628 \text{ J/s}}{4.18 \text{ J/cal}}\right)(300 \text{ s}) = (600 \text{ g})(0.9 \text{ cal/g·°C})\Delta t$; $\Delta t = 0.084°C$.

14-C5 (*a*) The heat is absorbed in three stages. To warm the solid requires $m(0.46 \text{ cal/g·°C})(7°C)$; to melt the salt requires $m(60 \text{ cal/g})$; to warm the liquid requires $m(0.68 \text{ cal/g·°C})(13°C)$. Adding these gives $\Delta Q = (72.1 \text{ cal/g})m$. To store 10^6 kcal (= 10^9 cal) requires that the mass be $m = (10^9 \text{ cal})/(72.1 \text{ cal/g}) = 1.39 \times 10^7$ g = 13.9 metric tons.   (*b*) $V = m/d = (1.39 \times 10^7 \text{ g})/(1.46 \text{ g/cm}^3) = 9.5 \times 10^6$ cm^3 = 9.5 m^3. [See also Prob. 19-B22.]

14-C6 $\left(6 \times 10^5 \dfrac{\text{kcal}}{\text{s}}\right)\left(\dfrac{86\,400 \text{ s}}{1 \text{ day}}\right)\left(\dfrac{4180 \text{ J}}{1 \text{ kcal}}\right)\left(\dfrac{1 \text{ kWh}}{3.6 \times 10^6 \text{ J}}\right)\left(\dfrac{\$0.01}{1 \text{ kWh}}\right) = \$602\,000.$

14-C7 (*a*) 1000 MW + 1800 MW = 2800 MW.   (*b*) Efficiency = output/input
$=$ (1000 MW)/(2800 MW) = 36%.   (*c*) $\dfrac{\Delta Q}{\Delta T} = \dfrac{mc\,\Delta t}{\Delta T}$; $1800 \times 10^6 \dfrac{\text{J}}{\text{s}}$
$= \left(\dfrac{5 \times 10^8 \text{ kg}}{3600 \text{ s}}\right)\left(4180 \dfrac{\text{J}}{\text{kg·°C}}\right)\Delta t$; $\Delta t = 3.1°C$.   [See also Example 16-6 on p. 363.]

14-C8 (*a*) Work performed $= mgh = (70 \text{ kg})(9.8 \text{ N/kg})(2923 \text{ m}) = 2.00 \times 10^6$ J; the power is $P = W/t = (2.00 \times 10^6 \text{ J})/(8 \times 3600 \text{ s}) = 69$ W.   (*b*) The basal metabolic rate, 90 W, is equivalent to
$\left(90 \dfrac{\text{J}}{\text{s}}\right)\left(\dfrac{1 \text{ kcal}}{4180 \text{ J}}\right)\left(\dfrac{86\,400 \text{ s}}{1 \text{ day}}\right) = 1860$ kcal/day.
The caloric intake attributable to the climb was (10 000 − 1860) kcal = 7140 kcal. The mechanical work performed was 2000 kJ or 480 kcal. The efficiency was (480 kcal)/(7140 kcal) = 7%.

14-C9 Use the solar constant given on p. 324.

Power = $(20 \text{ m})(50 \text{ m})\left(8.13 \dfrac{\text{J}}{\text{cm}^2 \cdot \text{min}}\right)\left(\dfrac{10^2 \text{ cm}}{1 \text{ m}}\right)^2 \left(\dfrac{1 \text{ min}}{60 \text{ s}}\right)(10\%) = 1.36 \times 10^5$ W
= 136 kW.
[This is 182 horsepower.]

14-C10 The projected area of the earth's surface, broadside to the sun, is $\pi R^2 = \pi (6.4 \times 10^6 \text{ m})^2 = 1.287 \times 10^{14} \text{ m}^2$. In 10 years the trapped energy available to melt ice is

$(1.287 \times 10^{14} \text{ m}^2)\left(1\% \times 1.94 \dfrac{\text{cal}}{\text{cm}^2 \cdot \text{min}}\right)\left(\dfrac{1 \text{ min}}{60 \text{ s}}\right)\left(\dfrac{10^2 \text{ cm}}{1 \text{ m}}\right)^2 (10 \times 3.156 \times 10^7 \text{ s})(10\%)$
$= 1.31 \times 10^{22}$ cal

Using 8×10^4 cal/kg for the latent heat of fusion of ice, we calculate the depth H of water from the melted ice (here the surface area of the oceans is used, $4.0 \times 10^{14} \text{ m}^2$):
1.31×10^{22} cal = $(1000 \text{ kg/m}^3)(4 \times 10^{14} \text{ m}^2)(H)(8 \times 10^4 \text{ cal/kg})$; $H = 0.41$ m.

14-C11 $4\pi(6.4 \times 10^6 \text{ m})^2 (1.0 \text{ m})\left(1000 \dfrac{\text{kg}}{\text{m}^3}\right)\left(540 \dfrac{\text{kcal}}{\text{kg}}\right)\left(\dfrac{4180 \text{ J}}{1 \text{ kcal}}\right) = 1.2 \times 10^{24}$ J

This energy can be traced back to the sun, which supplied the heat to vaporize the water that formed the clouds.

14-C12 0.86, 0.83, 0.59, 0.35, all in cal/cm$^3 \cdot °$C; 6.1, 5.9, 5.9, 6.3, all in cal/mole$\cdot°$C. [The specific heats per mole of metals are all close to 6 cal/mole$\cdot°$C (law of Dulong and Petit). Specific heats per gram or per cm^3 show no such regularity.]

14-C13 Measure the slopes of tangents to the graph of Fig. 14-1. From $Q = mc\,\Delta t$,
$c = \dfrac{1}{m}\lim(\Delta Q/\Delta t) = \dfrac{1}{m}(dQ/dt)$. At $-260°$C, $c = (1/200 \text{ g})(4.0 \text{ cal}/12.5°\text{C})$
≈ 0.0016 cal/g$\cdot°$C; At $-252°$C, $c = \left(\dfrac{1}{200 \text{ g}}\right)\left(\dfrac{6.6 \text{ cal}}{5°\text{C}}\right) \approx 0.0066$ cal/g$\cdot°$C.

14-C14 See Table 4 in the Appendix for the conversion of cm^2 to ft^2. A possible chain of conversion factors is the following:
$K = 1 \dfrac{\text{cal}\cdot\text{cm}}{\text{cm}^2 \cdot \text{s} \cdot °\text{C}} \left(\dfrac{1 \text{ Btu}}{252 \text{ cal}}\right)\left(\dfrac{1 \text{ in.}}{2.54 \text{ cm}}\right)\left(\dfrac{929 \text{ cm}^2}{1 \text{ ft}^2}\right)\left(\dfrac{3600 \text{ s}}{1 \text{ h}}\right)\left(\dfrac{1 °\text{C}}{1.8 °\text{F}}\right)$
[Handbooks give this factor as 2902.]

Chapter 15   Thermal Behavior of Gases

Questions

15-1 Although molecular sizes differ, they are all very much less than the average separation of the molecules in the gas, so the correction is a small one, whatever the composition of the gas.

15-2 $V_1/T_1 = V_2/T_2$. There is some confusion over the naming of this law, which should be credited to Gay-Lussac, not Charles. See W. J. Lyons, "Inaccuracies in the Textbook Discussions of the Ordinary Gas Laws," *Am. J. Phys.* **6**, 256 (1938).

15-3 In applying $P = nRT/V$, the number of moles n increases very rapidly as molecules evaporate to keep the vapor saturated. This is evident from the rapid increase of density of saturated water vapor.

15-4 There are two viewpoints. The latent heat of vaporization comes from the random KE of the molecules, thereby cooling the liquid. Also, the faster-moving molecules leave the liquid more readily than the slower ones, causing the average KE of the remaining molecules to decrease.

15-5 Yes, by reducing the pressure to below 17.55 torr (Table 15-2). The liquid would be at room temperature and not warm to the touch.

15-6 The ice would melt (the state would move upward along a vertical line through $-5\,°C$).

15-7 It changes from a liquid to a vapor, i.e., it boils.

15-8 The moist thermometer is cooled by evaporation; this is the principle of the wet- and dry-bulb hygrometer.

15-9 Since 1000 lb/in.^{2} $\approx$ 68 atm $\approx$ 52 000 torr, the material is in the liquid region of the phase diagram (Fig. 15-8).

15-10 A gas is a substance that is above its critical temperature. A vapor is gaseous, but below the critical temperature; a vapor can be liquefied if enough pressure is applied.

15-11 The saturated vapor pressure of hydrogen is 760 torr at $-253\,°C$.

15-12 Reduce the pressure to below 31.86 torr (see Table 15-2).

15-13 If liquid air is at, say, $-196\,°C$, the nitrogen is at its boiling point and is being vaporized, whereas the oxygen is below its boiling point. An old flask of liquid air consists almost entirely of liquid oxygen (and is an explosion hazard).

15-14 (a) Vapor; (b) vapor; (c) liquid; (d) no.

Multiple Choice

15-15 (c); **15-16** (c); **15-17** (c); **15-18** (b); **15-19** (b); **15-20** (a).

Problems

15-A1 (24 cm)(1 atm) = x(3 atm); x = 8 cm from B; 16 cm from A.

15-A2 45 lb/in.^{2} of gauge pressure is (15 + 45) = 60 lb/in.^{2} = 4 atm absolute pressure. (1 atm)(1200 ft^3) = (4 atm)V; V = 300 ft^3 of air. Hence, the volume of water is (1200 $-$ 300) ft^3 = 900 ft^3.

15-A3 N(2 ft^3)(20 atm) = (20 000 ft^3)(1 atm); N = 500 tanks.

15-A4 1 mole of H_2O is 18 g; 360 g is 20 moles.

15-A5 1 mole of H_2O is 18 g; 360 g is 20 moles. Whether the H_2O is solid, liquid, or gaseous is immaterial.

15-A6 $(8 \times 10^6 \text{ N/m}^2)(0.1 \text{ m}^3) = P(0.5 \text{ m}^3)$; $P = 1.6 \times 10^6$ N/m^2.

15-A7 313 K; 193 K; 293 K; 373 K.

15-A8 $V = (30 \text{ liters})\left(\dfrac{1500 \text{ K}}{300 \text{ K}}\right)\left(\dfrac{1 \text{ atm}}{3 \text{ atm}}\right) = 50 \text{ liters.}$

15-A9 $P = (5 \times 10^5 \text{ N/m}^2)\left(\dfrac{350 \text{ K}}{300 \text{ K}}\right) = 5.83 \times 10^5 \text{ N/m}^2.$

15-A10   The initial absolute pressure is $(25 + 15) \text{ lb/in.}^2 = 40 \text{ lb/in.}^2$. $P = (40 \text{ lb/in.}^2)$
$\times \left(\dfrac{303 \text{ K}}{278 \text{ K}}\right) = 43.6 \text{ lb/in.}^2$; new gauge pressure is $(43.6 - 15.0) \text{ lb/in.}^2$
$= 28.6 \text{ lb/in.}^2$.

15-A11 $P = (30 \text{ lb/in.}^2)\left(\dfrac{20 \text{ ft}^3}{5 \text{ ft}^3}\right)\left(\dfrac{500 \text{ K}}{200 \text{ K}}\right) = 300 \text{ lb/in.}^2.$

15-A12   At 30°C, the air could hold 30.37 g/m^3 (Table 15-2). Relative humidity is
$r = (27 \text{ g/m}^3)/(30.37 \text{ g/m}^3) = 89\%.$

15-A13 $(17.30 \text{ g/m}^3)(0.40) = 6.92 \text{ g/m}^3.$

15-A14   From Table 15-2, the temperature is 99°C.

15-A15   From Table 15-2, the pressure is 526 torr.

15-B1   Pressure due to the plug is $\dfrac{F}{A} = \dfrac{(5.00 \text{ kg})(9.8 \text{ N/kg})}{\pi(2.00 \times 10^{-2} \text{ m})^2} = 0.39 \times 10^5 \text{ N/m}^2$. Final
pressure $= (1.013 + 0.390) \times 10^5 \text{ N/m}^2 = 1.403 \times 10^5 \text{ N/m}^2$. In the cylinder, the
volumes are proportional to the heights.
$H = (42 \text{ cm})\left(\dfrac{1.013}{1.403}\right) = 30.3 \text{ cm.}$

15-B3   In the barometer, the space above the mercury column is evacuated, so the
absolute pressure on the bubble is just that due to the height of mercury column. The volume has increased by a factor of 8, and pressure is proportional
to height. $V_1(52 \text{ cm}) = (8V_1)(H)$; $H = 6.5 \text{ cm}$ from the top of the column.

15-B4 (a) $n = (1 \text{ mol})\left(\dfrac{40 \text{ liters}}{22.4 \text{ liters}}\right)\left(\dfrac{273 \text{ K}}{323 \text{ K}}\right)\left(\dfrac{8 \text{ atm}}{1 \text{ atm}}\right) = 12.07 \text{ mol}$; (b) $m = (12.07 \text{ mol})$
$\times (44.06 \text{ g/mol}) = 532 \text{ g}$; (c) $N = 7.27 \times 10^{24} \text{ molecules.}$ [The abbrevi-
ation l for liter is sometimes confused with the numeral 1. It is likely that in
the near future the symbol L will be adopted for "liter."]

15-B5   Since m is proportional to the number of moles present, PV/mT is constant.
$\dfrac{(900 \text{ torr})(V)}{(54 \text{ g})(T)} = \dfrac{(870 \text{ torr})(V)}{m_2(T)}$; $m_2 = 52.2 \text{ g}$. $\Delta m = (54.0 - 52.2) \text{ g} = 1.8 \text{ g}.$

15-B6   1 kg of SO_2 is $(1000 \text{ g})/(64 \text{ g/mol}) = 1000/64 \text{ mol.}$
$P = (1 \text{ atm})\left(\dfrac{1000/64 \text{ mol}}{1 \text{ mol}}\right)\left(\dfrac{22.4 \text{ liters}}{100 \text{ liters}}\right)\left(\dfrac{323 \text{ K}}{273 \text{ K}}\right) = 4.14 \text{ atm.}$

15-B7 $P = (1 \text{ atm})\left(\dfrac{100 \text{ mol}}{1 \text{ mol}}\right)\left(\dfrac{22.4 \text{ liters}}{300 \text{ liters}}\right)\left(\dfrac{343 \text{ K}}{273 \text{ K}}\right) = 9.38 \text{ atm.}$

15-B8 (a) Recall that $1 \text{ m}^3 = 1000 \text{ liters}$. From $n'T'/P'V' = n_0 T_0/P_0 V_0$ we have
$n' = n_0\left(\dfrac{T_0}{T'}\right)\left(\dfrac{V'}{V_0}\right)\left(\dfrac{P'}{P_0}\right) = (1 \text{ mol})\left(\dfrac{273 \text{ K}}{223 \text{ K}}\right)\left(\dfrac{5 \times 10^3 \text{ liters}}{22.4 \text{ liters}}\right)\left(\dfrac{7.2 \text{ atm}}{1 \text{ atm}}\right) = 1967 \text{ mol}$
$= 1.97 \text{ kmol.}$ (b) $m = (1.97 \times 10^3 \text{ mol})(0.028 \text{ kg/mol}) = 55.1 \text{ kg.}$

15-B9   We apply ratio factors to the density at STP, for which 1 mol occupies 22.4
liters.
$d = \left(\dfrac{48 \text{ g}}{22.4 \text{ liters}}\right)\left(\dfrac{440 \text{ torr}}{760 \text{ torr}}\right)\left(\dfrac{273 \text{ K}}{333 \text{ K}}\right) = 1.02 \text{ g/liter.}$

15-B10   The molecular weight of NO_2F is $(14 + 32 + 19) = 65$. Initially,
$n_1 = (1 \text{ mol})\left(\dfrac{273 \text{ K}}{300 \text{ K}}\right)\left(\dfrac{80 \text{ liters}}{22.4 \text{ liters}}\right) = 3.25 \text{ mol}$; $m_1 = (3.25 \times 65) \text{ g} = 211.25 \text{ g.}$

After 15 g leaks out, $m_2 = (211.25 - 15)$ g $= 196.25$ g;

$P_2 = (760 \text{ torr})\left(\dfrac{196.25 \text{ g}}{211.25 \text{ g}}\right) = 706$ torr.

15-B11 $d = \left(\dfrac{20.179 \text{ g}}{22.4 \text{ liters}}\right)\left(\dfrac{20 \text{ atm}}{1 \text{ atm}}\right)\left(\dfrac{273 \text{ K}}{573 \text{ K}}\right) = 8.58$ g/liter.

15-B12   The molecular weight of UF_6 is $238 + 6(19) = 352$; that of N_2 is $2(14) = 28$. The density ratio is $\left(\dfrac{352}{28}\right)\left(\dfrac{300 \text{ K}}{1000 \text{ K}}\right) = 3.77$.

15-B13   (a) $V = (22.4 \text{ liters/mol})(20 \text{ mol}) = 448$ liters $= 0.448$ m^3.   (b) Weight of helium $= (4.00 \times 10^{-3} \text{ kg/mol})(20 \text{ mol})(9.8 \text{ N/kg}) = 0.784$ N. BF = weight of displaced air $= (0.448 \text{ m}^3)\left(\dfrac{29 \times 10^{-3} \text{ kg}}{0.0224 \text{ m}^3}\right)(9.8 \text{ N/kg}) = 5.684$ N. Useful payload $=$ BF $-$ dead load $= (5.684 - 0.784 - 0.80)$ N $= 4.10$ N.

15-B14   (a) Initially, the ball contained n_1 moles of air (use absolute pressures):
$n_1 = (1 \text{ mol})\left(\dfrac{273 \text{ K}}{293 \text{ K}}\right)\left(\dfrac{28 \text{ lb/in.}^2}{15 \text{ lb/in.}^2}\right)\left(\dfrac{2.24 \text{ liters}}{22.4 \text{ liters}}\right) = 0.1739$ mol; $m_1 = (0.1739 \text{ mol})$
$\times (29 \text{ g/mol}) = 5.043$ g.   (b) At the new temperature, there must be fewer moles in the ball, whose volume has not changed.
$n_2 = (1 \text{ mol})\left(\dfrac{273 \text{ K}}{303 \text{ K}}\right)\left(\dfrac{28 \text{ lb/in.}^2}{15 \text{ lb/in.}^2}\right)\left(\dfrac{2.24 \text{ liters}}{22.4 \text{ liters}}\right) = 0.1682$ mol;
$m_2 = (0.1682 \text{ mol})(29 \text{ g/mol}) = 4.88$ g. The amount to be let out of the ball is $(0.1739 - 0.1682)$ mol $= 0.0057$ mol, and $m_2 - m_1 = (0.0057 \text{ mol})(29 \text{ g/mol}) = 0.165$ g ≈ 0.17 g.

15-B15   (a) The partial pressure due to each gas is calculated from the new pressure and the new volume (1 m^3). For H_2, $P' = 1$ atm; for N_2, $P' = (0.5 \text{ atm})$ $\times [(4 \text{ m}^3)/(1 \text{ m}^3)] = 2$ atm; for O_2, $P' = (2 \text{ atm})[(3 \text{ m}^3)/(1 \text{ m}^3)] = 6$ atm.
(b) Total pressure is $(1 + 2 + 6)$ atm $= 9$ atm.   (c) Masses are found from the number of moles; recall that at STP 1 mole of any ideal gas occupies 0.0224 m^3, so 1 m^3 contains $1/0.0224 = 44.65$ mol. The number of moles is also proportional to pressure. For H_2, $n = (1)(44.65) = 44.65$ mol; $m = (2.02 \text{ g/mol})(44.65 \text{ mol}) = 89$ g. For N_2, $n = (2)(44.65) = 89.3$ mol; $m = (28 \text{ g/mol})(89.3 \text{ mol}) = 2500$ g. For O_2, $n = (6)(44.65) = 267.9$ mol; $m = (32 \text{ g/mol})(267.9 \text{ mol}) = 8571$ g. Total mass of all the gas is $(89 + 2500 + 8571)$ g $= 11.16$ kg.

15-B16   The oxygen expands from 4 liters to 31 liters to give a pressure of $(2480 \text{ torr})(4/31) = 320$ torr. The hydrogen expands from 27 liters to 31 liters to give a pressure of $(310 \text{ torr})(27/31) = 270$ torr. Total pressure is $(320 + 270)$ torr $= 590$ torr.

15-B17   (a) Volumes are proportional to heights measured inside the diving bell. Use Boyle's law (remember that absolute pressures are needed): $(12 \text{ ft})(15 \text{ lb/in.}^2)$ $= (5 \text{ ft})P$; $P = 36$ lb/in.^{2}.   (b) The gauge pressure of the trapped air is $(36 - 15)$ lb/in.$^2 = 21$ lb/in.^{2}. This pressure equals the pressure due to h feet of water, where h is the depth from the lake surface to the surface of the enclosed water. Then $P = hdg$ is used, with $dg = 62.4$ lb/ft^3 for water:
$h = \dfrac{P}{dg} = \left(\dfrac{21 \text{ lb./in.}^2}{62.4 \text{ lb/ft}^3}\right)\left(\dfrac{144 \text{ in.}^2}{1 \text{ ft}^2}\right) = 48.5$ ft.
There is 7 ft of water in the diving bell, so the depth of the lake is $(48.5 + 7)$ ft $= 55.5$ ft.

15-B18   The initial pressure is $(760 - 740)$ torr $= 20$ torr. The volume of trapped air increases from 60 units to 100 units. Then $(20 \text{ torr})(60 \text{ units}) = P'(100 \text{ units})$;

P' = 12 torr, due to the trapped air. True barometric pressure is 700 torr + 12 torr = 712 torr.

15-B19 One of several ways to approach this problem is the following: from $K = 273.16 + C$, $K = 273.16 + \frac{5}{9}(F - 32)$. If $K = F$, we have $F = 273.16 + \frac{5}{9}(F - 32)$, whence $F = 574.61°$.

15-B20 $P_1 = (14.7 \text{ lb/in.}^2)\left(\frac{4 \text{ mol}}{1 \text{ mol}}\right)\left(\frac{0.0224 \text{ m}^3}{40 \text{ m}^3}\right)\left(\frac{573 \text{ K}}{273 \text{ K}}\right) = 0.0691 \text{ lb/in.}^2$ [Note that if the first parentheses contained 760 torr, the answer would be 3.57 torr.]

15-B21 Dew at 10°C means that the air actually had 9.40 g/m^3 (Table 15-2); at 20°C this would be less dense: $(9.40 \text{ g/m}^3)(283/293) = 9.09 \text{ g/m}^3$. At 20°C the air *could* hold 17.30 g/m^3, so the relative humidity is $r = (9.09 \text{ g/m}^3)/(17.30 \text{ g/m}^3)$ = 52.5%.   [As indicated in the footnote on p. 342, a simpler calculation uses saturated vapor pressures: $(9.21/17.55) = 52.5\%$.]

15-B22 $(9.40 \text{ g/m}^3)(0.75) = 7.05 \text{ g/m}^3$; $(9.40 - 7.05) \text{ g/m}^3 = 2.35 \text{ g/m}^3$.

15-B23 2.21×10^7 Pa; 218 atm; 3210 lb/in.^{2}; 0.318 g/cm^3.   [For pressure, use conversion factors on p. 272 or in Appendix Table 4 on p. 803.]

15-B24 $(31.86 \text{ torr})(0.60) = 19.1 \text{ torr}$.

15-B25 (*a*) Outdoors, the density of water vapor is $(0.70)(4.85 \text{ g/m}^3) = 3.395 \text{ g/m}^3$; $m = (3.395 \text{ g/m}^3)(40 \text{ m}^3) = 127 \text{ g}$.   (*b*) When heated to 20°C, the density becomes $(3.395 \text{ g/m}^3)(273/293) = 3.163 \text{ g/m}^3$; $r = 3.163/17.30 = 18.3\%$. (*c*) This classroom is too dry for comfort and health.

15-C1 At 20°C, the pressure due to air was $(628.0 - 17.55) \text{ torr} = 610.45 \text{ torr}$. Apply the gas law to the *air* pressure (volume is constant): $P_2 = (610.45 \text{ torr})\left(\frac{333 \text{ K}}{293 \text{ K}}\right)$ = 693.8 torr. Now the vapor pressure is found to be $(843.2 - 693.8) \text{ torr}$ = 149.4 torr.

15-C5 (*a*) One would not expect water vapor at 100°C and 1 atm to be an ideal gas, since it is at the point of condensation into water, and cohesive forces between the molecules must surely be significant. However, part (*b*) shows that it is remarkably close to being ideal.

(*b*) Density = $\left(\frac{18 \text{ g}}{0.0224 \text{ m}^3}\right)\left(\frac{273 \text{ K}}{373 \text{ K}}\right) = 588 \text{ g/m}^3$.   [This is within 2% of the experimental value 598 g/m^3 listed in Table 15-2.]

15-C3 As shown in the footnote on p. 343, the pressure of the trapped air decreases from 742.45 torr to 27 torr. Now apply the general gas law to the trapped air (the number of moles n is constant).
$$\frac{P_2 V_2}{T_2} = \frac{P_1 V_1}{T_1}; \quad \frac{(27 \text{ torr})(V_2)}{372 \text{ K}} = \frac{(742.45 \text{ torr})(1 \text{ mm}^3)}{293 \text{ K}}; \quad V_2 = 34.9 \text{ mm}^3$$

15-C4 $(5 \text{ m})(10 \text{ m})(3 \text{ m})(30.37 \text{ g/m}^3)(0.90) = 4100.0 \text{ g}$. At 20% relative humidity, the same volume would hold $(150 \text{ m}^3)(30.37 \text{ g/m}^3)(0.20) = 911 \text{ g}$. We must remove $(4100 - 911) \text{ g} = 3189 \text{ g} = 3.2 \text{ kg}$.   [This much water would be 3.2 liters, which *could* be comfortably contained in a 4-liter jug.]

15-C5 (*a*) Since 6.8 cm $H_2O = (68/13.6) \text{ torr} = 5.0 \text{ torr}$, the total pressure is 755 torr. Of this, 17.5 torr is due to water vapor, leaving $(755 - 17.5) \text{ torr} = 737.5 \text{ torr}$ due to the H_2 gas. Now use the general gas law:
$$\frac{(737.5 \text{ torr})(380 \text{ cm}^3)}{n(293 \text{ K})} = \frac{(760 \text{ torr})(22\,400 \text{ cm}^3)}{(1 \text{ mol})(273 \text{ K})}; \quad n = 0.0153 \text{ mol}.$$
(*b*) Corrected to STP, $V = (380 \text{ cm}^3)\left(\frac{273 \text{ K}}{293 \text{ K}}\right)\left(\frac{737.5 \text{ torr}}{760 \text{ torr}}\right) = 344 \text{ cm}^3$. Alternatively, $V = (22\,400 \text{ cm}^3/\text{mol})(0.0153 \text{ mol}) = 344 \text{ cm}^3$.

15-C6 We calculate the density using the ideal gas law:
$$d = \left(\frac{18 \text{ g}}{0.0224 \text{ m}^3}\right)\left(\frac{166\,000 \text{ torr}}{760 \text{ torr}}\right)\left(\frac{273 \text{ K}}{647 \text{ K}}\right) = 74 \times 10^3 \text{ g/m}^3.$$
This is about $\frac{1}{4}$ the observed value given in Table 15-2. At such a large specific gravity, the vapor molecules are so close together that cohesive forces become important and the observed density is larger than calculated using the ideal gas law.

Chapter 16   The Theory of Heat

Questions

16-1 Heat is quantity of thermal energy, measured in J or cal; temperature is proportional to average translational KE per molecule. The same question was asked in Chap. 14 (Ques. 14-1); the student can now give a more precise answer, although considerations about absolute zero (Sec. 16-9) make even the statement on p. 351 somewhat incomplete.

16-2 The helium is hotter; internal rotational energy does not contribute to the temperature. Note that the internal rotational energy of the oxygen molecules is a little less than $\frac{2}{5}$ the total energy (see Sec. 16-11); the oxygen is evidently cool enough so that quantum effects are noticeable.

16-3 At a given temperature, $\frac{1}{2}mv^2$ is constant, hence $v \propto \sqrt{1/m}$. The ^{20}Ne molecules (atoms, really, since neon is monatomic) are moving faster and would diffuse more readily through a porous membrane. This selective diffusion is used to separate the nuclear fuel ^{235}U from ^{238}U (see Prob. 16-C5).

16-4 Volume of molecules not negligible; cohesive forces between molecules not negligible.

16-5 More collisions per unit time; greater pressure. Van der Waals' equation of state (a better approximation to the behavior of real gases) is $(P + a/V^2)(V - b) = nRT$. The small constant b represents the volume of the molecules themselves and is subtracted from the volume V of the container to give the volume of the empty space in the container; the larger b is, the larger is the calculated P. The constant a is related to the cohesive forces between molecules; solving the equation for P shows that the cohesive forces cause a decrease of pressure.

16-6 By the law of conservation of momentum, the component of momentum in any given direction (such as the x axis) remains unaltered during collision. Therefore the same total change of momentum takes place at the wall, even though no single molecule is likely to pass unimpeded from wall to wall.

16-7 Greater for alcohol since only a fraction of the absorbed heat is effective in giving translational KE to the molecules. Experiment bears this out (Table 16-1 on p. 376).

16-8 The numerator in Eq. 16-6 for first-law efficiency can be made larger if T_1 is larger. Thus $(700 - 300)/700 = 0.57$, which is greater than $(400 - 300)/400 = 0.25$.

16-9 Work is done on the gas by the muscle that "suddenly" pushes the plunger down. The process is adiabatic.

16-10 Work done to separate the molecules comes from the KE of the molecules; the gas therefore cools. See the photo on p. 351, which illustrates this point.

16-11 The idea is theoretically sound, if a volatile working substance such as alcohol or ether is used. Attempts at practical exploitation of oceanic temperature differences have not yet been successful.

16-12 No. The refrigerator rejects the same amount of heat to the room as it removes from the ice cube compartment; a structure on the rear of the refrigerator allows for this heat exchange. You can't beat the first law of thermodynamics; the refrigerator and the room together constitute a thermally isolated system.

16-13 The zero-point energy is unavailable and hence does not conflict with the Kelvin definition of absolute zero.

16-16 The bar would become warmer if it were clamped; compare Fig. 16-3. The effect is small, however, on account of the smaller coefficient of expansion of a solid as compared with a gas, and c_p for a solid is only slightly greater than c_v.

Multiple Choice

16-14 (c);   **16-15** (c);   **16-16** (c);   **16-17** (b);   **16-18** (c);   **16-19** (b).

Problems

16-A1 Can: $(4.4 \times 10^6 \text{ J})/(5 \text{ gal}) = 8.8 \times 10^5 \text{ J/gal}$.   Pool: $(8 \times 10^{10} \text{ J})/(10^5 \text{ gal}) = 8.0 \times 10^5 \text{ J/gal}$. The water in the can is warmer.   [See also Prob. 16-B10, where the temperatures are calculated.]

16-A2 $(3.2 \times 10^5 \text{ J})\left(\dfrac{400 \text{ cm}^3}{1000 \text{ cm}^3}\right) 1.3 = 1.66 \times 10^5 \text{ J}$.   [See also Prob. 16-B11.]

16-A3 $v = (0.80 \text{ m})/(\frac{1}{800} \text{ s}) = 640 \text{ m/s}$.   [See also Prob. 16-B12.]

16-A4 $e = \text{output/input} = (4.18 \text{ J})/[(5 \text{ cal})(4.18 \text{ J/cal})] = 20\%$.

16-A5 $(500 \text{ K} - 340 \text{ K})/(500 \text{ K}) = 32\%$.

16-A6 Input $= 2000 \text{ J} + 8000 \text{ J}$; $e = (2000 \text{ J})/(10\,000 \text{ J}) = 20\%$.

16-A7 $Q_1 = (180 \text{ J})/(0.10) = 1800 \text{ J}$.

16-A8 $(500 \text{ K} - T_2)/(500 \text{ K}) = 0.30$; $T_2 = 350 \text{ K}$.

16-B1 $\Delta v = [250 - (-250)] \text{ m/s} = 500 \text{ m/s}$; $1/\Delta t = 20$ per s $= 20 \text{ s}^{-1}$. Rate of change of momentum is $(m \, \Delta v)/\Delta t = (0.1 \text{ kg})(500 \text{ m/s})(20 \text{ s}^{-1}) = 1000 \text{ N}$.

16-B2 As in Example 16-1 (p. 353), assume 1 mole of H_2 is present. The volume is $(0.0224 \text{ m}^3)\left(\dfrac{1092 \text{ K}}{273 \text{ K}}\right)\left(\dfrac{1 \text{ atm}}{3 \text{ atm}}\right) = 0.02987 \text{ m}^3$. Now $v = \sqrt{3PV/Nm}$, and the total mass M is Nm. Thus,

$$v = \frac{3PV}{M} = \sqrt{\frac{3(3 \times 1.01 \times 10^5 \text{ N/m}^2)(0.02987 \text{ m}^3)}{2 \times 10^{-3} \text{ kg}}} = 3690 \text{ m/s}$$

[Note that the pressure 3 atm in fact canceled out, since $V \propto 1/P$. Some instructors may wish to derive here a more useful equation: Since the number of moles is $n = M/W$, where W is the molecular weight, we obtain $v = \sqrt{\frac{3nRT}{M}}$ $= \sqrt{\frac{3(M/W)RT}{M}} = \sqrt{\frac{3RT}{W}}$. This shows clearly that molecular speeds depend on temperature and molecular weight, not on pressure, volume, or total mass. In this problem,

$$v = \sqrt{\frac{3RT}{W}} = \sqrt{\frac{3(8.31 \text{ J/mol·K})(1092 \text{ K})}{2 \times 10^{-3} \text{ kg/mol}}} = 3690 \text{ m/s}.$$

See also Sec. 16-13, where a similar approach is used to derive a formula for the speed of sound in a gas.]

16-B3 From Eq. 16-2, $(2.4 \times 10^4 \text{ N/m}^2)(8 \text{ m}^3) = \frac{1}{3}(3.0 \text{ kg})v^2$; $v = 438$ m/s.

16-B4 The volume would be $1/P$ of the original volume (Boyle's law), and PV (hence v^2) would be the same. [See also remarks on Probs. 16-B2 and 16-C1.]

16-B5 (a) KE $= \frac{1}{2}\left(\frac{0.032 \text{ kg}}{6.02 \times 10^{23}}\right)(460 \text{ m/s})^2 = 5.62 \times 10^{-21}$ J. (b) $mgh = \left(\frac{0.032 \text{ kg}}{6.02 \times 10^{23}}\right)$ $\times (9.8 \text{ N/kg})(2 \text{ m}) = 1.04 \times 10^{-24}$ J. (c) The PE is less than 0.1% of the KE.

16-B7 (a) $v = \sqrt{3PV/M} = \sqrt{3(5 \times 1.01 \times 10^5 \text{ N/m}^2)(4 \text{ m}^3)/(100 \text{ kg})} = 246$ m/s.

(b) $\frac{PV}{nT} = \frac{P_0 V_0}{n_0 T_0}$, $\frac{(5 \text{ atm})(4 \text{ m}^3)}{n(323 \text{ K})} = \frac{(1 \text{ atm})(0.0224 \text{ m}^3)}{(1 \text{ mol})(273 \text{ K})}$; $n = 755$ mol.

The molecular weight is $(100 \times 10^3 \text{ g})/(755 \text{ mol}) = 133$ g/mol.

16-B8 $v \propto \sqrt{T}$; $v' = v\sqrt{(673 \text{ K})/(373 \text{ K})} = 1.34v$

16-B9 $v \propto T$; $v' = v\sqrt{(2500 \text{ K})/(10\,000 \text{ K})} = \frac{1}{2}v$

16-B10 Use $T = \frac{2}{3}(\text{KE})/nR$ (from Eq. 16-5). Can: $T = \frac{2}{3}(4.4 \times 10^6 \text{ J})/(5 \times 210 \text{ mol})$ $\times (8.31 \text{ J/mol·K}) = 336$ K $= 63°$C.

Pool: $T = \frac{2}{3}(8 \times 10^{10} \text{ J})/(3 \times 10^5 \times 210 \text{ mol})(8.31 \text{ J/mol·K}) = 305.6$ K $= 32°$C.

16-B11 1 liter of Hg is $(1000 \text{ cm}^3)(13.6 \text{ g/cm}^3)(1 \text{ mol}/200 \text{ g}) = 68$ mol. From Eq. 16-5, $T = \frac{2}{3}(\text{KE})/nR = \frac{2}{3}(3.2 \times 10^5 \text{ J})/(68 \text{ mol})(8.31 \text{ J/mol·K}) = 378$ K $= 105°$C.

16-B12 Mass of a single O_2 molecule is $(0.032 \text{ kg})/N_A$. This corresponds to $n = 1/N_A$ of a mole. Now, from Eq. 16-5,

$$T = \frac{mv^2}{3nR} = \frac{(0.032 \text{ kg})(640 \text{ m/s})^2}{3(1 \text{ mol})(8.31 \text{ J/mol·K})} = 526 \text{ K} = 253°\text{C}.$$

[N_A cancels out.]

16-B13 KE $= \frac{3}{2}nRT = \frac{3}{2}(5 \text{ mol})(8.31 \text{ J/mol·K})(400 \text{ K}) = 24.9$ kJ.

16-B14 (a) $\left(\frac{6.02 \times 10^{23} \text{ molecules}}{22.4 \times 10^3 \text{ cm}^3}\right)\left(\frac{10^{-12} \text{ torr}}{760 \text{ torr}}\right) = 3.5 \times 10^4$ molecules/cm^3.

(b) $(3.5 \times 10^4 \text{ molecules/cm}^3)(x^3) = 1 \text{ cm}^3$; $x = 0.03$ cm.

16-B15 From KE $= \frac{3}{2}nRT$, the constant is $\frac{3}{2}nR = \frac{3}{2}\left(\frac{1 \text{ mole}}{6.02 \times 10^{23} \text{ molecules}}\right)\left(8.31 \frac{\text{J}}{\text{mol·K}}\right)$ $= 2.07 \times 10^{-23}$ J/molecule.

16-B16 In Example 16-5, we found 6290 J for the increase in internal energy of 2.50 mol, corresponding to a temperature increase of 202 K. The specific heat is, therefore, $C_v = \frac{(6290/4.18) \text{ cal}}{(2.50 \text{ mol})(202 \text{ K})} = 2.98$ cal/mol·K. [This agrees with the value in column 2 of p. 354, also the value in Table 16-1 on p. 376.]

16-B17 (a) From Table 15-2, the temperature is 300°C. (b) Carnot efficiency is $\Delta T/T_1 = (200 \text{ K})/(573 \text{ K}) = 34.9\%$. (c) Only 70% of the mechanical output is useful; overall efficiency is $(0.70)(0.349) = 24.4\%$.

16-B18 $e = (400 \text{ K})/(1000 \text{ K}) = 0.40$; $Q_{in} = Q_{out}/e = (1400 \text{ kW})(1 \text{ h})/0.40 = 3500 \text{ kWh}$. The amount "lost" is $3500 \text{ kWh} - 1400 \text{ kWh} = 2100 \text{ kWh} = 7.56 \times 10^9 \text{ J}$.

16-B19 $30 \text{ kcal} = 125.4 \text{ kJ}$. The useful work is 20 kJ. Hence, the efficiency is
$$e = \frac{20 \text{ kJ}}{125.4 \text{ kJ}} = \frac{1000 \text{ K} - T_2}{1000 \text{ K}}; \quad T_2 = 841 \text{ K}.$$

16-B20 $e = (200 \text{ K})/(500 \text{ K}) = 40\%$. If 40% of Q_{in} is useful work, 60% of the input is waste heat. Thus $Q_1(0.60) = 1500 \text{ cal}$; $Q_1 = 2500 \text{ cal}$, and $W = (2500 \text{ cal})(0.40) = 1000 \text{ cal} = 4180 \text{ J}$.

16-B21 (a) $e = (400 \text{ K})/(1000 \text{ K}) = 0.40$. (b) Mechanical power $= 25 \text{ kW} + 5 \text{ kW} = 30 \text{ kW}$; power input $= (30 \text{ kW})/0.40 = 75 \text{ kW}$. In 1 hour, the energy input is $(30 \times 10^3 \text{ J/s})(3600 \text{ s})/0.40 = 2.70 \times 10^8 \text{ J}$. (c) Overall efficiency is $(25 \text{ kW})/(75 \text{ kW}) = 33\%$.

16-B22 (a) $e = (100 \text{ K})/(393 \text{ K}) = 25.4\%$. (b) There would be no fuel cost; the costs are those of drilling and maintaining the well, and pumping a fluid to serve as a heat exchanger.

16-B23 (a) $e = (20 \text{ K})/(295 \text{ K}) = 6.78\%$. (b) Input $= (100 \text{ MW})/0.0678 = 1475 \text{ MW}$. Rate of rejection of heat $= (1475 - 100) \text{ MW} = 1375 \text{ MW}$. (c) There would be no fuel cost. Difficulties include those involved in constructing a floating power station, and possible ecological damage by the large amount of waste heat.

16-B24 (a) $e = (180 \text{ K})/(500 \text{ K}) = 36\%$. Input $= (800 \text{ MW})/0.36 = 2222 \text{ MW}$; waste heat $= (2222 - 800) \text{ MW} = 1422 \text{ MW}$. (b) $\Delta T = \dfrac{\Delta Q}{mc} = \dfrac{1.422 \times 10^9 \text{ J/s}}{(2 \times 10^5 \text{ kg/s})(4180 \text{ J/kg·°C})}$ $= 1.70°\text{C}$.

16-B25 (a) $\text{COP}_{max} = T_{hot}/\Delta T = (318 \text{ K})/(38 \text{ K}) = 8.37$. (b) Actual COP $= 8.37(0.33)$ $= 2.76$. (c) From COP $= \Delta Q/\text{work input}$, we have: power input $= \dfrac{\Delta Q/\Delta t}{\text{COP}}$ $= \dfrac{24 \text{ kW}}{2.76} = 8.7 \text{ kW}$.   [This is about 12 horsepower.]

16-B26 (a) $\text{COP}_{max} = T_{cold}/\Delta T = (252 \text{ K})/(48 \text{ K}) = 5.25$. (b) Actual COP $= (5.25)(0.25) = 1.313$. (c) First calculate the heat that must be moved by the refrigerator. To cool 1 kg of water: $(1 \text{ kg})(4180 \text{ J/kg·°C})(27°\text{C}) = 113 \text{ kJ}$; to freeze 1 kg of water: $(1 \text{ kg})(80 \text{ kcal/kg})(4.18 \text{ kJ/kcal}) = 334 \text{ kJ}$; to cool 1 kg of ice: $(1 \text{ kg})(2090 \text{ J/kg·°C})(21°\text{C}) = 44 \text{ kJ}$. Total $\Delta Q = 491 \text{ kJ}$. Hence the work required is $\Delta Q/\text{COP} = (491 \text{ kJ})/1.313 = 374 \text{ kJ}$. The cost is (374 kJ) $\times \left(\dfrac{1 \text{ kWh}}{3600 \text{ kJ}}\right)\left(\dfrac{3¢}{1 \text{ kWh}}\right) = 0.31¢$.

16-C1 See the comments on Prob. 16-B2.

16-C2 Since Nm = mass of gas, the density d is Nm/V, and hence $P = \frac{1}{3}dv^2$.

16-C4 $v = \sqrt{\dfrac{3RT}{W}} = \sqrt{\dfrac{3(8.31 \text{ J/mol·K})(600 \text{ K})}{22.99 \times 10^{-3} \text{ kg/mol}}} = 807 \text{ m/s}$.

16-C5 Since $v \propto 1/\sqrt{W}$, the ratio is $\sqrt{352/349} = 1.0043$. [This small difference, about 0.4%, is the basis of the enrichment of uranium for use in nuclear power plants and weapons.]

16-C6 (a) Greater (by the first law of thermodynamics). (b) Work $= \tau\theta = (0.8 \text{ N})$ $\times (3 \times 10^{-3} \text{ m})(2\pi \times 10 \text{ rad}) = 0.1508 \text{ J}$. Then, from $\Delta Q = mc \Delta T$,
$$T = \frac{0.1508 \text{ J}}{(0.140 \text{ kg})(4180 \text{ J/kg·°C})} = 2.6 \times 10^{-4} \text{ °C}.$$

16-C7 This problem and the next one, taken together, give some (not all) of the theory of the Carnot cycle. See any advanced text for the proof that all reversible engines have the same efficiency when operating between the same temperatures T_1 and T_2. (a) The internal energy of a gas depends only on the temperature; for generality, denote this internal energy function as $U(T)$. (The function would be given by KE $= \frac{3}{2}nRT$ if the only internal energy were translational KE; but there can be other forms of internal energy, including rotational and vibrational molecular energy.) Now apply the first law: Work done by gas = decrease in internal energy + heat input. But part b of the cycle is adiabatic, the heat input is 0, and so the work done by the gas is a function only of the initial and final temperatures, and is given by $U(T_1) - U(T_2)$. (b) In part d of the cycle, the work done by the gas is $U(T_2) - U(T_1)$. Therefore, during the four parts of the entire cycle, the work done by the gas is $W_1 + [U(T_1) - U(T_2)] - W_2 + [U(T_2) - U(T_1)]$, which reduces to $W_1 - W_2$.

16-C8 (a) During part a of the cycle, the internal energy does not change (T is constant), hence the heat input is entirely converted to work. Thus, $W_1 = Q_1$. Similarly, $W_2 = Q_2$. (b) The efficiency $(W_1 - W_2)/Q_1$ is, therefore, $(Q_1 - Q_2)/Q_1$.

16-C9 (a) 2.0; (b) 2.4; (c) 2.9.

16-C10 The equation below Eq. 16-15 on p. 375 can be written $N\overline{v^2} = \Sigma v^2$. Multiply by $\frac{1}{2}m$ and expand the sum, obtaining $\frac{1}{2}Nm\overline{v^2} = \frac{1}{2}\Sigma mv^2 = \frac{1}{2}mv_1^2 + \frac{1}{2}mv_2^2 + \frac{1}{2}mv_3^2\cdots$. But $Nm = M$, the total mass, hence the total translational KE of the molecules is $\frac{1}{2}Mv^2$.

16-C11 (a) $C_p = (0.25 \text{ cal/g·°C})(28 \text{ g/mol}) = 7.0 \text{ cal/mol·°C}$. Since $C_p - C_v = R = 2.0$ cal/mol·°C for any ideal gas, we must have $C_v = 5.0 \text{ cal/mol·°C}$, or 0.179 cal/g·°C. (b) $\gamma = C_p/C_v = 7.0/5.0 = 1.40$. (c) The value of γ indicates that the gas is diatomic. [It is, in fact, N_2.]

16-C12 $C_p = \gamma C_v$; $C_p - C_v = (\gamma - 1)C_v$. Hence $(1.29 - 1)C_v = 2.15 \text{ cal/mol·K}$; $C_v = 7.41 \text{ cal/mol·K}$, and $C_p = (7.41 + 2.15) = 9.56 \text{ cal/mol·K}$. [The difference $C_p - C_v$ is not 2.0 cal/mol·K, since SO_2 is not an ideal gas at the temperature and pressure of these data.]

16-C13 (a) Refer to Fig. 15-9 on p. 347. Let x be the distance of the plunger from B when the cork pops out. The adiabatic gas law gives

$(1 \text{ atm})(24 \text{ cm})^{1.4} = (3 \text{ atm})(x)^{1.4}$; $\left(\dfrac{x}{24 \text{ cm}}\right)^{1.4} = \dfrac{1}{3}$; $\dfrac{x}{24 \text{ cm}} = \left(\dfrac{1}{3}\right)^{1/1.4}$;

$x = (24 \text{ cm})\left(\dfrac{1}{3}\right)^{0.7143} = 10.95 \text{ cm}$. The plunger has moved a distance

$(24 - 10.95) \text{ cm} = 13.05 \text{ cm}$. (b) The final temperature is found from $T/PV = T_0/P_0V_0$:

$T = T_0\left(\dfrac{P}{P_0}\right)\left(\dfrac{V}{V_0}\right) = (293 \text{ K})\left(\dfrac{3 \text{ atm}}{1 \text{ atm}}\right)\left(\dfrac{10.95 \text{ cm}}{24.00 \text{ cm}}\right) = 401 \text{ K} = 128°\text{C}$.

16-C14 (a) For neon, a monatomic gas, $\gamma = 5/3 = 1.67$. The adiabatic gas law gives $\dfrac{760 \text{ torr}}{900 \text{ torr}} = \left(\dfrac{V}{400 \text{ cm}^3}\right)^{5/3}$; whence $V = 361 \text{ cm}^3$.

(b) $T = (290 \text{ K})\left(\dfrac{900 \text{ torr}}{760 \text{ torr}}\right)\left(\dfrac{361 \text{ cm}^3}{400 \text{ cm}^3}\right) = 310 \text{ K} = 37°\text{C}$.

16-C15 Use C_v from Table 16-1. $\Delta Q = MC_v \Delta T = (2 \text{ mol})(10.30 \text{ cal/mol·K})(10 \text{ K}) = 206 \text{ cal}$.

16-C16 (a) If we double the volume at constant pressure, the final temperature is found from the gas law. $T = T_0\left(\dfrac{V}{V_0}\right)\left(\dfrac{P}{P_0}\right) = (273 \text{ K})\left(\dfrac{2V_0}{V_0}\right)\left(\dfrac{P_0}{P_0}\right) = 576 \text{ K}$; $\Delta T = 273°\text{C}$. Using C_p from Table 16-1 gives $\Delta Q = MC_p\Delta T = (3 \text{ mol}) \times (7.03 \text{ cal/mol·°C})(273°\text{C}) = 5.76 \text{ kcal}$. (b) At constant volume, the

73

gas law gives $T = (273 \text{ K})\left(\dfrac{V_0}{V_0}\right)\left(\dfrac{2P_0}{P_0}\right) = 576$ K; $\Delta T = 273°$C. Although
the temperature change is the same as in part (a), we now use
C_v: $\Delta Q = MC_v \Delta T = (3 \text{ mol})(5.03 \text{ cal/mol·°C})(273°\text{C}) = 4.12$ kcal.

16-C17 At any given temperature, the density d is proportional to the pressure P, and
the speed, which is $\sqrt{\gamma P/d}$, is unaffected by change of pressure. [On the
other hand, change in temperature affects d alone, and hence $v_w \propto \sqrt{T}$.]

16-C18 $v_w = \sqrt{\dfrac{\gamma R T}{W}} = \sqrt{\dfrac{(1.32)(8.31 \text{ J/mol·K})(673 \text{ K})}{0.044 \text{ kg/mol}}} = 410$ m/s.

16-C19 $v_w = (360 \text{ m/s})\sqrt{\dfrac{773 \text{ K}}{523 \text{ K}}} = 438$ m/s.

16-C20 $300 \text{ m/s} = \sqrt{\dfrac{(1.40)(8.31 \text{ J/mol·K})(T)}{0.029 \text{ kg/mol}}}$; $T = 224$ K $= -49°$C. Alternatively, use the

value 331 m/s at 0°C (p. 231): $300 = 331\sqrt{\dfrac{T}{273 \text{ K}}}$; $T = 224$ K $= -49°$C.

16-C21 For the closed pipe, $\lambda = 4L = 320$ cm; $v_w = \lambda\nu = (320 \text{ cm})(105.0 \text{ Hz}) = 336$ m/s
at 300 K. From $v_w = \sqrt{\dfrac{\gamma R T}{W}}$, we have $336 \text{ m/s} = \sqrt{\dfrac{\gamma(8.31 \text{ J/mol·K})(300 \text{ K})}{0.028 \text{ kg/mol}}}$,
whence $\gamma = 1.27$. [This is comparable to the values for simple polyatomic
molecules in Table 16-1.]

16-C22 For Prxxg, $v_w = \lambda\nu = (2.40 \text{ m})(210 \text{ Hz}) = 504$ m/s at a temperature T. The
speed was 480 m/s at 333 K. Hence $504 = 480\sqrt{T/(333 \text{ K})}$; $T = 367$ K.

Chapter 17 Electric Charge

Questions

17-1 Magnetism is the subdivision of electricity that deals with charges in motion.
In advanced work, the laws of electromagnetism result naturally when the
theory of relativity is applied to the laws of electrostatics.

17-2 There are, in fact, two kinds of charge, $+$ and $-$. However, most large-scale
manifestations of electricity involve the drift of charges of one sign (negative
electrons) through metallic conductors.

17-3 No; protons are components of the nuclei, which are fixed in a crystal lattice.
The lattice may not be geometrically perfect, and the nuclei may be in thermal
oscillation (vibration about their equilibrium positions), but the *protons* are
not separated from nuclei and take no part in electrical conduction.

17-4 Many points on the pen make contact with the coat sleeve when the pen is
rubbed rather than merely touched to the cloth.

17-5 If a positively charged rod is brought near a positively charged electroscope,
electrons are attracted toward the knob, leaving additional excess $+$ charges
on the leaves, which diverge a bit.

17-6 Pieces of paper slowly acquire negative charges by conduction from the rod;
the charges eventually fly off because like charges repel each other. On a
damp day it is difficult to maintain charge on the rubbed comb because of
conduction by a surface film of moisture on the comb.

17-7 He could have charged one ball by letting it touch a large charged body and then placing the charged ball in contact with an identical uncharged ball.

17-8 The charge on the raindrop was 463 μC.

17-9 The plane may have become positively or negatively charged by friction while airborne; this charge is shared with the earth by grounding the plane, thereby lessening the chance of a spark.

17-10 Use a proof plane and an electroscope that has previously been given a charge of known sign.

17-11 6.02×10^{23} electrons are needed.

17-12 $(82 - 4) = 78$ electrons.

Multiple Choice

17-13 (*b*);　　**17-14** (*b*);　　**17-15** (*c*);　　**17-16** (*b*);　　**17-17** (*a*);　　**17-18** (*c*).

Problems

17-A1 $I = (4800 \text{ C})/(300 \text{ s}) = 16 \text{ A}.$
17-A2 $Q = (30 \text{ C/s})(6 \times 3600 \text{ s}) = 6.48 \times 10^5 \text{ C}.$
17-A3 $(10^{-12} \text{ C})/(1.6 \times 10^{-19} \text{ C/electron}) = 6.25 \times 10^6$ electrons.
17-A4 $Q = (0.3 \text{ C/s})(1200 \text{ s}) = 360 \text{ C}.$
17-A5 $(10^6 \text{ electrons/s})(1.6 \times 10^{-19} \text{ C/electron}) = 1.6 \times 10^{-13} \text{ C/s} = 0.16 \text{ pA}.$
17-A6 $F = 9 \times 10^9 \dfrac{\text{N·m}^2}{\text{C}^2} \dfrac{(10^{-10} \text{ C})(5 \times 10^{-8} \text{ C})}{(3 \text{ m})^2} = 5 \times 10^{-9} \text{ N}.$
17-A7 Since $F \propto 1/r^2$, $F = (1/2^2)(16 \text{ mN}) = 4 \text{ mN}.$
17-A8 $10^{-6} \text{ N} = 9 \times 10^9 \dfrac{\text{N·m}^2}{\text{C}^2} \dfrac{(10^{-6} \text{ C})^2}{r^2}$; $r = 94.9 \text{ m}.$
17-A9 $(121.75 \text{ g})/3 = 40.6 \text{ g}.$
17-A10 $(207.2 \text{ g})/4 = 51.8 \text{ g}.$
17-A11 (*a*) $8Q_F = 8(96\,500 \text{ C}) = 7.72 \times 10^5 \text{ C}.$　　(*b*) $(7.72 \times 10^5 \text{ C})/(1.6 \times 10^{-19} \text{ C/elec-tron}) = 4.83 \times 10^{24}$ electrons. Alternatively, since N_A electrons neutralize 1 g.e.w., the number of electrons needed is $8N_A = 8(6.02 \times 10^{23}) = 4.82 \times 10^{24}$ electrons.　　[Rounding errors cause these answers to differ slightly. More precise numerical values are: $e = 1.602 \times 10^{-19}$ C (p. 388); $N_A = 6.022 \times 10^{23}$ (p. 22); $Q_F = 9.649 \times 10^4$ C (p. 391). The answer to part (*b*) is 4.818×10^{24} from $8N_A$, and 4.818×10^{24} from $8Q_F/e$.]
17-A12 $5N_A = 3.01 \times 10^{24}$ electrons.
17-A13 Since 3 faradays are required to deposit 1 mole, the charge of 18 faradays will deposit 6 moles.

17-B1 (*a*) $F_e = \left(9 \times 10^9 \dfrac{\text{N·m}^2}{\text{C}^2}\right) \dfrac{(1.60 \times 10^{-19} \text{ C})^2}{(0.53 \times 10^{-10} \text{ m})^2} = 8.2 \times 10^{-8} \text{ N}.$

(*b*) $F_g = \left(6.67 \times 10^{-11} \dfrac{\text{N·m}^2}{\text{kg}^2}\right) \dfrac{(1.67 \times 10^{-27} \text{ kg})(9.11 \times 10^{-31} \text{ kg})}{(0.53 \times 10^{-10} \text{ m})^2} = 3.6 \times 10^{-47} \text{ N}.$

(*c*) The electric force is 2.3×10^{39} times as large as the gravitational force.

17-B2   The charge of 1 g of electrons is $\dfrac{1.60 \times 10^{-19}\ \text{C}}{(9.11 \times 10^{-31}\ \text{kg})}(10^{-3}) = 1.756 \times 10^{8}\ \text{C}$.

$$F = \left(9 \times 10^{9}\ \frac{\text{N·m}^{2}}{\text{C}^{2}}\right) \frac{(1.756 \times 10^{8}\ \text{C})^{2}}{(3.70 \times 10^{8}\ \text{m})^{2}} = 2.03 \times 10^{9}\ \text{N}.$$

17-B3 $(9.11 \times 10^{-31}\ \text{kg})\left(9.8\ \dfrac{\text{N}}{\text{kg}}\right) = \left(9 \times 10^{9}\ \dfrac{\text{N·m}^{2}}{\text{C}^{2}}\right) \dfrac{(1.60 \times 10^{-19}\ \text{C})^{2}}{r^{2}};\ \ r = 5.08\ \text{m}.$

17-B4 $F = \left(9 \times 10^{9}\ \dfrac{\text{N·m}^{2}}{\text{C}^{2}}\right) \dfrac{(2 \times 1.60 \times 10^{-19}\ \text{C})^{2}}{(10^{-11}\ \text{m})^{2}} = 9.22 \times 10^{-6}\ \text{N}.$

17-B5 $F = \left(9 \times 10^{9}\ \dfrac{\text{N·m}^{2}}{\text{C}^{2}}\right) \dfrac{(26 \times 1.60 \times 10^{-19}\ \text{C})(1.60 \times 10^{-19}\ \text{C})}{(10^{-9}\ \text{m})^{2}} = 5.99 \times 10^{-9}\ \text{N} = 6.0\ \text{nN}.$

17-B6 $F = \left(9 \times 10^{9}\ \dfrac{\text{N·m}^{2}}{\text{C}^{2}}\right) \dfrac{(1.60 \times 10^{-19}\ \text{C})^{2}}{(5 \times 10^{-15}\ \text{m})^{2}} = 9.22\ \text{N}.$ [This repulsive Coulomb

force is balanced by attractive nuclear forces, which do not depend on the presence or absence of charge. See p. 16.]

17-B7 $F = \left(9 \times 10^{9}\ \dfrac{\text{N·m}^{2}}{\text{C}^{2}}\right) \dfrac{(1.60 \times 10^{-19}\ \text{C})(6 \times 1.60 \times 10^{-19}\ \text{C})}{(10^{-10}\ \text{m})^{2}} = 1.38 \times 10^{-7}\ \text{N}.$

17-B8   Upward force: $F_{e} = \left(9 \times 10^{9}\ \dfrac{\text{N·m}^{2}}{\text{C}^{2}}\right) \dfrac{(8 \times 10^{-9}\ \text{C})(5 \times 10^{-9}\ \text{C})}{(0.03\ \text{m})^{2}} = 4.00 \times 10^{-4}\ \text{N}.$

Downward force: $mg = (0.06 \times 10^{-3}\ \text{kg})(9.8\ \text{N/kg}) = 5.88 \times 10^{-4}\ \text{N}.$
$a = (\text{net } F)/m = (1.88 \times 10^{-4}\ \text{N})/(0.06 \times 10^{-3}\ \text{kg}) = 3.13\ \text{m/s}^{2}.$

17-B9   Force of Q_{1} on Q_{2} is $\left(9 \times 10^{9}\ \dfrac{\text{N·m}^{2}}{\text{C}^{2}}\right) \dfrac{(10 \times 10^{-6}\ \text{C})(2 \times 10^{-6}\ \text{C})}{(5\ \text{m})^{2}} = 7.2\ \text{mN}.$

Similarly, force of Q_{3} on Q_{2} works out to be 1.8 mN. Both forces are toward the right; total force is 9.0 mN, toward Q_{3}.

17-B10   Force on A due to B is $\left(9 \times 10^{9}\ \dfrac{\text{N·m}^{2}}{\text{C}^{2}}\right)$

$\times \dfrac{(30 \times 10^{-6}\ \text{C})(160 \times 10^{-6}\ \text{C})}{(4\ \text{m})^{2}} = 2.7\ \text{N}$, to the left

(away from B). Similarly, the force on A due to C works out to be 2.7 N, upward (toward C). The resultant force is $\sqrt{(2.7)^{2} + (2.7)^{2}} = 3.82\ \text{N}$, $45°$ from AC, $135°$ from AB.

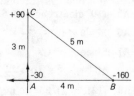

Prob. 17-B10

17-B11   (a) Force on one of the end charges is

$\left(9 \times 10^{9}\ \dfrac{\text{N·m}^{2}}{\text{C}^{2}}\right)(20 \times 10^{-6}\ \text{C})^{2}\left[\dfrac{1}{(3\ \text{m})^{2}} + \dfrac{1}{(6\ \text{m})^{2}}\right]$

$= 0.50\ \text{N}$, away from the center.   (b) The net force on the central charge is 0.

17-B12 $F_{1} = F_{2} = \left(9 \times 10^{9}\ \dfrac{\text{N·m}^{2}}{\text{C}^{2}}\right) \dfrac{(20 \times 10^{-6}\ \text{C})^{2}}{(0.3\ \text{m})^{2}} = 40\ \text{N}.$

$F_{3} = \frac{1}{2}F_{1} = 20\ \text{N}$, since the distance is $\sqrt{2}$ as large. The vector sum is $(40\sqrt{2} + 20)\ \text{N} = 76.5\ \text{N}$, outward along the diagonal.

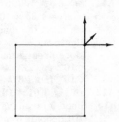

Prob. 17-B12

17-B13 $F_1 = F_2 = \left(9 \times 10^9 \dfrac{\text{N·m}^2}{\text{C}^2}\right)\dfrac{(4 \times 10^{-6} \text{ C})^2}{(2 \text{ m})^2} = 0.036$ N. The resultant force is found by the component method, or by the law of cosines. By symmetry, the force is 30° below the base line (extended); $F = 2F_1 \cos 30°$ = 2(0.036 N)(0.866) = 0.0624 N, away from triangle, perpendicular to the opposite side.

Prob. **17-B13**

17-B14 $\dfrac{(48 \times 10^{-12} \text{ C/s})(10^{-6} \text{ s})}{1.60 \times 10^{-19} \text{ C/electron}} = 300$ electrons

17-B15 $\left(\dfrac{112.40}{2}\dfrac{\text{g}}{\text{g.e.w.}}\right)\left(\dfrac{1 \text{ g.e.w.}}{96\,500 \text{ C}}\right)(40 \text{ C/s})(8 \times 3600 \text{ s}) = 671$ g.

17-B16 $\left(\dfrac{63.54}{2}\dfrac{\text{g}}{\text{g.e.w.}}\right)\left(\dfrac{1 \text{ g.e.w.}}{96\,500 \text{ C}}\right)(1 \text{ C}) = 3.29 \times 10^{-4}$ g = 0.329 mg.

17-B17 Mass deposited = 22.441 g − 22.043 g = 0.398 g.

0.398 g $= \left(\dfrac{63.54}{n}\dfrac{\text{g}}{\text{g.e.w.}}\right)\left(\dfrac{1 \text{ g.e.w.}}{96\,500 \text{ C}}\right)\left(0.400 \dfrac{\text{C}}{\text{s}}\right)(1500 \text{ s})$; $n = 0.99$; within experimental error this is ≈ 1, so the ion was Cu^+.

17-B18 (a) $m_H = \left(\dfrac{1.008}{1}\dfrac{\text{g}}{\text{g.e.w.}}\right)\left(\dfrac{1 \text{ g.e.w.}}{96\,500 \text{ C}}\right)\left(100 \dfrac{\text{C}}{\text{s}}\right)(3.6 \times 10^4 \text{ s}) = 37.6$ g. The molecular weight of H_2 gas is 2.016, so 37.6 g is 18.65 mol.

$V = (22.4 \text{ liters})\left(\dfrac{18.65 \text{ mol}}{1 \text{ mol}}\right)\left(\dfrac{300 \text{ K}}{273 \text{ K}}\right) = 459$ liters.   (b) For O^{2+}, m_0

$= \left(\dfrac{16.00}{2}\dfrac{\text{g}}{\text{g.e.w.}}\right)\left(\dfrac{1 \text{ g.e.w.}}{96\,500 \text{ C}}\right)\left(100 \dfrac{\text{C}}{\text{s}}\right)(3.6 \times 10^4 \text{ s}) = 298$ g. The molecular weight of O_2 gas is 32.000, so 298 g is 9.33 mol.

$V = (22.4 \text{ liters})\left(\dfrac{9.33 \text{ mol}}{1 \text{ mol}}\right)\left(\dfrac{300 \text{ K}}{273 \text{ K}}\right) = 230$ liters.   [This solution is given in great detail. If solved in symbols, the ratio of volume of H_2 to that of O_2 turns out to be exactly 2, the reciprocal of the ratio of the charges of the ions. This can be seen to be a consequence of the fact that for a given charge Q through the cell, the number of moles released is Q/nQ_F.]

17-B19 (a) 8000 g $= \left(\dfrac{35.45}{1}\dfrac{\text{g}}{\text{g.e.w.}}\right)\left(\dfrac{1 \text{ g.e.w.}}{96\,500 \text{ C}}\right)(I)(86\,400 \text{ s})$; $I = 252$ C/s = 252 A.

(b) $V = (22.4 \text{ liters})\left(\dfrac{8000/70.9 \text{ mol}}{1 \text{ mol}}\right)\left(\dfrac{1 \text{ atm}}{100 \text{ atm}}\right) = 25.3$ liters.

17-C1 Consider the forces on one of the balls. By similar triangles, $F_e/mg = (30 \text{ cm})/(40 \text{ cm})$; $F_e = \frac{3}{4}mg$ $= \frac{3}{4}(0.010 \text{ kg})(9.8 \text{ N/kg}) = 0.0735$ N. Now use Coulomb's law:

$0.0735 \text{ N} = \left(9 \times 10^9 \dfrac{\text{N·m}^2}{\text{C}^2}\right)\dfrac{Q^2}{(0.60 \text{ m})^2}$; $Q = 1.71$ $\times 10^{-6}$ C = 1.71 μC.

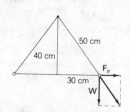

Prob. **17-C1**

17-C2 This is similar to Example 5-1 on p. 84; use the component method to find the required horizontal force. $\frac{3}{5}T = (0.01 \text{ kg})(9.8 \text{ N/kg})$; $T = 0.163$ N; $F = \frac{4}{5}T = 0.1307$ N. Now use Coulomb's law to find the charge:

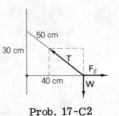

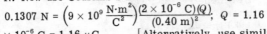

$0.1307 \text{ N} = \left(9 \times 10^9 \frac{\text{N} \cdot \text{m}^2}{\text{C}^2}\right)\frac{(2 \times 10^{-6} \text{ C})(Q)}{(0.40 \text{ m})^2}$; $Q = 1.16$

$\times 10^{-6}$ C $= 1.16$ μC.   [Alternatively, use similar triangles as in the solution for Prob. 17-C1 (above): $F_e/mg = (40 \text{ cm})/(30 \text{ cm})$; $F_e = \frac{4}{3}mg = 0.1307$ N as before.]

Prob. 17-C2

17-C3 Let Q_1 and Q_2 be expressed in units of nC ($= 10^{-9}$ C). Coulomb's law gives

$5 \times 10^{-5} \text{ N} = \left(9 \times 10^9 \frac{\text{N} \cdot \text{m}^2}{\text{C}^2}\right)\frac{Q_1 Q_2 \times 10^{-18} \text{ C}^2}{(3 \times 10^{-2} \text{ m})^2}$; this reduces to $Q_1 Q_2 = 5$.

Also, $Q_1 + Q_2 = 6$. Solve simultaneously, obtaining $Q_1 = 2$ nC, $Q_2 = 3$ nC.

17-C4 It should be apparent that the charge Q_3 must be to the right of Q_2; if between Q_1 and Q_2 the two forces are both to the left (if Q_3 is +), and cannot cancel. If Q_3 is to the left of Q_1, the attractive force is always greater than the repulsive force (r is less, Q is greater). If x is in m, we must have

$\frac{4}{(x+2)^2} = \frac{1}{(x-3)^2}$; $\left(\frac{x+2}{x-3}\right)^2 = \frac{4}{1}$; $\frac{x+2}{x-3} = 2$; $x = 8$ m.

[Using the negative root, $\frac{x+2}{x-3} = -2$, gives x between Q_1 and Q_2, which is physically unacceptable.]

17-C5 We add the forces by the component method. Due to $+5$ μC at the origin,

$F = \left(9 \times 10^9 \frac{\text{N} \cdot \text{m}^2}{\text{C}^2}\right)\frac{(5 \times 10^{-6} \text{ C})(3 \times 10^{-6} \text{ C})}{(2 \text{ m})^2} = 0.03375$ N $= 33.75$ mN;

$F_x = -33.75$ mN; $F_y = 0$. Due to $+8$ μC at $y = 2$ m,

$F = \left(9 \times 10^9 \frac{\text{N} \cdot \text{m}^2}{\text{C}^2}\right)\frac{(8 \times 10^{-6} \text{ C})(3 \times 10^{-6} \text{ C})}{(2\sqrt{2} \text{ m})^2} = 0.027$ N $= 27.0$ mN; $F_x = -19.09$

mN, $F_y = +19.09$ mN.

Adding components, we have $\Sigma F_x = -52.84$ mN, $\Sigma F_y = +19.09$ mN, $F = \sqrt{(\Sigma F_x)^2 + (\Sigma F_y)^2} = 56.2$ mN. From $\tan \theta = (\Sigma F_y)/(\Sigma F_x)$, we obtain $\theta = 20°$ from the negative x axis.

17-C6 $m = (0.2 \text{ A})(1800 \text{ s})\left(107.87 \frac{\text{g}}{\text{g.e.w.}}\right)\left(\frac{1 \text{ g.e.w.}}{96\,500 \text{ C}}\right) = 0.4024$ g. Using the density of silver from Table 2-1, we have $0.4204 \text{ g} = (30 \text{ cm}^2)(x)(10.5 \text{ g/cm}^3)$; $x = 0.00128$ cm.

17-C7 $(80 \text{ cm}^2)(2 \times 10^{-3} \text{ cm})(19.3 \text{ g/cm}^3) = \left(\frac{196.97}{3} \frac{\text{g}}{\text{g.e.w.}}\right)\left(\frac{1 \text{ g.e.w.}}{96\,500 \text{ C}}\right)(3 \text{ A})(t)$;

$t = 1512$ s $= 25.2$ min.

17-C8 The mass of lead sheath is found using the average diameter: $m = \pi(4.8 \text{ cm})$ $\times (0.2 \text{ cm})(400 \text{ cm})(10.3 \text{ g/cm}^3) = 12.43 \times 10^3$ g. The equation for electrolysis gives

$12.43 \times 10^{-3} \text{ g} = \left(\frac{207.2}{4} \frac{\text{g}}{\text{g.e.w.}}\right)\left(\frac{1 \text{ g.e.w.}}{96\,500 \text{ C}}\right)(0.02 \text{ A})(t)$;

$t = 1.158 \times 10^9$ s $= 36.7$ years. The cable lasted about 37 years and was not serviceable in 1976.

17-C9 $\pi(1.5 \text{ cm})^2(2)(80 \times 10^{-4} \text{ cm})\left(10.5 \frac{\text{g}}{\text{cm}^3}\right) = \left(\frac{107.87}{1} \frac{\text{g}}{\text{g.e.w.}}\right)\left(\frac{1 \text{ g.e.w.}}{96\,500 \text{ C}}\right)(120 \text{ s})(I)$;

$I = 8.85$ A.

17-C10 5.73×10^{-3} g $= \left(\dfrac{107.87}{1} \dfrac{g}{g.e.w.} \right) \left(\dfrac{1\ g.e.w.}{96\,500\ C} \right)$ (0.0041 C)(N); $N = 1250$ heartbeats in 800 s; the rate was 94 min^{-1}.

Chapter 18   Electric Field

Questions

18-1 Electric field strength is a vector quantity, since force is a vector quantity; electric potential is a scalar quantity, since work is a scalar quantity.

18-2 A large test charge might significantly alter the distribution of the charges that cause the field that is to be measured.

18-3 Draw equipotential lines everywhere perpendicular to the field lines. Close to the charges, the equipotentials are circles (spheres, in three dimensions) as in Fig. 18-11. Another equipotential surface for these two charges of equal magnitude is a straight line (a plane in three dimensions) that is the perpendicular bisector of the line joining the two charges. All points on this line (plane) are equidistant from the two charges, and the algebraic sum of the two potentials is zero on this line (plane). It would require no work to bring a test charge along this line (plane) from ∞ to a point midway between the charges, since the electric force would at all times be perpendicular to the displacement.

18-4 A mascon causes a small perturbation of the motion of an artificial satellite orbiting the moon. It is believed that mascons that lie under lunar "seas" (maria) may be the remains of large meteorites that impacted long ago, or the upwelling of volcanic material somewhat denser than the surrounding area.

18-5 If the field lines were not perpendicular to the surface of the metal, the component of **E** parallel to the surface would cause free charges to move, and the system of charges would not be in equilibrium. This argument does not apply to insulators (dielectrics) where there are no free charges; lines of force may intersect the surface of a dielectric at an angle. An analogy with gravitational field may be helpful: At the earth's surface, the field lines are vertical; field lines can intersect any nonhorizontal *solid* surface (such as the sloping side of a pyramid) but cannot do this for a liquid surface whose molecules are free to move. Hence the liquid surface must be horizontal, perpendicular to the field lines.

18-6 Upward. The PE increases when the diver's height above the water increases, and decreases when the height decreases; $\Delta W/\Delta z$ is positive. This correlates with the fact that the field strength (the *downward* gravitational field) is the negative of the potential gradient (p. 403).

18-7 Zero. (See Sec. 7-2 on p. 148).

18-8 A circle (intersection of a plane and a spherical equipotential surface). In the general orbit, which is an ellipse, the gravitational PE is *not* constant and the KE changes (correlate with Kepler's law of areas).

18-9 The wind velocities illustrate a vector field; the temperatures represent a scalar field; the temperature gradients are perpendicular to the isothermal lines. The temperature gradient is greatest near Arkansas, where a 10° change occurs over a distance of about 150 km (90 mi).

18-10 The boomerang is thrown *away* from the intended receiver, swings around, and is received from behind. The thrower is pushed toward the receiver by the recoil of his throw, and the receiver is pushed toward the thrower when struck from behind by the boomerang.

18-11 Potential difference is a difference of potential energy *per unit charge*.

18-12 If one part of the conductor were at a different potential, electrons would flow to the position where their PE is least. The redistributed charge would be distributed in such a way that now all points of the conductor *would* be at the same potential. A hydrostatic analogy is helpful here.

18-13 The original system of charges in Fig. 18-7b was in equilibrium (a configuration of minimum PE). Hence *any* redistribution of the system of charges increases the PE of the system. It is somewhat loose to speak of the PE "of the sphere"; more precisely, the PE is that of the entire system of charges shown in the figure (see the discussion of the PE of C and O_2 on p. 121).

18-14 C decreases (Eq. 18-9); Q is the same; therefore, V is greater. Hence the field (given by the potential gradient) is greater.

Multiple Choice

18-13 (a); **18-14** (a); **18-15** (a); **18-16** (b); **18-17** (c); **18-18** (b).

Problems

18-A1 $E = F/Q = (0.36 \text{ N})/(3 \times 10^{-7} \text{ C}) = 1.2 \times 10^6 \text{ N/C}$. The field is downward, since by definition the field is measured by the force per unit *positive* test charge.

18-A2 $F = EQ = (4 \times 10^4 \text{ N/C})(5 \times 10^{-8} \text{ C}) = 2 \times 10^{-3} \text{ N}$.

18-A3 $E = (3.2 \times 10^{-17} \text{ N})/(1.6 \times 10^{-19} \text{ C}) = 200 \text{ N/C}$, downward.

18-A4 $F = (30 \times 10^{-6} \text{ C})(250 \text{ N/C}) = 7.5 \times 10^{-3} \text{ N}$.

18-A5 PD $= (6 \text{ J})/(15 \text{ C}) = 0.4 \text{ J/C} = 0.4 \text{ V}$.

18-A6 PD $= (118 - 100) \text{ V} = 18 \text{ V}$; $W = VQ = (18 \text{ J/C})(5 \text{ C}) = 90 \text{ J}$.

18-A7 $\Delta V/\Delta s = (60 \text{ V})/(0.25 \text{ m}) = 240 \text{ V/m}$.

18-A8 (a) $\Delta V/\Delta s = (2000 \text{ V})/(2 \times 10^{-3} \text{ m}) = 10^6 \text{ V/m}$. (b) The magnitude of the electric field strength is the same as the potential gradient, i.e., 10^6 N/C. This is a strong field; as mentioned on p. 409, it is about sufficient to cause a spark in dry air.

18-A9 $C = Q/V = (4000 \times 10^{-6} \text{ C})/(500 \text{ V}) = 8 \times 10^{-6} \text{ F} = 8 \ \mu\text{F}$.

18-A10 $Q = CV = (50 \times 10^{-6} \text{ F})(9 \text{ V}) = 450 \ \mu\text{C}$.

18-A11 $Q = CV = (20 \times 10^{-6} \text{ F})(450 \text{ V}) = 9 \times 10^{-3} \text{ C}$.

18-A12 $C = Q/V = (10^{11} \times 1.6 \times 10^{-19} \text{ C})/(800 \text{ V}) = 2 \times 10^{-11} \text{ F} = 20 \text{ pF}$.

18-B1 (a) $E_1 = \left(9 \times 10^9 \ \dfrac{\text{N·m}^2}{\text{C}^2}\right) \dfrac{(100 \times 10^{-6} \text{ C})}{(5 \text{ m})^2} = 3.6 \times 10^4 \text{ N/C}$ (to the right).

(b) $E_2 = \left(9 \times 10^9 \ \dfrac{\text{N·m}^2}{\text{C}^2}\right) \dfrac{(40 \times 10^{-6} \text{ C})}{(2 \text{ m})^2} = 9.0 \times 10^4 \text{ N/C}$ (to the right).

(c) $E = 12.6 \times 10^{-4} \text{ N/C}$ (to the right).

18-B2 Using $E = kQ/r^2$ gives $E_1 = 9.0 \times 10^4 \text{ N/C}$ (to the right), $E_2 = 13.5 \times 10^4 \text{ N/C}$ (to the left); resultant $E = 4.5 \times 10^4 \text{ N/C}$ (to the left, toward the 40 μC charge).

18-B3 The fields due to two of the charges are equal and opposite, and the resultant is due to one charge only:
$$E = \left(9 \times 10^9 \frac{\text{N·m}^2}{\text{C}^2}\right)\frac{(8 \times 10^{-6}\ \text{C})}{(\sqrt{2}\ \text{m})^2} = 3.6 \times 10^4\ \text{N/C},$$
directed toward the empty corner.   [See also Prob. 18-C2.]

18-B4 From Newton's law of gravitation, $G(M/x^2) = G(\frac{1}{81}M/y^2)$; $y = \frac{1}{9}x$.

18-B5 (a) $F = EQ = (4000\ \text{V/m})(1.60 \times 10^{-19}\ \text{C}) = 6.40 \times 10^{-16}\ \text{N}$.   (b) $a = F/m$
= $(6.40 \times 10^{-16}\ \text{N})/(9.11 \times 10^{-31}\ \text{kg}) = 7.03 \times 10^{14}\ \text{m/s}^2$.

18-B6 The electric force balances the weight of the drop: $(150 \times 1.60 \times 10^{-19}\ \text{C})$
$\times (300\ \text{N/C}) = \frac{4}{3}\pi r^3(1000\ \text{kg/m}^3)(9.8\ \text{N/kg})$; $r = 5.60 \times 10^{-7}\ \text{m} = 0.56\ \mu\text{m}$.

18-B7 The PD is $(1.8\ \text{J})/(0.3 \times 10^{-3}\ \text{C}) = 6000\ \text{V}$. E = potential gradient = $(6000\ \text{V})/$
$(0.20\ \text{m}) = 3 \times 10^4\ \text{V/m} = 30\ \text{kV/m}$.

18-B8 The change in PE is $(11 \times 10^{-6} - 2 \times 10^{-6})\ \text{J} = 9 \times 10^{-6}\ \text{J}$; this is the work done against *electric* forces. $V = W/Q = (9 \times 10^{-6}\ \text{J})/(3 \times 10^{-8}\ \text{C}) = 300\ \text{V}$.

18-B9 $V = (9.6 \times 10^{-13}\ \text{J})/(1.60 \times 10^{-19}\ \text{C}) = 6 \times 10^6\ \text{V} = 6\ \text{MV}$. Point Y is at higher potential.

18-B10 $a = v^2/2s = (2 \times 10^5\ \text{m/s})^2/2(4 \times 10^{-2}\ \text{m}) = 5 \times 10^{11}\ \text{m/s}^2$. $F = ma = EQ$ gives $(1.67 \times 10^{-27}\ \text{kg})(5 \times 10^{11}\ \text{m/s}^2) = E(1.60 \times 10^{-19}\ \text{C})$; $E = 5.22 \times 10^3\ \text{V/m}$.

18-B11 $\frac{1}{2}(9.11 \times 10^{-31}\ \text{kg})v^2 = (1.60 \times 10^{-19}\ \text{C})(120\ \text{V})$; $v = 6.49 \times 10^6\ \text{m/s}$.   [The nonrelativistic formula $\frac{1}{2}mv^2$ for KE can be used here, since v turns out to be much less than c.]

18-B12 The absorbed energy is $(50\ \text{C})(800\ \text{MJ/C})(0.01) = 4 \times 10^8\ \text{J} = 9.57 \times 10^4\ \text{kcal}$. To boil water, starting at 30°C, requires 70 kcal/kg + 540 kcal/kg = 610 kcal/kg. Hence $m = (9.57 \times 10^4\ \text{kcal})/(610\ \text{kcal/kg}) = 157\ \text{kg}$.

18-B13 $C = \dfrac{KA}{4\pi kd} = \dfrac{(5)(0.04\ \text{m})(0.04\ \text{m})}{4\pi(9 \times 10^9\ \text{N·m}^2/\text{C}^2)(1.2 \times 10^{-3}\ \text{m})} = 58.9 \times 10^{-12}\ \text{F} = 58.9\ \text{pF}$.

18-B14 $V = Q/C = (32 \times 10^{-6}\ \text{C})/(0.04 \times 10^{-6}\ \text{F}) = 800\ \text{V}$; E = potential gradient = V/d
= $(800\ \text{V})/(0.5 \times 10^{-3}\ \text{m}) = 1.6 \times 10^6\ \text{V/m}$.   [This capacitor is close to breakdown; see p. 409.]

18-B15 $V = (8 \times 10^{-17}\ \text{J})/(1.60 \times 10^{-19}\ \text{C}) = 500\ \text{V}$; E = potential gradient = $(500\ \text{V})/$
$(4 \times 10^{-3}\ \text{m}) = 1.25 \times 10^5\ \text{V/m} = 125\ \text{kV/m}$.

18-B16 During each shock, $Q = CV = (20 \times 10^{-6}\ \text{F})(1.4\ \text{V}) = 28\ \mu\text{C}$. $I = \Delta Q/\Delta t$
= $(28\ \mu\text{C})/(0.25\ \text{s}) = 112\ \mu\text{A}$.

18-B17 $Q = 1000(200 \times 10^{-6}\ \text{C})(25\ \text{V}) = 5\ \text{C}$; $m = \left(\dfrac{63.54}{2}\ \dfrac{\text{g}}{\text{g.e.w.}}\right)\left(\dfrac{1\ \text{g.e.w.}}{96\,500\ \text{C}}\right)(5\ \text{C}) = 1.65$
$\times 10^{-3}\ \text{g} = 1.65\ \text{mg}$.

18-B18 $Q = C(9\ \text{V})$; $V' = Q/C' = Q/(\frac{1}{5}C) = C(9\ \text{V})/(\frac{1}{5}C) = 45\ \text{V}$.   [According to Eq. 18-13, the energy stored in the capacitor has increased, since Q has remained the same, C has decreased, and V has increased. This added energy has come from the work done (perhaps by a muscle) against an opposing force when the slab is pulled out. The opposing force is the attraction between charges on each plate and induced charges of opposite sign on the adjacent faces of the dielectric slab.]

18-B19 $C_1 = Q_1/V = (2\ \mu\text{C})/(800\ \text{V}) = 0.0025\ \mu\text{F}$. In benzene, the capacitance is K times as large: $C_2 = (0.0025\ \mu\text{F})(2.28)$. $Q_2 = C_2V$; $\Delta Q = Q_2 - Q_1 = (C_2 - C_1)V$
= $(KC_1 - C_1)V = (K - 1)C_1V = (2.28 - 1)\left(\dfrac{2\ \mu\text{C}}{800\ \text{V}}\right)(800\ \text{V}) = 2.56\ \mu\text{C}$.

18-B20 (a) In parallel, $C = (5 + 10 + 30)\ \mu\text{F} = 45\ \mu\text{F}$.   (b) In series, $1/C$
= $(1/5 + 1/10 + 1/30)$; $C = 3\ \mu\text{F}$.

18-B21 (a) PD = 45 V for each capacitor. (b) Using $Q = CV$, we find $Q_1 = (15\ \mu F)$ $\times$ (45 V) = 675 μC; $Q_2 = (10\ \mu F)(45\ V) = 450\ \mu C$. [Check: Combined $C = (15 + 10)\ \mu F = 25\ \mu F$; total charge = $(25\ \mu F)(45\ V) = 1125\ \mu C$, which checks with 675 μC + 450 μC.]

18-B22 (a) Combined C is found from $1/C = 1/15 + 1/10$; $C = 6\ \mu F$. Charge on each capacitor = charge on combination = $(6\ \mu F)(45\ V) = 270\ \mu C$. (b) Using $V = Q/C$, we find $V_1 = (270\ \mu C)/(15\ \mu F) = 18\ V$; $V_2 = (270\ \mu C)/(10\ \mu F) = 27\ V$. [Check: 18 V + 27 V = 45 V across the series combination.]

18-C1 (a) Using Newtonian mechanics, we apply the energy principle. The electron's increase of energy is $(1.02 \times 10^6\ J/C)(1.60 \times 10^{-19}\ C) = 1.63 \times 10^{-13}\ J$; equate (illegally) to $\frac{1}{2}(9.11 \times 10^{-31}\ kg)v^2$, whence $v = 6.0 \times 10^8\ m/s$. (b) A correct solution uses the relativistic formula for KE (Eq. 7-8 on p. 162), from which $m = m_0 + KE/c^2 = 9.11 \times 10^{-31}\ kg + (1.63 \times 10^{-13}\ J)/(3 \times 10^8\ m/s)^2 = 27.2$ $\times 10^{-31}\ kg = 3m_0$. Now $m = m_0/\sqrt{1 - v^2/c^2}$ gives $v = (\sqrt{8}/3)c = 2.83 \times 10^8\ m/s$.

18-C2 E_1, E_2, and E_3 each have magnitude
$$\frac{kQ}{r^2} = \left(9 \times 10^9\ \frac{N \cdot m^2}{C^2}\right)\frac{8 \times 10^{-6}\ C}{(\sqrt{2}\ m)^2} = 3.6 \times 10^4\ N/C.$$
E_1 and E_3 combine to give $7.2 \times 10^4\ N/C$, $45°$ above the x direction; the resultant E is $\sqrt{(7.2)^2 + (3.6)^2} \times 10^4 = 8.05$ $\times 10^4\ N/C$. The direction is found from $\tan \theta = 3.6/7.2$; $\theta = 27°$. The resultant field is $8.05 \times 10^4\ N/C$, $27°$ from the diagonal joining the corners with charges of opposite sign.

18-C3 (a) $t = (0.04\ m)/(5 \times 10^7\ m/s) = 8 \times 10^{-10}\ s$. (b) Impulse = $Ft = Eqt$ = $[(80\ V)/(0.01\ m)](1.60 \times 10^{-19}\ C)(8 \times 10^{-10}\ s) = 1.024 \times 10^{-24}\ N \cdot s$. (c) Since impulse = change in momentum, $1.024 \times 10^{-24}\ N \cdot s = (9.11 \times 10^{-31}\ kg)v$; $v = 1.12$ $\times 10^6\ m/s$. [This is agreeably much less than c, confirming the use of the electron's rest mass.]

18-C4 (a) $1/6 + 1/3 = 1/C_S$; $C_S = 2\ \mu F$; total C is $7\ \mu F + 2\ \mu F = 9\ \mu F$. (b) The PD across the series combination is also 12 V; each of the series capacitors has charge $Q = C_S V = (2\ \mu F)(12\ V) = 24\ \mu C$. Thus the PD across the 6 μF capacitor is $V = Q/C = (24\ \mu C)/(6\ \mu F) = 4\ V$.

18-C5 Allowing a safety factor of 5, we assume that a PD of 5000 V could be applied. The breakdown field is $(10^5\ V)/(10^{-3}\ m) = 10^8\ V/m$. From $E = V/d$, $d = V/E$ = $(5000\ V)/(10^8\ V/m) = 5 \times 10^{-5}\ m = 50\ \mu m$. Now, from Eq. 18-9,
$$A = \frac{4\pi k d C}{K} = \frac{4\pi (9 \times 10^9\ N \cdot m^2/C^2)(5 \times 10^{-5}\ m)(10^{-7}\ F)}{3} = 0.188\ m^2.$$

18-C6 (a) $10^{-12}\ kg = \frac{4}{3}\pi r^3 (1000\ kg/m^3)$; $r = 6.203 \times 10^{-6}\ m$ or 6 μm. Surface area = $4\pi r^2 = 4\pi (6.203 \times 10^{-6}\ m)^2 = 4.84 \times 10^{-10}\ m^2$.
(b) $C = \frac{KA}{4\pi k d} = \frac{(5)(4.84 \times 10^{-10}\ m^2)}{4\pi (9 \times 10^9\ N \cdot m^2/C^2)(100 \times 10^{-9}\ m)} = 2.14 \times 10^{-13}\ F = 0.21\ pF$.
(c) $Q = CV = (2.14 \times 10^{-13}\ F)(100 \times 10^{-3}\ V) = 2.14 \times 10^{-14}\ C$. This represents $(2.14 \times 10^{-14})/(1.60 \times 10^{-19}) \approx 1.3 \times 10^5$ electronic charges clustered around the cell.

18-C7 $C = \frac{A}{4\pi k d}$; $Q = CV = \frac{AV}{4\pi k d} = \frac{A}{4\pi k}\left(\frac{V}{d}\right)$; where V/d is the breakdown field strength or potential gradient. Here,
$$Q = \frac{(0.20\ m)(0.50\ m)}{4\pi (9 \times 10^9\ N \cdot m^2/C^2)} (3 \times 10^6\ V/m) = 2.65 \times 10^{-6}\ C = 2.65\ \mu C$$

18-C8 (a) $Q = CV = \frac{AV}{4\pi k d} = \frac{A}{4\pi k}E$; $Q/A = E/4\pi k$. The surface density depends only on the field E.

(b) $\dfrac{Q}{4\pi R^2} = \dfrac{E}{4\pi k}$; $R = \sqrt{\dfrac{kQ}{E}} = \sqrt{\dfrac{(9 \times 10^9 \text{ N·m}^2/\text{C}^2)(0.1 \text{ C})}{3 \times 10^6 \text{ N/C}}} = 17.3$ m

[Discussion of this problem can include mention of lightning rods, where one wishes to encourage discharge from a sharply pointed rod with small radius of curvature. Conversely, the high-voltage electrodes of a Van de Graaf generator are surrounded by gently curved surfaces with large radius of curvature, to minimize breakdown (Fig. 31-1 on p. 740).]

18-C9 $\text{PE} = \frac{1}{2}CV^2 = \frac{1}{2}(50 \times 10^{-3} \text{ F})(20 \text{ V})^2 = 10$ J.

18-C10 (a) The PD is $(80 \times 10^3 \text{ V/m})(2 \times 10^{-3} \text{ m}) = 160$ V. $\text{PE} = \frac{1}{2}QV = \frac{1}{2}(5 \times 10^{15}$ $\times 1.60 \times 10^{-19} \text{ C})(160 \text{ V}) = 0.064$ J. (b) $W = Vq = (160 \text{ V})(1.60 \times 10^{-19} \text{ C})$ $= 2.56 \times 10^{-17}$ J.

18-C11 (a) At any point between the charges, the two fields are in the same direction and cannot cancel; at any point beyond $x = +5$ m the field due to -100 μC will always be larger than the field due to $+25$ μC. Therefore, the point of zero field is at a distance d to the *left* of the origin.

$\dfrac{25}{d^2} = \dfrac{100}{(5+d)^2}$; $\left(\dfrac{5+d}{d}\right)^2 = \dfrac{100}{25}$; $\dfrac{5+d}{d} = 2$; $d = 5$ m. The field E is zero at

$x = -5$ m. (b) For a point between the charges, $\dfrac{25}{x} + \dfrac{-100}{5-x} = 0$; $x = +1$ m.

For a point to the left of the origin, $\dfrac{25}{d} + \dfrac{-100}{5+d} = 0$; $d = 1.67$ m; $x = -1.67$ m.

[There are two points on the x axis where $V = 0$. These represent the points where the $V = 0$ equipotential surface crosses the x axis.]

18-C12 The potential at one corner due to the other three charges is

$3\left[\dfrac{(9 \times 10^9 \text{ N·m}^2/\text{C}^2)(50 \times 10^{-6} \text{ C})}{2 \text{ m}}\right] = 675$ kV. At the center, the potential is

$3\left[\dfrac{(9 \times 10^9 \text{ N·m}^2/\text{C}^2)(50 \times 10^{-6} \text{ C})}{\sqrt{2} \text{ m}}\right] = 954.6$ kV. The PD is $(955 - 675)$ kV $= 280$

kV; the work is $W = Q.\Delta V = (50 \times 10^{-6} \text{ C})(280 \times 10^3 \text{ V}) = 14.0$ J.

18-C13 From $W = \frac{1}{2}CV^2$, $100 \text{ J} = \frac{1}{2}(C)(450 \text{ V})^2$; $C = 9.88 \times 10^{-4}$ F $= 988$ μF.

18-C14 Using Eq. 18-13 for energy density, we find the stored energy to be $\left(\dfrac{K}{8\pi k}E^2\right)$ (volume) $= \dfrac{(1)(100 \text{ V/m})^2(2 \text{ m})(91.4 \text{ m})(48.8 \text{ m})}{8\pi(9 \times 10^9 \text{ N·m}^2/\text{C}^2)} = 3.94 \times 10^{-4}$ J.

18-C15 (a) $Q_1 = (3 \text{ }\mu\text{F})(15 \text{ V}) = 45 \text{ }\mu\text{C}$; $Q_2 = (5 \text{ }\mu\text{F})(7 \text{ V}) = 35 \text{ }\mu\text{C}$; total charge on the parallel combination is $(45 + 35) \text{ }\mu\text{C} = 80 \text{ }\mu\text{C}$. The total capacitance is $(3 + 5)$ μF $= 8$ μF. Hence $V = Q/C = (80 \text{ }\mu\text{C})/(8 \text{ }\mu\text{F}) = 10$ V. (b) $Q_1' = (3 \text{ }\mu\text{F})(10 \text{ V})$ $= 30 \text{ }\mu\text{C}$; $Q_2' = (5 \text{ }\mu\text{F})(10 \text{ V}) = 50 \text{ }\mu\text{C}$. (c) Use $\text{PE} = \frac{1}{2}QV$. Before connecting the capacitors, we had $W_1 = \frac{1}{2}(45 \text{ }\mu\text{C})(15 \text{ V}) = 337.5 \text{ }\mu\text{J}$; $W_2 = \frac{1}{2}(35 \text{ }\mu\text{C})(7 \text{ V})$ $= 122.5 \text{ }\mu\text{J}$; total stored energy was $(337.5 + 122.5) \text{ }\mu\text{J} = 460 \text{ }\mu\text{J}$. After connection, $W = \frac{1}{2}(80 \text{ }\mu\text{C})(10 \text{ V}) = 400 \text{ }\mu\text{J}$. The loss of PE was $(460 - 400) \text{ }\mu\text{J}$ $= 60 \text{ }\mu\text{J}$. [The energy is dissipated as heat in the conducting wires, as charge oscillates back and forth; the frequency is very high, determined by the product LC (Fig. 23-1 on p. 540), where L is the very small self-inductance of the circuit wiring. Some of the energy is also lost by radiation from the accelerated charges (top of p. 550).]

Chapter 19   Electric Energy

Questions

19-1   Electrons leave the negative terminal of the cell; conventional current is directed away from the positive terminal of the cell.

19-2   The electrons are gaining electric PE from the chemical PE of the cell.

19-3   PD does not necessarily express the possibility of reversible transformation of energy.

19-4   Yes.

19-5   Yes; their cross sections would be different.

19-6   The resistivity is relatively constant with respect to temperature change.

19-7   The charge carriers are positive (holes, or absence of electrons); the resistivity decreases with increasing temperature.

Multiple Choice

19-8   (b);   19-9   (c);   19-10   (a);   19-11   (a);   19-12   (c);   19-13   (a).

Problems

19-A1 $P = I^2R$; $I = \sqrt{P/R} = \sqrt{(1100\ \text{W})/(44\ \Omega)} = 5$ A.
19-A2 $R = P/I^2 = (800\ \text{W})/(4\ \text{A})^2 = 50\ \Omega$.
19-A3 $P = VI = (6\ \text{V})(0.35\ \text{A}) = 2.1$ W.
19-A4 $I = V/R = (15\ \text{V})/(200\ \Omega) = 0.075$ A $= 75$ mA.
19-A5 $V = IR = (3 \times 10^{-3}\ \text{A})(4 \times 10^6\ \Omega) = 12\,000$ V $= 12$ kV.
19-A6 $R = V/I = (9\ \text{V})/(0.06\ \text{A}) = 150\ \Omega$.
19-A7 $P = VI = (120\ \text{V})(10\ \text{A}) = 1.2$ kW.
19-A8 $W = Pt = (200\ \text{J/s})(1200\ \text{s})\left(\dfrac{1\ \text{kWh}}{3.6 \times 10^6\ \text{J}}\right) = 0.067$ kWh.

19-A9   From $R = \rho L/A$, $R' = (100\ \Omega)\left(\dfrac{4L}{L}\right)\left(\dfrac{A}{5A}\right) = 80\ \Omega$.

19-B1   (a) $Q = (5\ \text{A})(30\ \text{s}) = 150$ C; $\varepsilon = (600\ \text{J})/(150\ \text{C}) = 4$ V.   [Each coulomb of charge passing through the battery gains 4 J of energy at the expense of the chemical PE of the battery.]   (b) $P = \varepsilon I = (4\ \text{V})(5\ \text{A}) = 20$ J/s $= 20$ W.

19-B2   Cost $= (25\ \text{W})\left(10\ \dfrac{\text{h}}{\text{day}}\right)\left(\dfrac{365\ \text{days}}{1\ \text{y}}\right)\left(\dfrac{\$0.03}{1000\ \text{Wh}}\right) = \$2.74/\text{y}$.

19-B3 $(10\ \text{W})\left(16\ \dfrac{\text{h}}{\text{day}}\right)\left(\dfrac{365\ \text{days}}{1\ \text{y}}\right)\left(\dfrac{1\ \text{kWh}}{1000\ \text{Wh}}\right) = 58.4$ kWh/y.

   (a) Monetary cost $= \left(58.4\dfrac{\text{kWh}}{\text{y}}\right)\left(\dfrac{\$0.03}{1\ \text{kWh}}\right) = \$1.75/\text{y}$.

   (b) Ecological cost $= \left(58.4\ \dfrac{\text{kWh}}{\text{y}}\right)\left(\dfrac{3.6 \times 10^6\ \text{J}}{1\ \text{kWh}}\right)\left(\dfrac{1\ \text{kcal}}{4180\ \text{J}}\right)\left(\dfrac{1\ \text{kg of coal}}{7000\ \text{kcal}}\right)$
   $= 7.19$ kg of coal per year; $7.19/0.35 = 20.5$ kg/y is used.

19-B4 $(200 \text{ kg})(40°C)\left(4180 \dfrac{J}{kg \cdot °C}\right)\left(\dfrac{1 \text{ kWh}}{3.6 \times 10^6 \text{ J}}\right)\left(\dfrac{2¢}{1 \text{ kWh}}\right) = 19¢.$

19-B5 $e = \dfrac{\text{power output}}{\text{power input}} = \dfrac{(\frac{1}{4} \text{ hp})(746 \text{ W/hp})}{(1.80 \text{ A})(115 \text{ V})} = 90.1\%.$

19-B6 60% of the power input goes to heating the iron.

$0.60(9 \text{ A})(120 \text{ V})(90 \text{ s})\left(\dfrac{1 \text{ cal}}{4.18 \text{ J}}\right) = (800 \text{ g})\left(0.11 \dfrac{\text{cal}}{g \cdot °C}\right)(\Delta t); \quad \Delta t = 158.5°C.$ Final
temperature $= 20°C + 159°C = 179°C.$

19-B7 Power for radio $= (12 \text{ V})(2 \text{ A}) = 24 \text{ W}$; total power $= (24 + 20) \text{ W} = 44 \text{ W}.$
$W = Pt = (44 \text{ J/s})(600 \text{ s}) = 2.64 \times 10^4 \text{ J}.$

19-B8 $I = P/V = (700 \text{ W})/(12 \text{ V}) = 58.3 \text{ A}.$

19-B9 $(4 \times 10^6 \text{ V})(25 \times 10^{-3} \text{ A})\left(\dfrac{60 \text{ s}}{1 \text{ min}}\right) = m\left(4180 \dfrac{J}{kg \cdot °C}\right)(50°C); \quad m = 28.7 \text{ kg/min}.$

19-B10 Copper melts at $1083°C$ (Table 14-2). The power input is $P = VI = (20 \times 10^9 \text{ V})$
$\times (25 \times 10^{-6} \text{ A}) = 500 \text{ kW}.$ Therefore,
$\left(500 \times 10^3 \dfrac{J}{s}\right)(t) = (2 \text{ kg})\left(0.11 \dfrac{\text{kcal}}{kg \cdot °C}\right)\left(\dfrac{4180 \text{ J}}{1 \text{ kcal}}\right)(1063°C); \quad t = 2.0 \text{ s.}$ [Without
cooling, as in Prob. 19-B9, the target would quickly melt.]

19-B11 After the water starts to boil, the temperature remains at $100°C$. The energy
input is $I^2Rt.$ $(120 \text{ g})\left(540 \dfrac{\text{cal}}{g}\right)\left(\dfrac{4.18 \text{ J}}{1 \text{ cal}}\right) = (4 \text{ A})^2(R)(600 \text{ s}); \quad R = 28.2 \; \Omega.$ See
photo on p. 425. [The specific heat of the cup is of no importance, since
the temperature of the cup does not change during the 10 min that the water
is boiling.]

19-B12 The heat of combustion of coal is 33 MJ/kg.

(a) $(48\,000 \text{ kWh})\left(\dfrac{1 \text{ kg}}{33 \text{ MJ}}\right)\left(\dfrac{3.6 \text{ MJ}}{1 \text{ kWh}}\right)\left(\dfrac{1}{0.40}\right) = 13.1 \times 10^3 \text{ kg} = 13 \text{ metric tons.}$

(b) Since efficiency $= 0.40 = W/Q_{\text{in}}, Q_{\text{in}} = W/0.40 = 2.5W.$ Hence, $Q_{\text{out}} = Q_{\text{in}}$
$- W = 2.5W - W = 1.5W = 1.5(48\,000 \text{ kWh}) = 72\,000 \text{ kWh.}$ Converting thermal
units gives, for the heat rejected to the environment by a family of 4,
$Q_{\text{out}} = (72 \times 10^3 \text{ kWh})\left(\dfrac{3.6 \times 10^6 \text{ J}}{1 \text{ kWh}}\right)\left(\dfrac{1 \text{ kcal}}{4180 \text{ J}}\right) = 6.2 \times 10^7 \text{ kcal.}$

19-B13 $V = IR = (866 \text{ A})(0.05 \text{ m})\left(12 \dfrac{\mu\Omega}{m}\right) = 520 \; \mu V.$

19-B14 The volume of metal is unaltered, hence the cross-sectional area has decreased to $\frac{1}{3}$ its original value. From $R = \rho L/A$ we find that the new resistance
is $R' = (2 \; \Omega)(3)/(\frac{1}{3}) = 18 \; \Omega.$

19-B15 $\rho = \dfrac{RA}{L} = \dfrac{(0.414 \; \Omega)[\pi(10^{-3} \text{ m})^2]}{50 \text{ m}} = 2.60 \times 10^{-8} \; \Omega \cdot m.$ From Table 19-1, the metal
is aluminum.

19-B16 $R = \dfrac{\rho L}{A} = \dfrac{(1.59 \times 10^{-8} \; \Omega \cdot m)(20 \times 10^3 \text{ m})}{\pi(0.32 \times 10^{-3} \text{ m})^2} = 989 \; \Omega.$

19-B17 $R_t = 2R_0; \; R_0(1 + \alpha t) = 2R_0; \; 1 + \alpha t = 2; \; t = 1/\alpha = 1/[0.0039 \;(°C)^{-1}] = 256°C.$

19-B18 (a) Hot resistance $= V^2/P = (120 \text{ V})^2/(100 \text{ W}) = 144 \; \Omega.$ (b) $144 \; \Omega$
$= (8 \; \Omega)[1 + (0.009)(°C)^{-1})t]; \; t = 1890°C.$

19-B19 (a) $R = \dfrac{\rho L}{A} = \dfrac{(49 \times 10^{-8} \; \Omega \cdot m)(40 \text{ m})}{\pi(0.4 \times 10^{-3} \text{ m})^2} = 38.99 \; \Omega = 39.0 \; \Omega$

(b) $R_t = R_0(1 + \alpha t) = (38.99 \; \Omega)[1 + 0.00001 \;(°C)^{-1}](50°C) = 39.01 \; \Omega = 39.0 \; \Omega.$
[To three significant figures, the resistance at $50°C$ is the same as the resis-
tance at $0°C.$]

19-B20 $\dfrac{100 \text{ cm}}{500 \text{ mV}} = \dfrac{x}{2 \text{ mV}};\ x = 0.40 \text{ cm} = 4.0 \text{ mm}.$

19-B21 $(a)\ W = I^2Rt = (7 \text{ A})^2(30\ \Omega)(8 \times 3600 \text{ s}) = 42.3 \text{ MJ}.$ (b) Energy density $= (42.3 \text{ MJ})/(2000 \text{ kg}) = 0.021 \text{ MJ/kg}.$

$(c)\ 42.3 \times 10^3 \text{ kJ} = (2000 \text{ kg})\Big(0.20\ \dfrac{\text{kcal}}{\text{kg}\cdot\text{°C}}\Big)\Big(\dfrac{4.18 \text{ kJ}}{1 \text{ kcal}}\Big)(\Delta t);\ \Delta t = 25.3\text{°C}.$ [The very small energy density for storage in hot bricks is to be compared with 33 MJ/kg for combustion of coal (Table 14-3).]

19-B22 $(3200 \text{ kg})/(1700 \text{ kg/m}^3) = 1.88 \text{ m}^3$ for the salt. Adding 10% for the container gives $(1.88 + 0.19) \text{ m}^3 = 2.07 \text{ m}^3.$ Total volume is $1.5(2.07 \text{ m}^3) = L^3;\ L = \text{cube}$ edge $= 1.46 \text{ m}.$

19-B23 $(a)\ \Big(8.13\ \dfrac{\text{J}}{\text{cm}^2\cdot\text{min}}\Big)\Big(\dfrac{1 \text{ kW}}{10^3 \text{ J/s}}\Big)\Big(\dfrac{1 \text{ min}}{60 \text{ s}}\Big)\Big(\dfrac{10^2 \text{ cm}}{1 \text{ m}}\Big)^2 = 1.36 \text{ kW/m}^2,$ about 1 hp/m²

$(b)\ (1.36 \text{ kW/m}^2)(0.67)(0.50)(0.90)A = (205 \text{ kWh})/(9 \text{ h});\ A = 56 \text{ m}^2.$

19-B24 $(5.56 \times 10^{13} \text{ J})/(6.30 \times 10^{10} \text{ kg}) = 882 \text{ J/kg} = 0.000882 \text{ MJ/kg}.$ [This energy density is less than 1% of the value for a lead-acid storage battery. See also Prob. 19-B25. In general, gravitationally stored energy density is mgh/m $= gh = 9.8 \times 10^{-6} \text{ MJ/kg}$ for a height difference of 1 m.]

19-B25 $(a)\ mgh = (20 \times 10^3 \text{ m})(2 \times 10^3 \text{ m})(1.8 \text{ m})(1000 \text{ kg/m}^3)(9.8 \text{ N/kg})(0.9 \text{ m}) = 6.35$ $\times 10^{11} \text{ J} = 6.35 \times 10^5 \text{ MJ}.$ $(b)\ P = W/t = (6.35 \times 10^5 \text{ MJ})(0.50)/(6.25 \times 3600 \text{ s})$ $= 14 \text{ MW}.$ (c) The power available from this tidal energy installation would be less than 1% of the load-leveling power output of the hydroelectric installation of Example 19-9. Tidal energy is unlikely to be a significant factor in the economy.

19-C1 Volume $= (3 \times 10^{-3} \text{ kg})/(19\,300 \text{ kg/m}^3) = 1.55 \times 10^{-7} \text{ m}^3.$ From $R = \rho L/A$, we have $R = \dfrac{\rho L^2}{LA} = \dfrac{\rho L^2}{V};$

$L = \sqrt{\dfrac{R V}{\rho}} = \sqrt{\dfrac{(80\ \Omega)(1.55 \times 10^{-7} \text{ m}^3)}{2.27 \times 10^{-8}\ \Omega\cdot\text{m}}} = 23.4 \text{ m}.$

19-C2 $(a)\ R = \dfrac{\rho m}{\pi^2 r^4 d};$ $(b)\ \dfrac{(11.0 \times 10^{-8}\ \Omega\cdot\text{m})(0.030 \text{ kg})}{\pi^2(10^{-3} \text{ m})^4(7860 \text{ kg/m}^3)} = 0.0425\ \Omega.$

19-C3 $(a)\ R = \dfrac{\rho L}{A} = \dfrac{(94 \times 10^{-8}\ \Omega\cdot\text{m})(1.0000 \text{ m})}{\pi(0.5 \times 10^{-3} \text{ m})^2} = 1.1968\ \Omega.$

$(b)\ \Delta L/L = 4 \times 10^{-4};\ \Delta A/A = -4 \times 10^{-4};$ total fractional change is 8×10^{-4} $= 0.08\%.$ [The change in resistance is $(8 \times 10^{-4})(1.1968\ \Omega) = 8 \times 10^{-4}\ \Omega.$]

19-C4 $5.0\ \Omega = R_0\{1 + [0.0039\ (\text{°C})^{-1}](20\text{°C})\};\ R_0 = 4.638\ \Omega.$
At 75°C, $R = (4.638\ \Omega)\{1 + [0.0039\ (\text{°C})^{-1}](75\text{°C})\} = 5.99\ \Omega = 6.0\ \Omega.$ [It would be only approximately correct to use the initial resistance: $R \approx (5.0\ \Omega)\{1 + [0.0039\ (\text{°C})^{-1}](55\text{°C})\} = 6.07\ \Omega.$ The coefficient $0.0039\ (\text{°C})^{-1}$ is large enough so it is essential to realize that it refers to the resistance at 0°C. A similar requirement was met in the discussion of thermal expansion of gases (p. 307); but for solids the linear expansion coefficients are so small that either the initial or final length can be used without significant error.]

19-C5 $(a)\ P = VI = (120 \text{ V})(3 \text{ A}) = 360 \text{ W}.$ $(b)\ e = (320 \text{ W})/(360 \text{ W}) = 89\%.$
(c) Power lost in Joule heat is $(360 - 320 - 22) \text{ W} = 18 \text{ W};\ I^2R = (3 \text{ A})^2(R)$ $= 18 \text{ W};\ R = 2\ \Omega.$

Chapter 20   Electric Circuits

20-1   Place little + signs at the left end of each of the resistors; place little − signs at the right end of each resistor.

20-2   For the suggested path, $+15 + 24 + 21 + 15 − 75 = 0$.

20-3   Polarization of the cell causes the resistance to increase (gas bubbles are a worse conductor than a liquid or a paste). Also, a "dry" cell tends to dry out with age.

20-4   The terminal voltage is greater than the emf if the battery is being charged (i.e., if charges are being forced through the battery opposite to the direction the emf would tend to send them). In Fig. 20-6 (Example 20-4), each battery's terminal voltage is greater than its emf. The + sign is used in Eq. 20-1 for a battery that is being charged.

20-5   Yes; for instance, when it is short circuited by a wire of zero resistance. The 8 V battery in Fig. 20-37 (Prob. 20-B13) has, by chance, a terminal voltage of 0 V.

20-6   No. The instruments differ electrically, because of the way in which shunts or multipliers are connected.

20-7   A voltmeter has a high-resistance series multiplier; an ammeter has a low-resistance shunt.

20-8   No; the bridge will still be balanced at the same point.

20-9   A potentiometer has two advantages: negligible current drawn from the source that is being measured and the possibility of great precision if the equivalent of a long wire is used in a carefully constructed instrument. The voltmeter is portable, rugged, and quick reading.

20-10   Apply Kirchhoff's second law to the bottom loop. Since the galvanometer current is 0, the IR drop across it is 0; hence $\varepsilon_x − V = 0$, or $\varepsilon_x = V$. In effect, we replace a standard cell by a standard voltmeter; this form of potentiometer has the same advantage as the usual form, in that no current is drawn from the unknown seat of emf.

20-11   The low-resistance voltmeter would draw too much current from the standard cell; electrolysis would permanently change the composition and the emf of the cell.

Multiple Choice

20-12 (*c*);   **20-13** (*b*);   **20-14** (*c*);   **20-15** (*a*);   **20-16** (*a*);   **20-17** (*c*).

Problems

20-A1 $+21$ V $− 12$ V $= 9$ V; P is positive relative to ground.

20-A2 One of several paths is $EACMN$: $+48$ V $+12$ V $= +60$ V; N is positive relative to E. [Paths $EAKHGDBN$ and $EFDBN$ give the same result.]

20-A3 Starting at H, path $HGDPC$ gives -12 V for the potential of C relative to H. [Path $HKAC$ gives the same result: $+15$ V -75 V $+48$ V $= -12$ V.]

20-A4 Using Kirchhoff's first law, we find the current through the 5 Ω resistor to be 4 A to the right. Now $V = IR$ gives 42 V across the 6 Ω resistor, 9 V across the 3 Ω resistor, and 20 V across the 5 Ω resistor.

20-A5 $12 \ \Omega + \frac{1}{10}(200 \ \Omega) = 32 \ \Omega$.

20-A6 In series, $R = 5(10 \ \Omega) = 50 \ \Omega$. In parallel, $R = \frac{1}{5}(10 \ \Omega) = 2 \ \Omega$.

20-A7 (a) 36 Ω; (b) 4 Ω; (c) 18 Ω; (d) 24 Ω in parallel with 12 Ω gives 8 Ω.

20-A8 (a) $(120 \text{ V})/8 = 15$ V. (b) With one bulb removed, there is no IR drop in the rest of the circuit; the PD across the empty socket is 120 V. (c) $IR = (0)R = 0$ V.

20-A9 $V = \varepsilon - Ir = 12.20$ V $- (150 \text{ A})(0.008 \ \Omega) = 11.00$ V.

20-A10 Assume $\varepsilon = 1.5$ V. $R = (1.5 \text{ V})/(30 \text{ A}) = 0.05 \ \Omega$. [We assume the resistance of the ammeter to be negligible because of a very low-resistance shunt. Using an ammeter of insufficient range will result in a damaged or burned-out meter.]

20-A11 $\dfrac{R_4}{200} = \dfrac{31.6}{100}$; $R_4 = 63.2 \ \Omega$.

20-A12 $\dfrac{x}{35 \ \Omega} = \dfrac{100 - x}{15 \ \Omega}$; $x = 70$ cm.

20-A13 $\dfrac{R_x}{25 \text{ cm}} = \dfrac{12 \ \Omega}{75 \text{ cm}}$; $R_x = 4 \ \Omega$.

20-B1 Repeated application of rules for resistances in series and in parallel, as in Example 20-6, gives $R = 10 \ \Omega$.

20-B2 Repeated application of rules for resistances in series and in parallel, as in Example 20-6, gives $R = 10 \ \Omega$.

20-B4 The circuit is equivalent to three 5 Ω resistors in parallel; $R = (5 \ \Omega)/3 = 1.67 \ \Omega$. [See Prob. 20-C17 where simultaneous equations are used to find the equivalent resistance between A and B to be 2.07 Ω.]

20-B5 The net resistance P to Q is easily worked out to be 5 Ω; $I = (20 \text{ V})/(5 \ \Omega) = 4$ A. [The emf and internal resistance of the battery need not be known separately, since the terminal voltage is given in the statement of the problem.]

20-B6 (a) 4 A through 12 Ω; 8 A through 6 Ω; 12 A through 5 Ω. (b) $P = \varepsilon I = (120 \text{ V})(12 \text{ A}) = 1440$ W. (c) Using I^2R for each resistor, we find 192 W in 12 Ω; 284 W in 6 Ω; 720 W in 5 Ω; and 144 W in the 1 Ω internal resistance of the battery. [Check: $(192 + 384 + 720 + 144)$ W $= 1440$ W, which equals the rate of conversion of chemical PE found in part (b).]

20-B7 (a) 1 A through 12 Ω; 2 A through 6 Ω; 3 A through 5 Ω. (b) $P = \varepsilon I = (36 \text{ V})(3 \text{ A}) = 108$ W. (c) Using I^2R for each resistor, we find 12 W in 12 Ω; 24 W in 6 Ω; 45 W in 5 Ω; and 27 W in the internal resistance of the battery. [Check: $(12 + 24 + 45 + 27)$ W $= 108$ W, which equals the rate of conversion of chemical PE found in part (b).]

20-B8 Straightforward application of formulas for series and parallel combinations (as in Example 20-6) gives $(6 + 3.6 + 0.4) \ \Omega = 10 \ \Omega$ for the net resistance seen by the battery. Hence $I = (20 \text{ V})/(10 \ \Omega) = 2$ A. [As an added check, the Joule heating (I^2R) in the six circuit elements totals 40 W, which also equals

εI. See also Prob. 20-C5, in which a heavy wire is connected between points A and B.]

20-B9 The parallel combination is equivalent to 2 Ω, so the current through each battery is $I = \dfrac{\text{net } \varepsilon}{\text{net } R} = \dfrac{80 \text{ V} - 14 \text{ V}}{(2 + 1 + 5 + 3)} = 6$ A. The PD across the parallel combination is $(6 \text{ A})(2 \text{ Ω}) = 12$ V. Now we find the answers to the questions: (a) $P = V^2/R = (12 \text{ V})^2/(6 \text{ Ω}) = 24$ W. (b) $I = 6$ A (see above). (c) V_{80} $= \varepsilon - Ir = 80 \text{ V} - (6 \text{ A})(3 \text{ Ω}) = 62$ V; $V_{14} = \varepsilon + Ir = 14 \text{ V} + (6 \text{ A})(1 \text{ Ω}) = 20$ V. [A power check is instructive. In this circuit, chemical PE is transformed into electric energy at the rate of 480 W in the 80 V battery; the 14 V battery is being charged and is *gaining* chemical PE at the rate of 84 W. The net energy transformation is at the rate of 480 W − 84 W = 396 W; this checks with the total of the six I^2R losses in the circuit (including the batteries' internal resistances).]

20-B10 $I = (9 \text{ V})/(900 \text{ Ω}) = 0.01$ A. The IR drop across the 300 Ω resistor is $(0.01 \text{ A}) \times (300 \text{ Ω}) = 3$ V, so A is $+3$ V relative to ground. Similarly, B is -6 V relative to ground.

20-B11 (a) $I = (12 \text{ V})/(1000 \text{ Ω}) = 0.012$ A. $V = \varepsilon - Ir = 12.0 \text{ V} - (0.012 \text{ A})(100 \text{ Ω})$ $= 10.8$ V. (b) $V_A = (0.012 \text{ A})(300 \text{ Ω}) = +3.6$ V relative to ground.

20-B12 (a) $6.20 \text{ V} + 0.20 \text{ V} + 12.45 \text{ V} + 0.60 \text{ V} = 19.45$ V. (b) $V = \varepsilon - Ir$; 19.45 V $= 21.00 \text{ V} - (20 \text{ A})r$; $r = 0.0775$ Ω.

20-B13 The current through the circuit is $I = (\text{net } \varepsilon)/(\text{net } R) = (24 \text{ V})/(6 \text{ Ω}) = 4$ A, counterclockwise around the circuit. Use $V = \varepsilon \pm Ir$ to find the terminal voltages: (a) $20 \text{ V} - (4 \text{ A})(1 \text{ Ω}) = 16$ V; (b) $8 \text{ V} - (4 \text{ A})(2 \text{ Ω}) = 0$ V; (c) $2 \text{ V} - (4 \text{ A})(2 \text{ Ω}) = -6$ V; (d) $6 \text{ V} + (4 \text{ A})(1 \text{ Ω}) = 10$ V. [The 8 V battery is an example of a battery that has an emf but whose terminal voltage is 0. The 2 V battery's terminal voltage is in the opposite direction from its emf. If we start at the upper left corner and go from a to b to c to d to a, the total change in potential is $(-16 + 0 + 6 + 10)$ V = 0, as it should be according to Kirchhoff's second law.]

20-B14 The net emf is now $(20 - 8 + 2 - 6)$ V = 8 V; $I = (8 \text{ V})/(6 \text{ Ω}) = 1\frac{1}{3}$ A. The terminal voltages are (a) $20 \text{ V} - (\frac{4}{3} \text{ A})(1 \text{ Ω}) = 18\frac{2}{3}$ V; (b) $8 \text{ V} + (\frac{4}{3} \text{ A})(2 \text{ Ω})$ $= 10\frac{2}{3}$ V; (c) $2 \text{ V} - (\frac{4}{3} \text{ A})(2 \text{ Ω}) = -\frac{2}{3}$ V (opposite to the battery's emf); (d) $6 \text{ V} + (\frac{4}{3} \text{ A})(1 \text{ Ω}) = 7\frac{1}{3}$ V.

20-B15 The current through each cell is $(2.1 \text{ V} - 1.5 \text{ V})/(2 \text{ Ω} + 1 \text{ Ω}) = 0.2$ A. Cell 1 is being charged: $V = \varepsilon + Ir = 1.5 \text{ V} + (0.2 \text{ A})(2 \text{ Ω}) = 1.9$ V. Cell 2 is being discharged: $V = \varepsilon - Ir = 2.1 \text{ V} - (0.2 \text{ A})(1 \text{ Ω}) = 1.9$ V. [As expected, the terminal voltages of the cells are equal, since they are connected in parallel (as seen by a high-resistance voltmeter that might be connected across the combination).]

20-B16 Hot resistance of each bulb is $V^2/P = (120 \text{ V})^2/(100 \text{ W}) = 144$ Ω. Each bulb's new resistance is 72 Ω, and when in series their combined resistance is 144 Ω. The total power is now $V^2/R = (120 \text{ V})^2/(144 \text{ Ω}) = 100$ W. [If connected in parallel across 120 V, the total power would have been (100 + 100) W = 200 W.]

20-B17 (a) $V_K = (2 \times 10^{-3} \text{ Ω})(3 \times 10^{-3} \text{ A}) = +6$ V; the cathode is $+6$ V relative to ground. (b) $V_P = 400 \text{ V} - (50 \times 10^3 \text{ Ω})(3 \times 10^{-3} \text{ A}) = +250$ V; the plate is $+250$ V relative to ground and $+244$ V relative to the cathode. (c) The grid is at 0 V, i.e., at ground potential, and is therefore -6 V relative to the cathode. [Since there is no grid current, there is no IR drop in the 10^6 Ω resistor.]

20-B18 Use the circuit of Fig. 20-21, with a series multiplier R. 10 V = (0.001 A) $\times (R + 100\ \Omega)$; $R = 9900\ \Omega$.

20-B19 Use the circuit of Fig. 20-21, with a series multiplier R. 20 V = (0.005 A) $\times (R + 50\ \Omega)$; $R = 3950\ \Omega$.

20-B20 Use the circuit of Fig. 20-20, with a shunt resistor R. The PD across the galvanometer movement is (0.001 A)(100 Ω) = 0.100 V. The same PD is across the shunt. The current through the shunt is 5 A $-$ 0.001 A = 4.999 A. Hence R = (0.100 V)/(4.999 A) = 0.0200 Ω.

20-B21 Use the circuit of Fig. 20-20 with a shunt resistor R. The PD across the milliammeter is (0.005 A)(40 Ω) = 0.200 V. The same PD is across the shunt. The current through the shunt is (2 A $-$ 0.005 A) = 1.995 A. Hence R = (0.200 V)/(1.995 A) = 0.1003 Ω.

20-B22 (*a*) The resistance of the ammeter is of no consequence for this part. There is 1.00 A through the parallel combination of the voltmeter and R. The PD across the voltmeter is 40.0 V (the voltmeter surely indicates correctly its own PD), and the current through the voltmeter is (40.0 V)/(2000 Ω) = 0.020 A. This leaves 1.00 A $-$ 0.02 A = 0.98 A through R. Hence R = (40.0 V)/(0.98 A) = 40.82 Ω. (*b*) The resistance of the voltmeter is of no consequence for this part. The IR drop across the ammeter is (0.020 Ω)(1.00 A) $-$ 0.020 V. The PD across R is 40.00 V $-$ 0.020 V = 39.98 V. Hence R = (39.98 V)/(1.00 A) = 39.98 Ω. [The naive result (40.00 V)/(1.00 A) = 40.00 Ω is incorrect for both connections, but is much closer to the true R (in this case) when connection (*b*) is used.]

20-B23 A and B are both positive relative to C. The currents are easily found: Through the bottom branch, I = (48 V)/(16 Ω) = 3 A; through the top branch, I = (48 V)/(30 Ω) = 1.6 A. (*a*) Take a Kirchhoff trip from C to A: V_A = (3 A)(11 Ω) = +33 V, or take a trip from C through the battery to D then to A: V_A = +48 V $-$ (3 A)(5 Ω) = +33 V. (*b*) Similarly, V_B = (1.6 A)(20 Ω) = +32 V. (*c*) The current would be from high potential to low potential, i.e., from A to B. (*d*) R/(10 Ω) = (11 Ω)/(5 Ω); R = 22 Ω. [It would be incorrect to calculate the current from A to B through an assumed galvanometer resistance R_g by using I_g = (33 V $-$ 32 V)/R_g, for the currents through the arms of the bridge would be altered. See Prob. 20-C17.]

20-B24 R/(10 Ω) = (11 Ω)/(20 Ω); R = 5.5 Ω.

20-B25 $R_{50} = R_0\{1 + [0.0052\ (°C)^{-1}](50°C)\}$ = 1.260R_0. $\dfrac{x}{100 - x} = \dfrac{1.260R_0}{R_0}$; x = 55.75 cm. Hence the contact should be moved 5.75 cm to the right.

20-B26 L/(11.000 m) = (1.0183 V)/(1.5604 V); L = 7.178 m. The precision of the potentiometer is such that slide-rule accuracy is not adequate. In this problem, the standard cell's internal resistance is of no consequence, since there is no current through it. Nor is the slide wire's resistance of any consequence, except for the assumption that the wire is of uniform cross section.

20-C1 Total power = 160 W; $R = V^2/P$ = (120 V)^2/(160 W) $\approx$ 90 Ω.

20-C2 The parallel combination of three resistors is equivalent to 2 Ω; then the parallel combination of 20 Ω and (3 + 2) Ω is 4 Ω. The PD across the 20 Ω resistor and also across the 5 Ω resistor is (60 A)(4 Ω) = 240 V. Continued application of Ohm's law gives 12 A through the 20 Ω resistor, 48 A (by subtraction) through the 3 Ω resistor and also through the 2 Ω combination. V = (48 A)(2 Ω) = 96 V across each of the three resistors in the parallel combination, hence I = (96 V)/(4 Ω) = 24 A through the 4 Ω resistor.

20-C3 Refer to the solution of Prob. 20-C2, where we found V across the 6 Ω resistor to be 96 V. $P = V^2/R = (96\text{ V})^2/(6\ \Omega) = 1536$ W.

20-C4 Using $R_p = \dfrac{R_1 R_2}{R_1 + R_2}$ for resistors in parallel, the resistance from A to B is $\dfrac{(2+R)(3)}{(2+R)+3} + 2$. Equate this expression to R and solve, obtaining $R = 4\ \Omega$.

20-C5 The 6 Ω resistor connected at A is shorted out and the shortcircuit carries all the current from the battery. The remaining four 6 Ω resistors combine to give $1/R = 1/6 + 1/9$; $R = 3.6\ \Omega$. The battery sees a net R of $(3.6 + 0.4)\ \Omega$ $= 4\ \Omega$; $I = (20\text{ V})/(4\ \Omega) = 5$ A.

20-C6 $\varepsilon - 10r = 110$, also $\varepsilon - 30r = 106$. Solve simultaneously: $\varepsilon = 112$ V, $r = 0.2\ \Omega$.

20-C7 The voltmeter's resistance is $(25\text{ V})/(0.025\text{ A}) = 1000\ \Omega$. The current I through the voltmeter is $(12.00\text{ V})/(1000\ \Omega) = 0.0120$ A (this current is delivered by the battery). From $V = \varepsilon - Ir$, we have $12.00\text{ V} = 12.24\text{ V} - (0.0120\text{ A})r$ $r = 20\ \Omega$.

20-C8 In each connection, $I = V/R$ where V is the terminal voltage (as read correctly by the voltmeter) and R is 200 Ω or (later) the parallel combination of 200 Ω and 200 Ω, i.e., 100 Ω. We now write $V = \varepsilon - Ir$ for the two situations;
$$\varepsilon - \left(\frac{1.5200}{200}\right)r = 1.5200; \quad \varepsilon - \left(\frac{1.5150}{100}\right)r = 1.5150.$$ Solving simultaneously gives $\varepsilon = 1.525$ V, $r = 0.662\ \Omega$.

20-C9 (a) $P = V^2/R$ becomes $P = V^2 G$; $G = P/V^2 = (1200\text{ W})/(200\text{ V})^2 = 0.03$ S.
(b) $G = G_1 + G_2 + G_3 + \cdots$.

20-C10 It is convenient to set up three equations for the total resistance: (1) $r + R = \varepsilon/I_1$; (2) $r + 2R = \varepsilon/I_2$; (3) $r + \frac{1}{2}R = \varepsilon/I_3$. Subtract (1) from (2), obtaining $R = \varepsilon(1/I_2 - 1/I_1)$; subtract (3) from (2), obtaining $\frac{3}{2}R = \varepsilon(1/I_2 - 1/I_3)$. Eliminate R; ε cancels out, and we obtain $2I_1 I_2 + I_1 I_3 = 3 I_2 I_3$.

20-C11 (a) The first measurement gives $R_1 = 2R_y$; the second measurement gives $R_2 = \frac{1}{2}R_y + R_x$. Eliminate R_y, obtaining $R_x = R_2 - \frac{1}{4}R_1$.   (b) $R_x = 17\ \Omega$ $- \frac{1}{4}(40\ \Omega) = 7\ \Omega$; this is an adequate ground.

20-C12 (a) $V = \varepsilon - Ir$; here $I = (12.60\text{ V})/(5.08\ \Omega) = 2.4803$ A; $V = 12.60$ V $- (2.4803\text{ A})(0.080\ \Omega) = 12.402$ V. Alternatively, $I = V/(5.00\text{ A})$; $V = \varepsilon - Ir$ becomes $V = 12.60 - [(V/5.00)](0.080)$; solve for V, obtaining $V = 12.402$ V.
(b) $I = 25 + V/5.00$; $V = \varepsilon - Ir$ becomes $V = 12.60 - [(25 + V)/5.00](0.080)$; solve for V, obtaining $V = 10.433$ V.   [This problem realistically illustrates why the headlights dim when the starter motor is used.]

20-C13 First find the shunt resistance. 49.99 A goes through the shunt and 0.01 A through the meter. The PDs are the same: $(49.99\text{ A})R = (0.01\text{ A})(40\ \Omega)$; $R = 8.002 \times 10^{-3}\ \Omega$. Using $R = \rho L/A$, we have
$$A = \frac{\rho L}{R} = \frac{(49 \times 10^{-8}\ \Omega\cdot\text{m})(0.10\text{ m})}{8.00 \times 10^{-3}\ \Omega} = 6.13 \times 10^{-6}\ \text{m}^2 = 6.13\ \text{mm}^2$$

20-C14 The potential of B relative to E is found by three paths. $EFAB$: $+(3\text{ A})(2\ \Omega)$ $+ (3\text{ A})(1\ \Omega) + 7\text{ V} = +16$ V; EB: $+(2\text{ A})(8\ \Omega) = +16$ V; $EDCB$: $-(5\text{ A})(3\ \Omega)$ $+ 36\text{ V} - (5\text{ A})(1\ \Omega) = +16$ V.

20-C15 The set of three equations are different (each coefficient for I_1 and I_2 is reversed in sign). The solutions are $I_1 = +3$ A, $I_2 = -5$ A, $I_3 = +2$ A. These currents have the same physical significance as the solution in the text.

20-C16 Joule heat is given by $I^2 R$ in the five resistors. The powers are found from the currents in Fig. 20-45; total $I^2 R = (9 + 18 + 32 + 25 + 75)\text{ W} = 159$ W.
[Check: The 36 V battery is being discharged; $I = (36\text{ V})(5\text{ A}) = 180$ W. The 7 V battery is being charged; $I = (7\text{ V})(3\text{ A}) = 21$ W. Net conversion of chemical PE is at the rate of $(180 - 21)\text{ W} = 159$ W.]

20-C17   (a) The problem can be solved by the direct
method (six unknown currents) or by the loop
method (three loops). The resulting currents
are shown in the figure. The current from
the battery is 75 A.   (b) The equivalent resistance between A and B is (155 V)/(75 A)
= 2.07 Ω.   [The potentials (relative to
ground) are V_A = +155 V, V_B = 0, V_C
= +100 V, and V_D = +75 V. As a check, it is
seen that $V = IR$ for each of the five resistors.
A power check is successful; the power delivered by the battery is (155 V)(75 A) = 11 625 W;

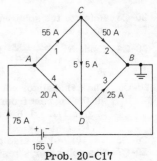

Prob. 20-C17

the sum of the I^2R values for the five resistors is also 11 625 W. If the 5 Ω
resistor were not present, we would have a simple circuit, with 3 Ω in parallel
with 7 Ω, yielding a combined resistance of 2.10 Ω. The added current path
from C to D must make the total resistance less than 2.10 Ω, unless by chance
the bridge is balanced (which is not true here). In this problem, 2.07 Ω is,
indeed, less than 2.10 Ω.

20-C18   (a) 0 A through the 10 V battery; 3 A through the 4 V battery; 3 A through
the 13 V battery; (b) 10 V.   [The 13 V battery is being discharged; the
4 V battery is being charged, and, as it happens, the 10 V battery is "floating"
with no current through it. Even if this problem is not assigned, it is instructive to show the consistency of the answers. Each battery's terminal voltage
is 10 V, as calculated from $V = \varepsilon + Ir$, and Kirchhoff's first law is satisfied
at each junction point. Also, a power check shows a total of 27 W of Joule
heating (from the sum of the I^2R values), and this equals the net transformation of energy in the seats of emf (39 W delivered by the 13 V battery, 12 W
absorbed by the 4 V battery).]

20-C19   (a) Use three unknown currents, or two Kirchhoff loops. The currents are:
1 A through the 10 V battery, 2.5 A through the 12 V battery; 3.5 A through
the 2 Ω resistor.   (b) PD = (3.5 A)(2 Ω) = 7 V.   [Check: For the 10 V
battery, V = 10 V − (1 A)(3 Ω) = 7 V; for the 12 V battery, V = 12 V − (2.5 A)
× (2 Ω) = 7 V. A power check is successful: each battery is delivering power
εI; (10 V)(1 A) + (12 V)(2.5 A) = 40 W. This is accounted for by the I^2R los-
ses: $(1 \text{ A})^2 (3 \text{ Ω}) + (2.5 \text{ A})^2 (2 \text{ Ω}) + (3.5 \text{ A})^2 (2 \text{ Ω}) = (3 + 12.5 + 24.5) \text{ W} = 40 \text{ W}.]$

20-C20   (a) There is no current through the 6 Ω resistor or the 12 V battery. The
current through the outer loop is everywhere the same, given by (18 V + 36 V)/
(2 Ω + 8 Ω + 3 Ω + 4 Ω + 1 Ω) = 3 A. Now take a Kirchhoff trip from X to Y
by either of the two paths, with the result that Y is +9 V relative to X.
(b) With the 7 Ω resistor between X and Y, this becomes a standard Kirchhoff
law problem with three unknown currents or two loops. The current through
the 7 Ω resistor works out to be 0.416 A, from Y to X.

20-C21   (a) $I = \varepsilon/(R + r)$; $P = I^2R = \varepsilon^2 R/(R + r)^2 = \varepsilon^2 R (R + r)^{-2}$.   (b) Use the
rule for differentiating a product (Appendix E, p. 797), to obtain dP/dR
$= \varepsilon^2 R(-2)(R + r)^{-3} + \varepsilon^2 (R + r)^{-2}$. This is 0 when $R = r$. Maximum power
transfer thus requires the load resistance to be equal to the internal resis-
tance of the battery; this is an example of "impedance matching."   (c) In
time Δt the energy dissipated as heat in the battery is $I^2 r\, \Delta t$, and the energy
delivered to the load is $I^2 R\, \Delta t$. If $r = R$ these energies are equal and $I^2 R\, \Delta t$
is half the total chemical PE which has been transformed.

Chapter 21   Electromagnetism

Questions

21-1 On the magnitude of charge and velocity, and on the direction of motion relative to the direction of the magnetic field.

21-2 A compass points in the direction of the field. A moving test charge experiences no force when moving in the direction of the field.

21-3 $T = \dfrac{N}{C \cdot (m/s)} \left(\text{same as } \dfrac{N \cdot s}{C \cdot m} \right);$ also $T = \dfrac{N}{A \cdot m}.$

21-4 Iron and other ferromagnetic substances have the ability to form domains.

21-5 No, if we consider the magnetism associated with electron spin to be due to "motion of electric charge." This interpretation may come perilously close to modelitis; electron spin is essentially a nonclassical phenomenon. The changing B-field in an e-m wave is caused by a changing E-field, which in turn was caused by motion of electric charge at the point of origin of the wave.

21-6 Each piece is another magnet, for either type of cut.

21-7 The conventional current is downward, and the right-hand rule (Fig. 21-14) shows that the field at a point east of the flagpole is horizontal, toward the south.

21-8 The conventional current is counterclockwise, as viewed from above. The B-field is upward (see Fig. 21-17).

21-9 (*a*) Right;   (*b*) up;   (*c*) left.   [In (*c*), the current segment ($q\mathbf{v}$) is from B to A; **B** is upward, away from the north pole of the magnet. Thus $\mathbf{F} = q\mathbf{v} \times \mathbf{B}$ gives a force to the left.]

21-10 The field at P is to the right; the force on the wire is upward.

21-11 $q\mathbf{E}$ is the electrostatic force, $q\mathbf{v} \times \mathbf{B}$ is the magnetic force.

21-12 The declination gives the navigator a correction for his compass direction.

21-13 Upward and to the north (see Fig. 21-25).

21-14 Use a current-carrying coil such as shown in Fig. 21-20*c* or Fig. 21-33.

21-15 A charged particle in the solar wind is moving at high speed and is equivalent to a current segment. A magnetic field is associated with the moving charges (Fig. 21-12). Since the solar wind is not constant, the magnetic effects are erratic and are called "magnetic storms."

21-16 On the strength and orientation of the magnetic field, the length of the conductor, and its speed.

21-17 As trains pound over the bridge, domains in the iron to the bridge are agitated, and those already aligned with the earth's magnetic field tend to grow, as in Fig. 21-21. As described, the girder is approximately aligned with the earth's magnetic field (for a point in the U.S.), so it becomes magnetized.

21-18 Magnetic induction is B, which is flux per unit area.

21-19 Conventional current in the falling rod must be toward the reader to give rise to an upward force (use $\mathbf{F} = q\mathbf{v} \times \mathbf{B}$). Electrons flow away from the reader.

21-20 (a) Electrons, carried toward the south, represent a conventional $q\mathbf{v}$ directed to the north. Only the vertical (downward) component of B is effective. From $\mathbf{F} = q\mathbf{v} \times \mathbf{B}$, we find **F** to be toward the west. The electrons accumulate on the right front hubcap (west end of the axle).   (b) Greater; $\sin \theta$ in the cross product is now 1 (if the dip is 70°).

21-21 No; the energy to run the motor comes from a battery or other seat of emf. The motor *will* lose effectiveness if the magnets are not truly permanent.

Multiple Choice

21-22 (b);   **21-23** (a);   **21-24** (b);   **21-25** (c);   **21-26** (a);   **21-27** (a).

Problems

21-A1 $B = F/qv = (8 \times 10^{-8}$ N$)/(1.60 \times 10^{-10}$ C$)(10^3$ m/s$) = 0.5$ T.   [Throughout the Solutions Manual, we give magnetic field strength in teslas (T), equivalent to N per C·m/s and to N/A·m.]

21-A2 $F = Bqv = (0.3$ T$)(1.60 \times 10^{-19}$ C$)(0.02 \times 3 \times 10^8$ m/s$) = 2.88 \times 10^{-13}$ N.

21-A3 $F = Bqv = (6 \times 10^{-5}$ T$)(10^{-11}$ C$)(250$ m/s$) = 1.5 \times 10^{-13}$ N.

21-A4 $F = BIl = (1.2$ T$)(2500$ A$)(0.05$ m$) = 150$ N. Yes, a strong man could easily supply this much force.

21-A5 $B = k'2I/R = (10^{-7}$ N/A$^2)(2)(15$ A$)/(0.05$ m$) = 6 \times 10^{-5}$ T.

21-A6 $F = BIl$; $I = F/Bl = (240$ N$)/(10^3$ T$)(0.3$ m$) = 0.8$ A.

21-A7 Horizontal component $B_h = (0.60 \times 10^{-4}$ T$)\cos 60° = 0.30 \times 10^{-4}$ T.

21-A8 $B = k'2\pi I/R$; 5×10^{-5} T $= (10^{-7}$ N/A$^2)(2\pi I)/(0.3$ m$)$; $I = 23.9$ A.

21-A9 $\varepsilon = Blv = (0.6$ T$)(0.03$ m$)(5$ m/s$) = 0.09$ V $= 90$ mV.   [It is assumed that B is perpendicular to the rod.]

21-A10 $\varepsilon = Blv = (0.06$ T$)(0.05$ m$)(4$ m/s$) = 0.012$ V $= 12$ mV.

21-A11 Use the vertical component of the earth's field (Fig. 21-27). $\Phi = BA$ $= (0.54 \times 10^{-4}$ T$)(0.3$ m$)(0.5$ m$) = 8.1 \times 10^{-6}$ Wb.

21-A12 $\varepsilon = \Delta\Phi/\Delta t = [-20$ Wb $- (+30$ Wb$)]/(0.4$ s$) = -125$ V.   [The $-$ sign has no particular significance for this problem.]

21-B1 (a) $F = qvB = (1.60 \times 10^{-19}$ C$)(3 \times 10^8$ m/s$)(1.9$ T$) = 9.12 \times 10^{-11}$ N.   (b) The weight of the proton (when at rest) is $(1.67 \times 10^{-27}$ kg$)(9.8$ N/kg$) = 1.64 \times 10^{-26}$ N. The ratio of magnetic force to gravitational force is 5.57×10^{15}. [Gravitational forces are negligible in the synchrotron.]

21-B2 $B = F/qv = (8 \times 10^{-13}$ N$)/(1.60 \times 10^{-19}$ C$)(1.96 \times 10^7$ m/s$) = 0.255$ T.

21-B3 (a) $F = qvB = (1.60 \times 10^{-19}$ C$)(3 \times 10^7$ m/s$)(0.2$ T$) = 9.6 \times 10^{-13}$ N. (b) $a = F/m = (9.6 \times 10^{-13}$ N$)/(2 \times 1.67 \times 10^{-27}$ kg$) = 2.87 \times 10^{14}$ m/s^2. (c) From $a = v^2/R$, we have $R = v^2/a = (3 \times 10^7$ m/s$)^2/(2.87 \times 10^{14}$ m/s$^2)$ $= 3.13$ m.   [In symbols, it turns out that $R = mv/qB$. This *result* is correct even for relativistic speeds, though the use of $a = v^2/R$ is valid only for nonrelativistic speeds.]

21-B4 (a) $F = qvB = (1.60 \times 10^{-19}$ C$)(6 \times 10^7$ m/s$)(8 \times 10^{-4}$ T$) = 7.68 \times 10^{-15}$ N.

(b) From $F = \dfrac{mv^2}{R}$, we have

$$R = \frac{mv^2}{F} = \frac{(9.11 \times 10^{-31} \text{ kg})(6 \times 10^7 \text{ m/s})^2}{7.68 \times 10^{-15} \text{ N}} = 0.427 \text{ m.}$$

Relativity effects depend on v^2/c^2; here $v/c = 0.2$ and $v^2/c^2 = 0.04$.]

21-B5 (a) The electric force on the (negative) electron is downward, given by qE. The magnetic force is upward, given by qvB. For balance, $qE = qvB$; $v = E/B$ = (1500 V/m)/(0.3 T) = 5000 m/s.   (b) The electron represents a conventional current toward the west. $\mathbf{F} = q\mathbf{v} \times \mathbf{B}$ shows that to have an upward force, $\mathbf{B}$ must be horizontal, toward the south.   [It is interesting that the charge q cancels out of the equation $v = E/B$ for the velocity selector.]

21-B6 (a) B is downward (use the right-hand rule shown in Fig. 21-14).   (b) For N turns,

$$B = Nk'\frac{2\pi I}{R} = (20)\left(10^{-7}\,\frac{\text{N}}{\text{A}^2}\right)\frac{(2\pi)(0.2 \text{ A})}{(0.06 \text{ m})} = 4.19 \times 10^{-5} \text{ T.}$$

(c) This is somewhat weaker than the earth's field shown in Fig. 21-27, which has magnitude $\sqrt{(5.4)^2 + (1.8)^2} \times 10^{-5} \text{ T} = 5.7 \times 10^{-5} \text{ T.}$

21-B7 $B = k'\dfrac{2\pi I}{R} = \left(10^{-7}\,\dfrac{\text{N}}{\text{A}^2}\right)\dfrac{(2\pi)(10^{-4} \text{ A})}{(0.5 \times 10^{-10} \text{ m})} = 1.26 \text{ T.}$ [It would require a strong laboratory electromagnet to produce a field of 1.26 T.]

21-B8 $I = (6 \times 10^{20} \times 1.60 \times 10^{-19})$ C/s = 96 A. The magnetic induction at the test segment is given by Eq. 21-7:

$$B = k'\frac{2I}{R} = \left(10^{-7}\,\frac{\text{N}}{\text{A}^2}\right)\frac{(2)(96 \text{ A})}{0.24 \text{ m}} = 8 \times 10^{-5} \text{ T}$$

Now use Eq. 21-4': $F = I\Delta l B = (4 \text{ A})(0.05 \text{ m})(8 \times 10^{-5} \text{ T}) = 1.6 \times 10^{-5} \text{ N}$ = 16 μN, toward the west.   [The direction of $\mathbf{B}$ is found from the right-hand rule (Fig. 21-14); the conventional current of 96 A is downward, so $\mathbf{B}$ at the segment is horizontal, toward the north. The conventional $q\mathbf{v}$ in the test segment is upward. Thus, in $\mathbf{F} = q\mathbf{v} \times \mathbf{B}$, $\mathbf{v}$ is upward, $\mathbf{B}$ is to the north, and $\mathbf{F}$ is toward the west. Another viewpoint is to note that the unlike currents repel each other (p. 480).]

21-B9 (a) To be perpendicular to B, the wire must be east-west.   (b) The magnitude of B is found from the components in Fig. 21-27 to be about 5.7×10^{-5} T. $F = BI\Delta l = (5.7 \times 10^{-5} \text{ T})(30 \text{ A})(0.01 \text{ m}) \approx 17 \mu$N.

21-B10 (a) A discussion similar to that on p. 480 for the attraction of like currents shows that unlike currents repel each other.   (b) B due to one wire is $k'(2I)/R = (10^{-7} \text{ N/A}^2)(2)(100 \text{ A})/(0.01 \text{ m}) = 2 \times 10^{-3}$ T. Hence $F = BI\Delta l$ = $(2 \times 10^{-3} \text{ T})(100 \text{ A})(0.01 \text{ m}) = 2 \times 10^{-3}$ N.

21-B11 $\varepsilon = Blv = (6 \times 10^{-5} \text{ T})(10 \text{ m})(8 \times 10^3 \text{ m/s}) = 4.8 \text{ V.}$ [Above the north magnetic pole, the earth's magnetic field is directed downward (Fig. 21-25).]

21-B12 $\varepsilon = N\dfrac{\Delta\Phi}{\Delta t} = NA\dfrac{\Delta B}{\Delta t}$; $0.05 \text{ V} = \dfrac{200(\pi)(0.10 \text{ m})^2 B}{0.040 \text{ s}}$; $B = 3.18 \times 10^{-4}$ T.   [Here $\Delta B = B$, since the final $B = 0$.]

21-B13 $\varepsilon = \Delta\Phi/\Delta t = (0.05 \text{ Wb/m}^2)(\pi)(0.05 \text{ m})^2/(200 \times 10^{-6} \text{ s}) = 1.963 \text{ V.}$ $I = \varepsilon/R$ = (1.936 V)/(4 Ω) = 0.491 A.

21-B14 $\varepsilon = N(\Delta\Phi/\Delta t) = NA(\Delta B/\Delta t) = (50)(\pi)(0.10 \text{ m})^2(80 \text{ T/s}) = 126 \text{ V.}$

21-B15 (a) From $\varepsilon = Blv$, $v = \varepsilon/Bl = (72 \times 10^{-6} \text{ V})/(0.02 \text{ T})(3 \times 10^{-3} \text{ m}) = 1.2 \text{ m/s.}$ (b) The sign of the induced emf is independent of the sign of the ions in the blood. $\mathbf{F} = q\mathbf{v} \times \mathbf{B}$ shows that positive ions would be forced upward, negative ions would be forced downward. These effects are both equivalent to an upward conventional current.   [An alert student may compare this to the

95

Hall effect (Fig. 21-11) in which the sign of charge carriers *does* affect the sign of the generated PD. The difference is that for blood flow we know the direction of v, whereas for electric current as in the Hall effect we only know the product qv.]

21-B16 A should be made negative.   [A forward force, given by $q\mathbf{v} \times \mathbf{B}$, requires $\mathbf{v}$ to be upward, from B to A, and the conventional current must be upward. This can also be considered in relation to Prob. 21-B11, using Lenz's law.]

21-C1 $\varepsilon = \dfrac{NA\,\Delta B}{\Delta t}$; $I = \dfrac{\varepsilon}{R} = \dfrac{NA\,\Delta B}{R\,\Delta t}$; $I\Delta t = \Delta Q = \dfrac{NA\,\Delta B}{R}$. Hence, $\Delta Q = (60)(\pi)(0.025\text{ m})^2$
$\times (0.8\text{ T})/(5 \times 10^{-3}\ \Omega) = 18.8$ C.   [The time interval Δt cancels out.]

21-C2 The induced emf is proportional to the component of **B** that is perpendicular to the motion. Thus $\varepsilon = (B\cos\alpha)lv$. The current is ε/R. The force on the current-carrying rod is proportional to the component of **B** that is perpendicular to the rod, i.e., to $B\cos\alpha$. Thus the general formula $F = BIl$ becomes $F = (B\cos\alpha)\left[\dfrac{B\cos\alpha\, lv}{R}\right]l$; equate this to $mg\sin\alpha$ and solve for v. If $\alpha = 0$ the solution gives $v = 0$ (a reasonable result). If **B** is reversed in direction B^2 is the same and the magnetic force still opposes the downhill motion (illustrating Lenz's law).

21-C3 (a) $Blv = (0.5\text{ T})(\cos 30°)(0.3\text{ m})(0.4\text{ m/s}) = 0.0520$ V. With $\mathbf{v}$ to the right and **B** downward, $q\mathbf{v} \times \mathbf{B}$ is directed from D to A, and the induced current is in the direction $DABCD$. The rod acts like a generator with the A end positive.
(b) $I = \varepsilon/R = (0.0520\text{ V})/(0.002\ \Omega) = 26.0$ A.   (c) $F = BIl = (0.5\text{ T})(\cos 30°)$
$\times (26.0\text{ A})(0.30\text{ m}) = 3.38$ N. The force must be applied toward the right.
(d) $P = Fv = (3.38\text{ N})(0.40\text{ m/s}) = 1.35$ W.   (e) $I^2R = (26.0\text{ A})^2(0.002\ \Omega)$
$= 1.35$ W.   (f) The answers to parts (d) and (e) are equal by the law of conservation of energy; the rod's KE is not changing, nor is its PE. All the work done by the muscles must appear as thermal energy in the rod.
[This problem is a numerical version of Example 21-6. The induced current, from D to A, is acted on by the vertical component of B. From $q\mathbf{v} \times \mathbf{B}$, with $\mathbf{v}$ from D to A, and **B** downward, this force on the rod is to the left, opposing the applied force to the right. This illustrates Lenz's law.]

21-C4 (a) The magnitude of ε is $N(d\Phi/dt) = NA\,(dB/dt) = (200)(0.5\text{ m})^2(0.01 - 0.012t + 0.0003t^2)$. Thus, $\varepsilon = 0.50 - 0.60t + 0.015t^2$; at $t = 0$, the magnitude of ε is 0.50 V.   (b) ε has a turning point when $d\varepsilon/dt = 0$; $0 = -0.60 + 0.03t$;
$t = 20$ s.   (c) Substituting $t = 20$ s into the expression for ε gives 5.50 V for the magnitude of ε at the turning point.   [The extremum for $|\varepsilon|$ is a minimum; since ε is a polynomial, $|\varepsilon|$ tends to infinity for large values of t, if the given expression for B remains valid for all time.]

21-C5 (a) For half of one side, $B = \displaystyle\int_{\phi = \pi/2}^{\phi = \pi/4} \left(-\dfrac{k'I}{a/2}\right)\sin\phi\,d\phi = \left(\dfrac{k'I}{a/2}\right)\left(\dfrac{\sqrt{2}}{2} - 0\right)$; total
$B = 8\sqrt{2}\,k'I/a$;   (b) Inscribed loop: use Eq. 21-8 with $R = a/2$, obtaining $B = 4\pi k'I/a$. Circumscribed loop: use Eq. 21-8 with $R = a\sqrt{2}/2$, obtaining $B = 2\sqrt{2}\,\pi k'I/a$.

21-C6 To obtain dB in terms of x and dx use $\sin\phi = a/\sqrt{x^2 + a^2}$ and $r^2 = x^2 + a^2$. For half of the wire, the integral to be evaluated is
$$B = k'Ia \int_{x=0}^{x=\infty} \dfrac{dx}{(x^2 + a^2)^{3/2}}.$$
See, e.g., *Handbook of Chemistry and Physics*, Formula 132.

Chapter 22   Applied Electricity

Questions

22-1   In the region where the current-carrying coil moves, the magnetic field is shaped by the cylindrical core so that the deflection θ is a linear function of the current.

22-2   Alternating current can be converted to pulsating direct current by the mechanical action of a commutator (Fig. 22-5) or by using a rectifier circuit (Figs. 22-26 and 22-36).

22-3   Alternating current allows use of transformers, making possible low-loss transmission at high voltages, and convenient manipulation of voltages used for various applications.

22-4   In each case, the lower terminal voltage at a light socket is caused by the IR drop in the house wiring. The refrigerator motor uses a heavy current only when starting. In a well-wired house, with separate circuits for appliances and for lights, the dimming (due only to the IR drop in the low-resistance heavy wires leading from pole transformer to house) may be imperceptible.

22-5   (a) The emf of the generator is proportional to the rate of change of flux; at higher angular velocity, the induced emf is greater.   (b) Mechanical energy is reversibly transformed into electric energy in the motor-generator combination. Electric energy is irreversibly transformed into thermal energy in the lamp filament.

22-6   Yes. Aluminum tracks would not be very practical except for a model train.

22-7   To reduce eddy current losses (see bottom of column 1 of p. 507).

22-8   The primary has the same number of turns as the secondary.

22-9   A current of many thousand amperes would cause the transformer to burn out. When connected to an ac voltage source, the back emf reduces the primary current to a small value.

22-11   Yes. The elevator gained mass and the water lost mass; the magnitude of the mass change is given by $\Delta m = \Delta E/c^2$.

22-12   No.

22-13   The controlled impurity atoms are electron donors in n-type material and are electron acceptors (i.e., donors of holes) in p-type material.

22-14   The resistance is greater when the diode is reverse biased.

22-15   The emitter and collector regions are both p-type material, and the device would still function as an amplifier, after a fashion. However, the amount of doping is not the same; the emitter is more heavily doped than the collector. Thus, one connection is more useful than the other.

22-16   The triode would not function as an amplifier if the plate potential were made negative relative to the cathode, for then thermionically emitted electrons would be repelled by the plate and there would be no plate current.

Multiple Choice

Problems

22-A1 $\frac{4}{5}(60°) = 48°$.

22-A2 $(95\%)(10\ \text{A}) = 9.50\ \text{A}$.   [Equation 22-1 shows that θ is proportional to B.]

22-A3 Back emf is proportional to speed; $\frac{400}{300}(48\ \text{V}) = 64\ \text{V}$.

22-A4 $(3000\ \text{rev/min})/(2000\ \text{rev/min})(120\ \text{V}) = 180\ \text{V}$.

22-A5 Turns ratio $= 20/800$; $\varepsilon_s = (20/800)(120\ \text{V}) = 3.0\ \text{V}$.

22-A6 $P = \varepsilon_s I_s = (3\ \text{V})(1\ \text{A}) = 3\ \text{W}$. $I_p = P/\varepsilon_p = (3\ \text{W})/(120\ \text{V}) = 0.025\ \text{A}$.

22-A7 In this step-up transformer, the turns ratio is $8000/200 = 40$. Hence, ε_s $= 40(120\ \text{V}) = 4800\ \text{V}$; $I_s = (1/40)(60\ \text{mA}) = 1.5\ \text{mA}$.

22-B1 The armature current is $(120\ \text{V} - 108\ \text{V})/(3\ \Omega) = 4\ \text{A}$. The field current is $(120\ \text{V})/(100\ \Omega) = 1.2\ \text{A}$. Total current is $(4 + 1.2)\ \text{A} = 5.2\ \text{A}$.

22-B2 The armature current is $(120\ \text{V} - 0\ \text{V})/(3\ \Omega) = 40\ \text{A}$. The field current is $1.2\ \text{A}$, as before. Total current is $(40 + 1.2)\ \text{A} = 41.2\ \text{A}$.

22-B3 (*a*) Armature current $= (120\ \text{V} - 108\ \text{V})/(4\ \Omega) = 3\ \text{A}$.   (*b*) Field current $= 5\ \text{A} - 3\ \text{A} = 2\ \text{A}$.   (*c*) $R = (120\ \text{V})/(2\ \text{A}) = 60\ \Omega$.

22-B4 (*a*) Clockwise;   (*b*) counterclockwise.   [In (*b*), the induced current must, by its action, give rise to a magnetic flux that is oppositely directed to the magnetic flux that is being built up by the action of the outer coil (Lenz's law). Thus the induced current is opposite to the primary current.]

22-B5 Clockwise.   [The induced current must, by its action, create a magnetic flux that tends to perpetuate the flux that is disappearing.]

22-B6 (*a*) Input power $= VI = (2\ \text{kV})(1000\ \text{A}) = 2000\ \text{kW} = 2\ \text{MW}$.   (*b*) Loss in line $= I^2R = (1000\ \text{A})^2(1.0\ \Omega) = 1\ \text{MW}$.   (*c*) Delivered power $= 2\ \text{MW} - 1\ \text{MW}$ $= 1\ \text{MW}$.   (*d*) Efficiency $= (1\ \text{MW})/(2\ \text{MW}) = 50\%$.

22-B7 $P = VI$; $I = P/V = (2 \times 10^6\ \text{W})/(20 \times 10^3\ \text{V}) = 100\ \text{A}$.   (*a*) Input power $= VI$ $= (20\ \text{kV})(100\ \text{A}) = 2\ \text{MW}$, the same as in Prob. 22-B6.   (*b*) Loss in line $= I^2R = (100\ \text{A})^2(1.0\ \Omega) = 0.01\ \text{MW}$.   (*c*) Delivered power $= 2.00\ \text{MW}$ $- 0.01\ \text{MW} = 1.99\ \text{MW}$.   (*d*) Efficiency $= (1.99\ \text{MW})/(2.00\ \text{MW}) = 99.5\%$.

22-B8 (*a*) $I = P/V = (80\ \text{kW})/(4\ \text{kV}) = 20\ \text{A}$; $I^2R = (20\ \text{A})^2(5\ \Omega) = 2000\ \text{W} = 2\ \text{kW}$. (*b*) Input power $= (80 + 2)\ \text{kW} = 82\ \text{kW}$. Efficiency $= (80\ \text{kW})/(82\ \text{kW}) = 97.6\%$. (*c*) $V = P/I = (82\ \text{kW})/(20\ \text{A}) = 4.1\ \text{kV} = 4100\ \text{V}$.

22-B9 From Eq. 22-6, $Z \approx 2\pi\nu L = 2\pi(5 \times 10^3\ \text{Hz})(20 \times 10^{-3}\ \text{H}) = 628\ \Omega$.

22-B10 $\varepsilon_b = L(\Delta I/\Delta t) = (0.3\ \text{H})[(15\ \text{A})/(0.003\ \text{s})] = 1500\ \text{V}$.   [See footnote on p. 511.]

22-B11 $Z \approx X_L = 2\pi\nu L$; $300\ \Omega = 2\pi(\nu)(0.02\ \text{H})$; $\nu = 2.39 \times 10^3\ \text{Hz} = 2.39\ \text{kHz}$.

22-B12 $Z = 2\pi(60\ \text{Hz})(5\ \text{H}) = 1885\ \Omega$; $I = V/Z = (120\ \text{V})/(1885\ \Omega) = 0.0637\ \text{A} = 63.7\ \text{mA}$.

22-B13 $Z \approx X_C = \dfrac{1}{2\pi\nu C}$; $\nu = \dfrac{1}{2\pi(30 \times 10^3\ \Omega)(0.02 \times 10^{-6}\ \text{F})} = 265\ \text{Hz}$.   [The approximation is valid, since the capacitor is "well insulated."]

22-B14 $Z = \dfrac{1}{2\pi\nu C} = \dfrac{1}{2\pi(600 \times 10^3\ \text{Hz})(200 \times 10^{-12}\ \text{F})} = 1326\ \Omega$. $I = (30\ \text{V})/(1326\ \Omega)$ $= 0.0226\ \text{A} = 22.6\ \text{mA}$.

22-B15 (a) -9 V $+ (3.1$ mA$)(1.5$ k$\Omega) = -4.35$ V; -9 V $+ (3.7$ mA$)(1.5$ k$\Omega) = -3.45$ V.
(b) A change of 10 μA caused an increase of 0.6 mA in the collector current; current gain $= (600\ \mu\text{A})/(10\ \mu\text{A}) = 60$.

22-B16 (a) 200 V $- (2.5$ mA$)(20$ k$\Omega) = 150$ V; 200 V $- (2.0$ mA$)(20$ k$\Omega) = 160$ V.
(b) A change of 0.4 V caused an increase of 10 V at the plate; voltage gain $= (10\ \text{V})/(0.4\ \text{V}) = 25$.

22-C1 (a) $e = \dfrac{\text{power out}}{\text{power in}} = \dfrac{1100\ \text{W}}{(24\ \text{V})(90\ \text{A})} = 51\%$. ($b$) $W = (24$ V$)(90$ A$)(1$ h$)$

$= 2160$ Wh $= 2.16$ kWh. (c) Cost per km $= \left(\dfrac{2.16\ \text{kWh}}{80\ \text{km}}\right)\left(\dfrac{3\cent}{1\ \text{kWh}}\right) = 0.08\cent/\text{km}$.

For the compact car, fuel cost per km $= \left(\dfrac{4\ \text{liters}}{40\ \text{km}}\right)\left(\dfrac{20\cent}{1\ \text{liter}}\right) = 2\cent/\text{km}$.
(d) Battery cost $= \left(\dfrac{6400\cent}{800\ \text{cycles}}\right)\left(\dfrac{1\ \text{cycle}}{80\ \text{km}}\right) = 0.1\cent/\text{km}$; total cost is $(0.1 + 0.08)$
$= 0.18\cent/\text{km}$.

22-C2 At half speed, $\varepsilon_b = 50$ V; armature current $= (110$ V $- 50$ V$)/(5\ \Omega) = 12$ A; field current $= 2$ A, as before; total current $= (12 + 2)$ A $= 14$ A.

22-C3 $\varepsilon_b = \frac{3}{4}(108$ V$) = 81$ V. Armature current $= (120$ V $- 81$ V$)/(4\ \Omega) = 9.75$ A. Field current $= 2$ A, as before. Total current $= (9.75 + 2)$ A $= 11.75$ A.

22-C4 Field current $= (220$ V$)/(200\ \Omega) = 1.1$ A. Hence armature current $= (9.1 - 1.1)$ A $= 8.0$ A. The back emf is found from 8.0 A $= (220$ V $- \varepsilon_b)/(2\ \Omega)$; $\varepsilon_b = 204$ V.

22-C5 Generated power $= 2700$ MW $+ 27$ MW $= 2727$ MW. $I = P/V = (2727 \times 10^6$ W$)/(800 \times 10^3$ V$) = 3409$ A. The power loss in the line is I^2R, hence $(27 \times 10^6$ W$) = (3409$ A$)^2R$; $R = 2.323\ \Omega$. Use the resistivity of aluminum to find the cross section:
$$A = \frac{\rho L}{R} = \frac{(2.6 \times 10^{-8}\ \Omega\text{·m})(2 \times 1350 \times 10^3\ \text{m})}{2.323\ \Omega} = 0.0302\ \text{m}^2.$$
[This transmission line would be equivalent in cross section to two cables, each 14 cm in diameter; in practice, many parallel cables would be used.]

22-C6 The coil acts as a seat of emf of value $L(dI/dt)$
$= (5$ H$)(60$ A$/$s$) = 300$ V. The IR drop in the coil is $(20$ A$)(0.8\ \Omega) = 16$ V. The total PD across the coil is $(300 + 16)$ V $= 316$ V. [The sign relationships are shown in the figure. Draw the self-inductance and the resistance of the coil in

Prob. 22-C6

the series, with a current toward the right. The $+$ and $-$ signs on the resistance are determined by the direction of the IR drop. The $+$ and $-$ signs on the inductance are determined by the fact that the current is *increasing*; Lenz's law tells us that the induced current must oppose the change (an increase) and hence tend to send conventional current to the left through the external circuit. Now it is seen that the two voltages add up. (If the current had been decreasing, the net PD across the coil would have been 284 V.) An analogy may be made with the expression for terminal voltage of a seat of emf, $V = \varepsilon \pm Ir$. Here the emf of the coil is arranged like a battery that is being charged.]

22-C7 Here $2\pi\nu = 2\pi (30$ rev$/$s$) = 188$ rad$/$s. (a) $\varepsilon_{\max} = 2\pi\nu NBA = (188$ rad$/$s$)\times (500$ turns$)(0.04$ T$)(0.05$ m$)(0.20$ m$) = 37.7$ V. Thus, the equation for ε as a function of time is $\varepsilon = 37.7 \sin 188\,t$. ($b$) $I_{\max} = \varepsilon_{\max}/R = (37.7$ V$)/(20\ \Omega) = 1.88$ A.

22-C8 From $Z = \sqrt{R^2 + X^2}$, $R = \sqrt{Z^2 - X^2} = \sqrt{(13)^2 - (5)^2} = 12\ \Omega$.

22-C9 The reactance is $X_L = \omega L = 2\pi(1000\ \text{Hz})(0.020\ \text{H}) = 125.6\ \Omega$.

$Z = \sqrt{(100)^2 + (125.6)^2} = 161\ \Omega$. From $\tan\phi = X/R$, we have $\tan\phi = 125.6/100$; $\phi = 51°$.

22-C10 The hot resistance of the bulb is $R = V^2/P = (120\ \text{V})^2/(5\ \text{W}) = 2880\ \Omega$. For the capacitor, $X_C = 1/2\pi\nu C = 1/(2\pi)(60\ \text{Hz})(40 \times 10^{-6}\ \text{F}) = 66\ \Omega$. Thus $Z = \sqrt{R^2 + X^2} = \sqrt{(2880)^2 + (66)^2} = 2881\ \Omega$. Since I, given by V/Z, equals V/R to within less than 0.1%, the current is essentially unaltered by the presence of the capacitor.

22-C11 $\nu = \dfrac{1}{2\pi}\sqrt{\dfrac{1}{LC}} = \dfrac{1}{2\pi}\sqrt{\dfrac{1}{(20 \times 10^{-6}\ \text{H})(0.002 \times 10^{-6}\ \text{F})}} = 796\ \text{kHz}$.

[The resistance of the coil does not enter into the problem. If desired, the appropriate formulas show that at resonance, X_L and X_C are each 100 Ω.]

22-C12 (a) If the power factor is 1.00, the circuit is at resonance. Then $X_L = X_C$, $Z = R = 200\ \Omega$, and $I = (220\ \text{V})/(200\ \Omega) = 1.10\ \text{A}$. (b) At resonance, $X_L = 1/\omega C$; $C = 1/\omega^2 L$. For 60 Hz, $C = 1/(377\ \text{rad/s})^2(5\ \text{H}) = 1.41\ \mu\text{F}$. (c) $X_C = 1/\omega C = 1/(377\ \text{rad/s})(1.41 \times 10^{-6}\ \text{F}) = 1881\ \Omega$. The peak current is $(1.10\ \text{A})\sqrt{2}$, and the peak voltage across the capacitor is $I_{max}X_C = (1.10\sqrt{2}\ \text{A})(1881\ \Omega) = 2926\ \text{V} = 2.93\ \text{kV}$. [This illustrates an easy way to blow out a capacitor when it is part of a resonant circuit. See also the discussion of Fig. 22-48.]

22-C13 First calculate the reactances. $X_L = (0.5\ \text{H})(377\ \text{rad/s}) = 188.5\ \Omega$; $X_C = 1/(10 \times 10^{-6}\ \text{F})(377\ \text{rad/s}) = 265.3\ \Omega$. (a) $Z = \sqrt{(X_C - X_L)^2 + R^2} = \sqrt{(265.3 - 188.5)^2 + (100)^2} = \sqrt{(76.8)^2 + (100)^2} = 126.06\ \Omega$. $I = V/Z = (220\ \text{V})/(126.06\ \Omega) = 1.75\ \text{A}$. (b) $\tan\phi = X/R = (76.8)/(100)$; $\phi = 37.5°$. (c) $\cos\phi = \cos 37.5° = 0.79$. (d) The circuit is capacitive, since $X_C > X_L$.

22-C14 $V_{max} = V_{rms}\sqrt{2} = (765\ \text{kV})\sqrt{2} = 1082\ \text{kV} = 1.08\ \text{MV}$. A serious environmental threat is posed by the large towers needed to support a million-volt transmission line.

22-C15 (a) $\cos\phi = P/VI = (30\ \text{W})/(120\ \text{V})(0.5\ \text{A}) = 0.50$; $\phi = 60°$. (b) $Z = V/I = (120\ \text{V})/(0.5\ \text{A}) = 240\ \Omega$; $R = Z\cos\phi = (240\ \Omega)(0.50) = 120\ \Omega$. (c) $X_L = \sqrt{Z^2 - R^2} = \sqrt{(240)^2 - (120)^2} = 207.8\ \Omega$. From $X_L = \omega L$, $L = X_L/\omega = (207.8\ \Omega)/(377\ \text{rad/s}) = 0.551\ \text{H}$.

Chapter 23   Electromagnetic Waves

Questions

23-1 Yes.

23-2 Yes.

23-3 3×10^8 m/s, the same as any other e-m wave.

23-4 There is a resonant L-C circuit at the "front end" of the receiver.

23-5 In Fig. 23-1c the charges are in motion; in the analogy of $\frac{1}{2}LI^2$ to $\frac{1}{2}mv^2$ we can say that the charges have inertia, as does the block in part 2 of Fig. 9-13. However, this is only an analogy; the "inertia" here introduced is not to be confused with the real inertia (F/m) of an electron, which for nonrelativistic speeds is 9.11×10^{-31} kg.

23-6 Vertical, so that the wave's electric field can move free electrons vertically (see Figs. 23-7 and 23-10). The induced emf in the loop antenna depends not on electric field, but on the rate of change of magnetic flux. When the plane of the coil is broadside to the distant source, both **E** and **B** are in the plane of the coil (Fig. 23-6) and the flux Φ has a constant value (equal to 0). Thus $\varepsilon\ (= d\Phi/dt)$ is zero, and the radio receiver indicates a minimum or zero signal.

23-7 B would be parallel to the plane of the coil; $\Phi = 0$ at all times, thus $\varepsilon = d\Phi/dt = 0$.

23-8 Different attributes of the wave are being modulated (changed) at the slow (audio) rate.

23-9 (*a*) About 6×10^{14} Hz;   (*b*) amplitude modulation.

23-10 Frequency modulation.

23-11 Information is "order," entropy is "disorder."

Multiple Choice

23-12 (*b*);   **23-13** (*a*);   **23-14** (*c*);   **23-15** (*c*);   **23-16** (*a*);   **23-17** (*b*).

Problems

23-A1 (*a*) $\lambda = c/\nu = (3 \times 10^8\ \text{m/s})/(20 \times 10^9\ \text{Hz}) = 0.015\ \text{m} = 1.5\ \text{cm}$.   (*b*) $\lambda = (3 \times 10^8\ \text{m/s})/(12 \times 10^9\ \text{Hz}) = 0.025\ \text{m} = 2.5\ \text{cm}$.

23-A2 $\lambda = (3 \times 10^8\ \text{m/s})/(108 \times 10^6\ \text{Hz}) = 2.78\ \text{m}$. The length of each section should be $\frac{1}{4}\lambda$, or 0.69 m.   [The antenna should be $\frac{1}{2}\lambda$ long, i.e., it should consist of two sections, each $\frac{1}{4}\lambda$ long, fed by an oscillator at the center. See Fig. 23-7, where antinodes of potential occur at the ends of the antenna; just as for all stationary waves, antinodes are $\frac{1}{2}\lambda$ apart.]

23-A3 $\nu = c/\lambda = (3 \times 10^8\ \text{m/s})/(0.012\ \text{m}) = 2.5 \times 10^{10}\ \text{Hz} = 25\ \text{GHz}$.

23-A4 $\lambda = (3 \times 10^8\ \text{m/s})/(1.42 \times 10^9\ \text{Hz}) = 0.211\ \text{m} = 21.1\ \text{cm}$.   [This radiation comes from hydrogen atoms in the space between the stars in our galaxy. Insofar as a model is possible, we think of the proton and the electron as tiny magnets whose axes of magnetization can be parallel or antiparallel to each other. One useful model relates the magnetism to the spin of the proton or electron. Suppose that the electron's magnetic axis is parallel to that of the proton; if the electron "flips" so that its magnetic axis is antiparallel to that of the proton, the energy of the system (the hydrogen atom) is slightly less. A photon is emitted whose frequency is given by $h\nu = \Delta E$ (Eq. 28-1).]

23-A5 $\nu = (3 \times 10^8\ \text{m/s})/(500 \times 10^{-9}\ \text{m}) = 6 \times 10^{14}\ \text{Hz} = 600$ terahertz (THz).

23-A6 $\lambda = (3 \times 10^8\ \text{m/s})/(750 \times 10^3\ \text{Hz}) = 400\ \text{m}$.

23-A7 $\lambda = (3 \times 10^8\ \text{m/s})/(91.9 \times 10^6\ \text{Hz}) = 3.26\ \text{m}$.

23-A8 (*a*) 5500 Å;   (*b*) 5000 Å;   (*c*) 5830 Å;   (*d*) 1.5×10^5 Å.

23-A9 (*a*) 5.461×10^{-7} m;   (*b*) 7.1×10^{-11} m;   (*c*) 1.5×10^{-5} m.

23-A10 (*a*) 5.00×10^{-5} cm;   (*b*) 1.54×10^{-10} m;   (*c*) $10^{-4}\ \mu\text{m}$;   (*d*) 589.3 nm;   (*e*) 2.0×10^5 Å.

23-B1 $W = \frac{1}{2}LI^2 \propto I^2$. $W = (100 \text{ J})[(12 \text{ A})/(3 \text{ A})]^2 = 1600 \text{ J}$.

23-B2 (a) $W = \frac{1}{2}LI^2 = \frac{1}{2}(20 \text{ H})(0.5 \text{ A})^2 = 2.5 \text{ J}$. (b) $2.5 \text{ J} = (1 \text{ kg})(9.8 \text{ N/kg})h$; $h = 0.255 \text{ m}$.

23-B3 $\nu \propto 1/\sqrt{C}$, hence $\nu = (300 \text{ kHz})\sqrt{200/800} = 150 \text{ kHz}$.

23-B4 $\nu = \dfrac{1}{2\pi} \sqrt{\dfrac{1}{(100 \times 10^{-3} \text{ Hz})(250 \times 10^{-12} \text{ F})}} = 31.8 \text{ kHz}$.

23-B5 $\nu = \dfrac{1}{2\pi} \sqrt{\dfrac{1}{(2 \text{ H})(0.5 \times 10^{-6} \text{ F})}} = 159 \text{ Hz}$.

23-B6 $\lambda = c/\nu = c(2\pi\sqrt{LC}) = (3 \times 10^8 \text{ m/s})(2\pi)\sqrt{(125 \times 10^{-6} \text{ H})(80 \times 10^{-12} \text{ F}} = 188 \text{ m}$.

23-B7 $\nu = c/\lambda = (3 \times 10^8 \text{ m/s})/(6 \text{ m}) = 5 \times 10^7 \text{ Hz}$. From $\nu = (1/2\pi)\sqrt{1/LC}$, $C = 1/4\pi^2\nu^2 L = 1/(4\pi^2)(5 \times 10^7 \text{ Hz})^2(1.6 \times 10^{-6} \text{ H}) = 6.33 \times 10^{-12} \text{ F} = 6.33 \text{ pF}$.

23-B8 $\nu \propto 1/\sqrt{C}$, hence $C \propto 1/\nu^2$. The ratio is $(1600/500)^2 = 10.2$. [The 10-fold capacitance change is usually made by rotating the plates of a variable capacitor (Fig. 18-18a), thus changing A in Eq. 18-7.]

23-B9 For maximum frequency, connect the two capacitors in series (giving $\frac{1}{2}C$); for minimum frequency, connect them in parallel (giving $2C$). The frequency ratio is $\sqrt{2C/\frac{1}{2}C} = 2:1$.

23-B10 From $\lambda = c/\nu = c(2\pi)\sqrt{LC}$, we obtain $L = \lambda^2/(4\pi^2)c^2C = (20 \text{ m})^2/(4\pi^2)$ $\times (3 \times 10^8 \text{ m/s})^2(50 \times 10^{-12} \text{ F}) = 2.25 \ \mu\text{H}$.

23-B11 (a) $\nu \propto 1/\sqrt{L}$, hence $L \propto 1/\nu^2$. The frequency ratio is $(88/108)$, hence $L = (54 \text{ nH})(88/108)^2 = 35.9 \text{ nH}$. (b) $C = 1/4\pi^2\nu^2 L = 1/4\pi^2(88 \times 10^6 \text{ Hz})^2$ $\times (54 \times 10^{-9} \text{ H}) = 6.06 \times 10^{-11} \text{ F} = 60.6 \text{ pF}$.

23-B12 Maximum KE is $\frac{1}{2}LI^2$, where I is the maximum current in the tank circuit. Maximum PE is $\frac{1}{2}Q^2/C$, where Q is the maximum charge on the plates of the capacitor. By the energy principle, $\frac{1}{2}LI^2 = \frac{1}{2}Q^2/C$; $I = Q\sqrt{1/LC}$, or (using Eq. 23-4) $I = 2\pi\nu Q$.

23-C1 (a) $2\pi\nu L = 1/2\pi\nu C$ yields $\nu = (1/2\pi)\sqrt{1/LC}$. Then $2\pi\nu = 1/\sqrt{LC}$ and $X_L = X_C$ $= \sqrt{L/C}$. (b) $\sqrt{(125 \times 10^{-6} \text{ H})/(80 \times 10^{-12} \text{ F})} = 1250 \ \Omega$.

23-C2 Using the chain rule (Appendix E, item c) gives $I = dQ/dt = 2\pi\nu Q_0 \cos 2\pi\nu t$, from which the maximum current is found to be $2\pi\nu Q_0$.

23-C3 (a) From $\nu = c/\lambda = (1/2\pi)\sqrt{1/LC}$, we have $C = \dfrac{\lambda^2}{4\pi^2 c^2 L} = \dfrac{(0.03 \text{ m})^2}{4\pi^2(3 \times 10^8 \text{ m/s})^2(10^{-9} \text{ H})} = 2.53 \times 10^{-13} \text{ F} = 0.253 \text{ pF}$.
(b) From $C = A/4\pi kd$, we have $l = \sqrt{A} = \sqrt{4\pi Ckd} = \sqrt{4\pi(2.53 \times 10^{-13} \text{ F})(9 \times 10^9 \text{ N·m}^2/\text{C}^2)(10^{-3} \text{ m})}$ $= 5.35 \times 10^{-3} \text{ m} = 5.35 \text{ mm}$.
(c) $X_L = 2\pi\nu L = 2\pi\left(\dfrac{3 \times 10^8 \text{ m/s}}{3 \times 10^{-2} \text{ m}}\right)(10^{-9} \text{ H}) = 20\pi \ \Omega = 62.8 \ \Omega$. [The formula derived in Prob. 23-C1 can also be used; $X_L = X_C = \sqrt{L/C}$ at resonance.]

Chapter 24   Geometrical Optics

Questions

24-1 Yes, one would not expect long-wave e-m radiation (radio) to behave differently from short wave e-m radiation (light). [Huygen's principle is, of course, a model and is not necessarily correct in every detail. For example, it fails to explain the lack of a backward-traveling wave front. A thorough and entirely successful treatment of light (and radio) propagation is based on Maxwell's equations, rather than Huygens' principle.]

24-2 "Straight" is a relative thing. Radar waves, for which λ/w is small, travel approximately in straight lines. See Sec. 24-2, also p. 595.

24-3 Specular reflection takes place at a mirror or at the surface of a quiet lake. Diffuse reflection takes place from almost any surface that is not smooth and polished, e.g., a page of a book or the side of a house. Scattering is illustrated by the blue skylight or the visible beam of a flashlight (or headlight) aimed forward on a foggy night.

24-4 Violet rays are deviated by a prism more than red rays.

24-5 No; for total reflection the angle of incidence must be in the optically more dense medium.

24-6 The first and third are converging, the second and fourth are diverging.

24-7 Yes, as in Fig. 24-22.

24-8 No.

24-9 The curvature is not changed by the plane mirror, so the initial wave front must be converging.

24-10 From $\sin \theta_c = 1/n$, the critical angle is less for diamond than for glass. A larger fraction of the rays striking a diamond–air interface (from inside the gem) will have an angle of incidence greater than θ_c; a properly cut diamond exploits these internal reflections to achieve a greater sparkle.

24-11 Yes, the wavelength is much less than the size of the obstacle. See p. 559, also the discussion on pp. 594–95.

24-12 The index of refraction of air depends on its density, hence on the temperature. Therefore, as the hot air rises (unsteadily), light from objects behind the air stream is bent erratically on its way to the eye.

Multiple Choice

24-13 (c); **24-14** (c); **24-15** (b); **24-16** (b); **24-17** (b); **24-18** (a).

Problems

24-A1 $c_n = c/n = (3 \times 10^8 \text{ m/s})/1.80 = 1.67 \times 10^8 \text{ m/s}$.
24-A2 $n = c/c_n = (3 \times 10^8 \text{ m/s})/(2.25 \times 10^8 \text{ m/s}) = 1.333$.
24-A3 $n = c/(\frac{3}{5}c) = \frac{5}{3} = 1.67$.
24-A4 $\lambda = [(3 \times 10^8 \text{ m/s})/2.00]/(6 \times 10^{14} \text{ Hz}) = 2.5 \times 10^{-7} \text{ m} = 250 \text{ nm}$.
24-A5 $\lambda = (500 \text{ nm})/1.33 = 375 \text{ nm}$.
24-A6 $c_1/c_2 = n_2/n_1 = (2.42)/(1.50) = 1.61$.
24-A7 $\sin \theta_{\text{air}} = \frac{4}{5}$; $\sin \theta_{\text{water}} = \frac{3}{5}$. Hence $n = \frac{4}{5}/\frac{3}{5} = \frac{4}{3} = 1.333$.
24-A8 $f = 1/\text{power} = 1/(12.5 \text{ m}^{-1}) = 0.08 \text{ m} = 8 \text{ cm}$. The lens is diverging.

24-A9 $f = 0.40$ m; power $= 1/f = 1/(0.40$ m$) = +2.5$ diopters. The lens is positive.

24-A10 1.00 m.   [The mirror extends from a point opposite the midpoint between the floor and the man's eyes to a point opposite the midpoint between the man's eyes and the top of his head.]

24-B1 (1) $\sin 60° = (1.333) \sin \theta_2$; $\theta_2 = 41°$.

24-B2 (1) $\sin 30° = (1.500) \sin \theta_2$; $\theta_2 = 19°$. The angle with the surface is $90° - 19° = 71°$.

24-B3 $n = 1/\sin \theta = 1/(3/5) = 5/3 = 1.67$.

24-B4 (1) $\sin 60° = (1.50) \sin \theta_2$; $\theta_2 = 35°$ N of E.

24-B5 If $\theta_1 =$ angle of incidence (in water), we have $\tan \theta_1 = (2$ m$)/(4$ m$)$; $\theta_1 = 26.57°$. Then $(1.333) \sin 26.57° = (1) \sin \theta_2$; $\theta_2 = 36.6°$.

24-B6 (1) $\sin \theta_1 = (1.333) \sin 35°$; $\theta_1 = 49.9°$; angle with the water surface is $90° - 49.9° = 40.1°$.

24-B7 $\sin \theta_c = 1/n = 1/2.42$; $\theta_c = 24°$.   [See Ques. 24-10.]

24-B8 $n = 1/\sin \theta_c = 1/\sin 45° = 1.414$.

24-B9 (a) 500 cm, diverging.   (b) Initial curvature as the wave front strikes the lens is $-1/(5$ m$) = 0.2$ m^{-1}. Adding the power of the lens to the initial curvature gives $(-0.20 + 0.25)$ m$^{-1} = +0.05$ m^{-1} for the curvature just as the light leaves the lens.   [A real image will be formed by this converging wave front.]   Radius of curvature $= 1/(0.05$ m$^{-1}) = 20$ m $= 2000$ cm.

24-B10 (a) *Ray method:* $1/3 + 1/q = 1/2$; $q = +6$ m beyond the lens.   [*Curvature method:* $-1/3 + 1/2 = 1/q$; $q = +6$ m beyond the lens.]   (b) Radius of curvature $= 6$ m.

24-B11 *Ray method:* $1/24 + 1/q = 1/(-8)$; $q = -6$ cm.   [*Curvature method:* $-1/24 - 1/8 = 1/q$; $q = -6$ cm.] *Either method:* $m = -q/p = -(-6$ cm$)/(24$ cm$) = +\frac{1}{4}$; $h = \frac{1}{4}(6$ mm$) = 1.5$ mm. Image is 6 cm to left of lens, virtual, erect, 1.5 mm high.

24-B12 *Ray method:* $1/24 + 1/q = 1/8$; $q = +12$ cm.   [*Curvature method:* $-1/24 + 1/8 = 1/q$; $q = +12$ cm.] *Either method:* $m = -(12$ cm$)/(24$ cm$) = -\frac{1}{2}$; $h = \frac{1}{2}(6$ mm$) = 3$ mm. Image is 12 cm to right of lens, real, inverted, 3 mm high.

24-B13 *Ray method:* $1/15 + 1/q = 1/20$; $q = -60$ cm.   [*Curvature method:* $-1/15 + 1/20 = 1/q$; $q = -60$ cm.] *Either method:* $m = -(-60$ cm$)/(15$ cm$) = +4$; $h = 4(2$ mm$) = 8$ mm. Image is 60 cm below lens, virtual, erect, 8 mm high.

24-B14 The virtual image formed by the first lens is at the focal point of the second lens. This point must be 10 cm to the left of the first lens, i.e., 40 cm to the left of the second lens. The focal length is therefore $+40$ cm.

24-B15 (a) $m = -(400$ cm$)/(5$ cm$) = -80$.   (b) *Ray method:* $1/5 + 1/400 = 1/f$; $f = 4.94$ cm.   [*Curvature method:* $-1/5 + 1/f = 1/400$; $f = 4.94$ cm.]

24-B16 The old image distance was 60.00 mm; the new image distance is found from $1/3000 + 1/q = 1/60$; $q = 61.22$ mm.   [*Curvature method:* $-1/3000 + 1/60 = 1/q$; $q = 61.22$ mm.] The lens must be moved away from the film by $(61.22 - 60.00)$ mm $= 1.22$ mm.

24-B17 Using $|m| = q/p$, we have $h = (3500 \times 10^3$ m$)\left(\dfrac{60 \times 10^{-3}\text{ m}}{3.84 \times 10^8\text{ m}}\right) = 5.5 \times 10^{-4}$ m $= 0.55$ mm.   [Another approach is to use the angular size of the moon: $\theta = (3500$ km$)/(3.84 \times 10^5$ km$) = 9.11 \times 10^{-3}$ rad $(\approx 0.52°)$. This is also the angle subtended by the image, as viewed from the center of the lens; $s = r\theta = (60$ mm$)(9.11 \times 10^{-3}$ rad$) = 0.55$ mm.]

24-B18 $f = 1/20 = 0.05$ m $= 5$ cm.   (*a*) *Ray method:* $1/p + 1/6 = 1/5$; $p = 30$ cm. [*Curvature method:* $-1/p + 1/5 = 1/6$; $p = 30$ cm.]   (*b*) $m = -(6 \text{ cm})/30$ cm) $= -\frac{1}{5}$; $h = \frac{1}{5}(2.0$ cm) $= 0.4$ cm.

24-B19   *Ray method:* $1/x + 1/4x = 1/60$; $x = 75$ cm.   [*Curvature method:* $-1/x + 1/60 = 1/4x$; $x = 75$ cm.]

24-B20   *Ray method:* $1/x + 1/(-4x) = 1/60$; $x = 45$ cm.   [*Curvature method:* $-1/x + 1/60 = -1/4x$; $x = 45$ cm.]

24-B21   The screen must be moved *away* from the lenses, as in Figs. 24-21 and 24-30. The first lens supplies a virtual object for the second lens; this object is at the original screen position, 30 cm to the right of the diverging lens. *Ray method:* $1/p + 1/q = 1/f$ becomes $1/(-30) + 1/(+45) = 1/f$; $f = -90$ cm. [*Curvature method:* $+1/30 + 1/f = +1/45$; $f = -90$ cm.]

24-B22   In Fig. 24-19, for the diverging lens of part (*a*) the described ray heads for the far focal point, strikes the lens about half way above the center, and emerges parallel to the axis. For the converging lens of part (*b*), the described ray heads upward from *B* toward the top edge of the lens and emerges parallel to the axis.

24-B23   (*a*) The image is a virtual one, behind the curved surface. The focal length is $-R/2 = -10$ cm. *Ray method:* $1/40 + 1/q = 1/(-10)$; $q = -8$ cm. [*Curvature method:* $-1/40 - 1/10 = 1/q$; $q = -8$ cm.]   (*b*) $m = -q/p$ $= -(-8 \text{ cm})/(40 \text{ cm}) = +0.20$.

24-B24   Use proportions from similar triangles: *BAF* similar to *ROF*: $\dfrac{p - f}{f}$ $= \dfrac{h}{h'}$; *BAO* similar to *B'A'O*: $\dfrac{p}{q} = \dfrac{h}{h'}$; whence $\dfrac{1}{p} + \dfrac{1}{q} = \dfrac{1}{f}$.

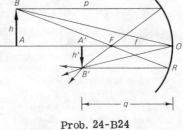

Prob. 24-B24

24-B25   (*a*) $f = +R/2 = +10$ cm.   (*b*) *Ray method:* $1/60 + 1/q = 1/10$; $q = 12$ cm.   [*Curvature method:* $-1/60$ $+ 1/10 = 1/q$; $q = 12$ cm.   (*c*) m $= -(12 \text{ cm})/(60 \text{ cm}) = -\frac{1}{5}$; $h = \frac{1}{5}(4$ cm) $= 0.8$ cm. The image is real, inverted, 0.8 cm high.

24-B26   (*a*) *Ray method:* $1/40 + 1/q = 1/(-10)$; $q = -8$ cm.   [*Curvature method:* $-1/40 - 1/10 = 1/q$; $q = -8$ cm.]   (*b*) $m = -q/p = -(-8 \text{ cm})/(40 \text{ cm}) = +\frac{1}{5}$; $h = \frac{1}{5}(2$ cm) $= 0.4$ cm. The image is virtual, erect, 0.4 cm high.

24-B27   (*a*) The magnification is $+3$, since it is a virtual image. $m = -q/p$ becomes $+3 = -q/(10 \text{ cm})$; $q = -30$ cm. The image is 30 cm behind the mirror. (*b*) The mirror is concave, since a convex mirror always gives a reduced virtual image of any real object.   (*c*) *Ray method:* $1/10 + 1/(-30) = 1/f$; $f = +15$ cm.   [*Curvature method:* $-1/10 + 1/f = -1/30$; $f = +15$ cm.]

24-C1   The index of refraction of glass relative to water is $1.500/1.333 = 1.125$; $\sin \theta_c = 1/1.125$; $\theta_c = 63°$. The ray must be incident in the optically more dense medium, i.e., the glass.

24-C2   The length of the ray from the corner to the center of an opposite face is $a\sqrt{3/2}$, where a is the cube edge. Hence, $\sin \theta_c = (a/\sqrt{2})/(a\sqrt{3/2}) = 1/\sqrt{3}$, and $n \geq \sqrt{3}$.

24-C3 The relative index of refraction is $1.66/1.333 = 1.245$. By the lens-maker's equation (Eq. 24-6), the power is proportional to $(n - 1)$. Hence,

$f = \left(\dfrac{1.245 - 1}{1.66 - 1}\right)$ (+5 diopters) = +1.86 diopters.   [See the discussion of underwater vision on p. 624.]

24-C4 The focal length is $1/10 = 0.10$ m $= 10$ cm. If x is the object distance, the image distance is $10x$. *Ray method:* $1/x + 1/10x = 1/10$; $x = 11$ cm. [*Curvature method:* $-1/x + 1/10 = 1/10x$; $x = 11$ cm.] The distance between object and image is $x + 10x = (11 + 110)$ cm $= 121$ cm.

24-C5 If x is the object distance, the image distance is $4x$. *Ray method:* $1/x + 1/4x = 1/8$; $x = 10$ cm.   [*Curvature method:* $-1/x + 1/8 = 1/4x$; $x = 10$ cm.] The distance between object and image is $x + 4x = (10 + 40)$ cm $= 50$ cm.

24-C6 (a) The lens is converging, since a diverging lens cannot form an enlarged image of a real object.   (b) The image is virtual for object at point A and real for object at point B. Applying the lens equation to each situation gives $\dfrac{1}{x} + \dfrac{1}{-5x} = \dfrac{1}{f}$ and $\dfrac{1}{x + 20} + \dfrac{1}{5(x + 20)} = \dfrac{1}{f}$. Solving simultaneously, we find $x = 40$ cm, $f = 50$ cm.   (c) A is 40 cm from the lens, B is 60 cm from the lens.

24-C7 For the first lens, $1/12 + 1/q = 1/10$; $q = 60$ cm. This image serves as a virtual object 20 cm to the right of the second lens: $1/(-20) + 1/q = 1/20$; $q = +10$ cm. The final image is 10 cm beyond the second lens. The overall magnification is $m_1 m_2 = \left(-\dfrac{60 \text{ cm}}{12 \text{ cm}}\right)\left(-\dfrac{10 \text{ cm}}{-20 \text{ cm}}\right) = -2.5$; $h = (2.5)(5 \text{ mm})$ $= 12.5$ mm. The image is real and inverted.

24-C8 (a) For the first lens, $1/30 + 1/q = 1/(-30)$; $q = -15$ cm. This image, although virtual as regards the first lens, serves as a real object 40 cm to the left of the second lens: $1/40 + 1/q = 1/8$; $q = +10$ cm. The final image is 10 cm beyond the second lens, i.e., 65 cm from the object.   (b) $m = m_1 m_2$ $= \left(-\dfrac{-15 \text{ cm}}{30 \text{ cm}}\right)\left(-\dfrac{10 \text{ cm}}{40 \text{ cm}}\right) = -\frac{1}{8}$. The size of the object is $(2 \text{ mm})/\frac{1}{8} = 16$ mm.

24-C9 (a) For the first lens, $1/60 + 1/q = 1/15$; $q = 20$ cm. This image serves as a real object 6 cm to the left of the second lens: $1/6 + 1/q = 1/(-12)$; $q = -4$ cm. The final image is 4 cm to the left of the second lens.

(b) $m = m_1 m_2 = \left(-\dfrac{20 \text{ cm}}{60 \text{ cm}}\right)\left(-\dfrac{-4 \text{ cm}}{6 \text{ cm}}\right) = -\frac{2}{9} = -0.22$.

24-C10 The magnified image is virtual and erect; the image distance is -60 cm. $1/30 + 1/(-60) = 1/f$; $f = 60$ cm; $R = 2f = 120$ cm; the mirror is concave.

24-C11 Both images are virtual; the first one is larger and therefore is formed by the concave side of the hubcap. $f = R/2$ and hence $1/f = 2/R$ for the concave side; $f = -R/2$ and hence $1/f = -2/R$ for the convex side. We have two equations in two unknowns: $1/p + 1/(-30) = +2/R$, also $1/p + 1/(-10) = -2/R$. Solving simultaneously gives   (a) $p = 15$ cm;   (b) $R = 60$ cm.

24-C12 Let a plane wave front strike the first lens. The curvature becomes $1/f_1$, and since the lenses are thin and are touching each other, the wave front's curvature is still $1/f_1$ when it reaches the second lens. The effect of the second lens is to add an additional curvature $1/f_2$, so the wave front leaving the second lens has curvature $1/f_1 + 1/f_2$. The combined effect of the two lenses is to give curvature $1/f_1 + 1/f_2$ to a wave front that originally had no curvature; it follows from the definition of power of a lens that the power of the combination is the sum of the powers of the separate lenses. In terms of focal lengths, $1/f = 1/f_1 + 1/f_2$.

24-C13   (a) Power $= 1/f = (n-1)(1/R_1 + 1/R_2) = (n-1)(1/R + 1/\infty) = (n-1)/R$.
(b) When the plane side is made reflecting, in effect we have a double convex lens; $1/f = (n-1)(1/R + 1/R) = 2(n-1)/R$.   (c) When the curved surface is made reflecting, we have three things in series: (1) a thin plano-convex lens as in part (a); (2) a concave mirror; and (3) another thin plano-convex lens. Adding the powers of the three devices (they are "touching," in the sense of Prob. 24-C12), we have $1/f = (n-1)/R + 2/R + (n-1)/R$, which reduces to $2n/R$.

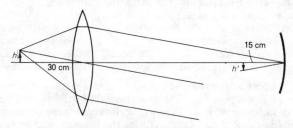

Prob. 24-C14

24-C14   The rays are parallel after the first trip through the lens and are brought to a focus 15 cm from the mirror. This image serves as a real object (75 cm from the lens) for the second trip through the lens: $1/75 + 1/q = 1/30$; $q = 50$ cm. The final real image is 50 cm to the left of the lens, or 20 cm to the left of the object. Calculation of the magnification is tricky, since the first image is at infinity. Using the rays shown in the diagram, we can draw two similar triangles showing that $h' = \frac{1}{2}h$; $m_1 = -\frac{1}{2}$. The magnification m_2 caused by the second trip through the lens is $-(50 \text{ cm})/(75 \text{ cm}) = -\frac{2}{3}$, so the overall magnification is $m = m_1 m_2 = (-\frac{1}{2})(-\frac{2}{3}) = +\frac{1}{3}$. The final image is real, erect, 20 cm to the left of the object.

24-C15   In Fig. 24-44, $x_2 + x_3 = (h^2/2)(1/R_1 + 1/R_2)$; here $x_2 + x_3 = 0.322$ cm and $h = 2.50$ cm, so $(1/R_1 + 1/R_2) = 0.1030 \text{ cm}^{-1}$. The lens-maker's equation now gives $n - 1 = 0.588$ (the data allow three significant figures). Thus $n = 1.558$, to four significant figures.

24-C16 $x = h^2/2R$ (saggital theorem) becomes 1 cm $= (5 \text{ cm})^2/2R$; $R = 12.5$ cm. The index of refraction of ice (from Table 24-2) is used in the lens-maker's formula (Eq. 24-6): $1/f = (1.31 - 1)[1/(12.5 \text{ cm}) + 1/\infty]$; $f = 40.3$ cm, and the power is $1/f = 1/0.403 \text{ m} = 2.48 \text{ m}^{-1} = 2.48$ diopters.

Chapter 25   Wave Optics

Questions

25-1   It must be known that the speed of light is slower in the medium of greater index of refraction.

25-2 The path lengths must differ by an integral number of wavelengths.

25-3 Yes; the path lengths differ by 4λ.

25-4 The spacing of the fringes would become $1/n$ as large, because the wavelength is given by c_n/ν, and c_n is $1/n$ as large as in air. The frequency is unaltered, but the frequency as such does not enter into the conditions for constructive and destructive interference.

25-5 From $n\lambda = a \sin \theta$, the violet light, which has shorter wavelength, peaks closer to O, in the first order, than does red light. Imagine superposing two interference patterns similar to the top part of Fig. 25-16, with peak separations in about a 2:1 ratio. The first maximum for violet light will approximately coincide with the first minimum for red light. Since white light also contains all wavelengths between violet and red, the overlapping of many such curves gives a very impure "spectrum" (if only two slits are used as in this example), but the predominant color near the central image is bluish.

25-6 The sources are only about 2 wavelengths apart, so a path difference of more than 2λ is not possible. The question asked for $2\frac{1}{2}\lambda$ or 3λ difference, manifestly impossible.   [The error survived three editions of the text; in the later printings of this fourth edition the question will be reworded.]

25-7 The locations of the main maxima are the same, but the grating maxima are much sharper (Fig. 25-16).

25-8 See Eq. 25-2 and Fig. 25-19.

25-9 The diffuseness is geometrical, caused by the broad source; wave effects are too small to be noticed here.

25-10 There is no coherence between the sources.

25-11 The half-silvered surface is at the right.

25-12 See the discussion just before Example 25-4 on p. 599.

25-13 The rays are in phase; both surfaces give a 180° phase shift, hence at each interface the reflection is against an optically more dense medium. The index of refraction of the oil must be between 1.00 and 1.33; this is less than the index for bulk oil.

25-14 Diffraction is usually considered to be the interference between broad beams where phase differences between parts of the beam are important (as in the single-slit diffraction pattern).

25-15 Polarization proves that light is a transverse phenomenon.

25-16 B sees a beam polarized in the E-W direction; A sees nothing.

25-17 See Fig. 25-38; P_1 is a polarizer and the identical Polaroid P_2 is used as an analyzer.

25-18 For the wave traveling to the right, the first slit is the polarizer and the second is the analyzer.

25-19 See Prob. 25-C8.

Multiple Choice

Problems

25-A1 $\lambda = (a \sin \theta)/n = (2.4 \times 10^{-6}$ m$)(\sin 30°)/3 = 4 \times 10^{-7}$ m $= 400$ nm.

25-A2 $\sin \theta = n\lambda/a = 2(4000 \times 10^{-9}$ m$)/(0.5 \times 10^{-3}$ m$) = 0.016$.

25-A3 $a = n\lambda/\sin \theta = 4(6 \times 10^{-7}$ m$)/(\sin 30°) = 4.80$ μm.

25-A4 (a) $\sin \theta = n\lambda/w = (1)(600 \times 10^{-9}$ m$)/(2 \times 10^{-6}$ m$) = 0.30$; $\theta = 17.5°$. (b) The second minimum is at $2(17.5°) = 35°$ from the central maximum. The first bright band is at approximately $\frac{1}{2}(17.5° + 35°) = 26.2°$.

25-A5 $\theta = \frac{1}{2}(60°) = 30°$. From $\sin \theta = n\lambda/w$, $0.500 = (1)(450$ nm$)/w$; $w = 900$ nm $= 0.9$ μm.

25-B1 The wavelength is $\lambda = (3 \times 10^8$ m/s$)/(60 \times 10^6$ Hz$) = 5$ m. The transmitters are driven $180°$ out of phase (equivalent to $\frac{1}{2}\lambda$), so the path difference must introduce an additional 0λ (manifestly impossible, if the observer is east of A), 1λ, 2λ, etc. Thus, if C is the position of the observer, the condition is $BC - AC = n\lambda$. If $x = BC$, we must have $\sqrt{x^2 + (10)^2} - x = n(5)$; $x = 10/n$ $-5n/2$. For $n = 1$, $x = 7.5$ m.   [For $n = 2$, $x = 0$ (observer still at A); for $n > 2$, x is negative and of no physical significance.]

25-B2 From the Pythagorean theorem, the path difference is $2\sqrt{153} - 24.000 = 0.7386$ cm. Equate this to $\frac{1}{2}\lambda$, $\frac{3}{2}\lambda$, or $\frac{5}{2}\lambda$ to obtain three wavelengths: $\lambda = (0.739)$ $\times [2, \frac{2}{3},$ or $\frac{2}{5}]$. Each ultrasonic frequency is $(34\,000$ cm/s$)/\lambda$, giving
$$\nu = \frac{34\,000 \text{ cm/s}}{(0.738 \text{ cm})(2)} \text{ (1, 3, or 5)} = 23.0 \text{ kHz}; \quad 69.0 \text{ kHz}; \quad 115.0 \text{ kHz}.$$

25-B3 $\lambda = (3 \times 10^8$ m/s$)/(750 \times 10^3$ Hz$) = 0.4$ km. For destructive interference, the path difference (found by using the Pythagorean theorem) must be $\frac{1}{2}\lambda$, $\frac{3}{2}\lambda$, $\frac{5}{2}\lambda$, etc. Thus, $2\sqrt{25 + h^2} - 10 = 0.2, 0.6, 1.0$, etc. Solving for h gives $h = 1.005$ km, 1.75 km, 2.29 km, etc. The minimum height is 1.005 km.   [Rounding errors are a source of confusion; if the data are exact, $h = 1.0049875$ km; rounding to 1.00 km would be misleading.]

25-B4 From $n\lambda = a \sin \theta$, for $\theta = 90°$ we have $n = a/\lambda = (10^{-5}$ m$)/(550 \times 10^{-9}$ m$)$ $= 18.18$. A total of 37 images can be seen: 18 on each side of center, plus the undeviated 0th order beam.

25-B5 (a) $\lambda = \dfrac{a \sin \theta}{n} = \left(\dfrac{0.054 \text{ m}}{20\,000 \text{ slits}}\right)\left(\dfrac{\sin 45°}{3}\right) = 636$ nm (red light). (b) For $\theta = 90°$, $\lambda = (636$ nm$)\left(\dfrac{\sin 90°}{\sin 45°}\right) = 900$ nm (infrared, not visible).

25-B6 (a) $\sin \theta = n\lambda/a = 2(525 \times 10^{-9}$ m$)/(10^{-5}$ m$) = 0.105$; $\theta = 6.027°$. $y = (3.00$ m$)\tan 6.027° = 0.317$ m $= 31.7$ cm.   [The approximation $\tan \theta \approx \sin \theta$ gives $y = 0.315$ m.] (b) As in part (a), find the deviations for the approximate limits of the green region (given in Table 24-1). For 490 nm, $y = 29.5$ cm; for 560 nm, $y = 33.8$ cm; the width of the green region on the screen is $(33.8 - 29.5)$ cm $= 4.3$ cm.   [The approximation $\tan \theta \approx \sin \theta$ gives 4.2 cm.]

25-B7 The grating space is $\dfrac{1}{2500}$ cm $= 4 \times 10^{-4}$ cm $= 4 \times 10^{-6}$ m. $\sin \theta = n\lambda/a$ $= 3(589 \times 10^{-9}$ m$)/(4 \times 10^{-6}$ m$) = 0.442$; $\theta = 26.2°$.

25-B8 $\sin \theta = n\lambda/a = 3(550 \times 10^{-9}\,\text{m})/(10^{-5}\,\text{m}) = 0.165$; $\tan \theta = 0.167$; $y = (2\,\text{cm})(0.167)$ $= 0.33\,\text{cm} = 3.3\,\text{mm}$.

25-B9 $\sin \theta = \lambda/a = (500.0 \times 10^{-9}\,\text{m})/(10^{-6}\,\text{m}) = 0.5000$; $\theta = 30.000°$. $\sin \theta' = (1.001)$ $\times (0.5000) = 0.5005$; $\theta' = 30.033°$. $\theta' - \theta = 0.033° \approx 2.0'$.   [This illustrates the high resolving power of a grating with many slits.]

25-B10 If $\lambda \geq w$, Eq. 25-2 gives $\sin \theta = n\lambda/w \geq 1$ for any value of n.

25-B11 First-order minimum occurs at $\sin \theta = \lambda/w = (6 \times 10^{-7}\,\text{m})/(10 \times 10^{-7}\,\text{m})$ $= 0.600$. Thus $\theta = 36.87°$; $\tan \theta = 0.750$; $y = (1.60\,\text{m})(0.750) = 1.20\,\text{m}$. The width of the central maximum is $2(1.20\,\text{m}) = 2.40\,\text{m}$.   [The approximation $\tan \theta \approx \sin \theta$ is not valid here.]

25-B12 The wavelength of the sound is $(340\,\text{m/s})/(2000\,\text{Hz}) = 0.17\,\text{m}$. The window serves as a slit, for which the first minimum is given by $\sin \theta = \lambda/w$ $= (0.17\,\text{m})/(0.68\,\text{m}) = 0.250$. Thus, $\tan \theta = 0.258$; $y = (5\,\text{m})(0.258) = 1.29\,\text{m}$. The distance from the corner of the room is $(2.50 - 1.29)\,\text{m} = 1.21\,\text{m}$. $[\lambda/w$ is large enough so that only the first minima occur at points on the facing wall.]

25-B13 $\tan \theta = (0.5\,\text{m})/(2\,\text{m}) = 0.250$; $\sin \theta = 0.243$; $\lambda = w \sin \theta = (2.2 \times 10^{-6}\,\text{m})(0.243)$ $= 5.34 \times 10^{-7}\,\text{m} = 534\,\text{nm}$. This is green light.

25-B14 For 68 fringes, the path difference at the wide end of the wedge is given by $2D = 68\lambda$; $D = 34\lambda = 34(589 \times 10^{-9}\,\text{m}) = 20 \times 10^{-6}\,\text{m} = 20\,\mu\text{m}$.   [See Fig. 25-28.]

25-B15 Refer to Fig. 25-28. (a) $\dfrac{x}{\frac{1}{2}\lambda} = \dfrac{12\,\text{cm}}{0.0025\,\text{cm}}$; with $\lambda = 500\,\text{nm}$, this gives

        $x = 1.2\,\text{mm}$. (b) In 12 cm there are 99 dark fringes plus one at each end of the plate.

25-B16 The round trip in the air film is 3λ; an extra $\frac{1}{2}\lambda$ is added (in effect) by the phase shift of the rays reflected from one glass plate. The total equivalent path difference is an odd number of half wavelengths.

25-B17 The wavelength in glass is $600\,\text{nm}/1.50 = 400\,\text{nm}$; the round trip is now $4\frac{1}{2}\lambda$. The phase shift at the front surface adds another $\frac{1}{2}\lambda$, making a total that is an integral number of wavelengths (5λ); the beams interfere constructively.

25-B18 There is a 180° phase shift both at the air–fluoride interface and at the fluoride–glass interface, since in each case light is being reflected at an interface separating the first medium from an optically more dense medium. These phase shifts cancel out, as also for the oil slick of Ques. 25-13 (Fig. 25-40). Since λ in fluoride is $500\,\text{nm}/1.25 = 400\,\text{nm}$, the round trip must be $\frac{1}{2}\lambda$, and the film thickness must be $\frac{1}{4}\lambda = 100\,\text{nm} = 0.100\,\mu\text{m}$.

25-B19 (a) At the left, where (by extrapolation) there is a dark fringe. (b) Each dark fringe corresponds to an extra $\frac{1}{2}\lambda$ in the thickness of the air wedge; about 9.5 fringes corresponds to $(4.75)(436\,\text{nm}) = 2.07\,\mu\text{m}$. The separation is about $2\,\mu\text{m}$.

25-B20 As in Example 25-4, we calculate the wavelengths for which destructive interference takes place. The first is 613 nm (orange light), the second is 307 nm (ultraviolet radiation). Between these wavelengths is the wavelength of light for which constructive interference takes place. We conclude that light of wavelength 459 nm (blue light) is strongly reflected.

25-B21 One path has been shortened by a total of 0.200 mm; $N = (0.200\,\text{mm})/(546 \times 10^{-9}\,\text{m}) = 366$ fringes.

25-B22 For Brewster's angle, $\tan \theta = n$ (stated on p. 603, proved in Prob. 25-C6). (a) In air, $n = 1.52 = \tan \theta$; $\theta = 57°$. (b) In water, the relative index of refraction is $1.52/1.333 = 1.140 = \tan \theta$; $\theta = 49°$.

25-B23 Brewster's angle, given by $\tan\theta = 1.333$, is $53°$. The angle of the sun above the horizon is $90° - 53° = 37°$.

25-C1 In Fig. 25-43, drop perpendiculars from each slit to the ray through the other slit. The path difference is equated to $n\lambda$, giving $n\lambda = a(\sin\theta_1 - \sin\theta_2)$. [In most problems in this chapter, $\theta_1 = 0$ and $|n\lambda| = a\sin\theta_2$.]

25-C2 The hints given in (a) and (b) amount to using the saggital theorem (see Sec. 24-12, also Mathematical Appendix C-1). (a) From Fig. 25-44, $y = R - \sqrt{R^2 - x^2}$. (b) Transposing R and squaring both sides gives $(R - y)^2 = R^2 - x^2$; $R^2 - 2Ry + y^2 = R^2 - x^2$; neglect y^2, to obtain $y = x^2/2R$, or $x = \sqrt{2Ry}$. (c) $x = \sqrt{2Rk(\frac{1}{2}\lambda)}$, or $x = \sqrt{k\lambda R}$, the desired formula for the radius of the kth ring. [Note that the radii are proportional to $\sqrt{1}$, $\sqrt{2}$, $\sqrt{3}$, $\sqrt{4}$, ...] (d) For $k = 1$, the first ring has radius $\sqrt{(1)(4 \times 10^{-7}\text{ m})(250\text{ m})}$ $= 10^{-2}$ m $= 1.0$ cm. The first six rings have radii 1.00, 1.41, 1.73, 2.00, 2.24, 2.45 cm.

25-C3 In the liquid, λ is replaced by λ/n. Then the equation becomes $x = \sqrt{k\lambda R/n}$, where λ is the wavelength in air. All radii are reduced by the factor $1/\sqrt{n}$; an unknown index of refraction can be found in this way.

25-C4 (a) For the 10th ring the segment y is $10(\frac{1}{2}\lambda) = 5\lambda$, and $x = 0.015$ m. By the saggital theorem, $x^2 \approx 2Ry$; $R = x^2/2y = (0.015\text{ m})^2/2(5 \times 450 \times 10^{-9}\text{ m})$ $= 50$ m. (b) By the lens-maker's equation (Eq. 24-6, p. 570), the focal length of this plano-convex lens is given by $1/f = (1.50 - 1)[1/50 + 1/\infty]$; $f = 100$ m. [This is a very long-focus lens, of power only $+0.01$ diopter.]

25-C5 The wavelength in cellophane is $(546 \times 10^{-9}\text{ m})/n$. The shift of 18 fringes means that there are 9 extra wavelengths in the cellophane path. Thus, $\dfrac{0.0082 \times 10^{-3}\text{ m}}{(546 \times 10^{-9}\text{ m})/n} - \dfrac{0.0082 \times 10^{-3}\text{ m}}{(546 \times 10^{-9}\text{ m})} = 9$; solving for n gives $n = 1.60$. [This experiment is shown in the film "Michelson Interferometer," listed in Reference 19 at the end of the chapter.]

25-C6 It is given that $\tan\theta_1 = n$, whence $\sin\theta_1 = n\cos\theta_1$. But from Snell's law, $\sin\theta_1 = n\sin\theta_2$. Hence $n\cos\theta_1 = n\sin\theta_2$; θ_1 and θ_2 are complementary angles. Since $\theta_1 + \theta_2 + \phi = 180°$, the angle ϕ between the reflected ray and the refracted ray is $90°$.

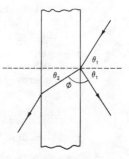

Prob. 25-C6

25-C7 (a) $(546.1\text{ nm})/1.320 = 413.7$ nm; $(546.1\text{ nm})/1.333$ $= 409.7$ nm. (b) Phase difference (in radians) $= 2\pi[(\text{path difference})/(\text{wavelength})]$. For one beam, $\phi_1 = 2\pi(1000\text{ nm})/(413.7\text{ nm}) = 15.188$ rad; for the other beam, $\phi_2 = 2\pi(1000\text{ nm})/(409.7\text{ nm})$ $= 15.336$ rad. The phase difference is $\phi_2 - \phi_1$ $= 0.148$ rad $= 8.5°$. [This illustrates the principle of the polarizing microscope that is discussed briefly on p. 630.]

25-C8 (a) Specific rotation $= \dfrac{147\text{ deg/dm}}{2.8\text{ g/cm}^3} = 52.5$ (deg/dm) per (g/cm^3).

(b) Concentration $= \dfrac{107\text{ deg/dm}}{52.5\text{ (deg/dm) per (g/cm}^3)} = 2.04$ g/cm^3. Alternatively, a simple proportion can be used, since the length of the cell is 10 dm in each case: concentration $= (2.8\text{ g/cm}^3)(107°/147°) = 2.04$ g/cm^3. [This is about the only place in physics that the decimeter (dm) is used. Dextrose is the same as d-glucose, with specific rotation $\alpha = +52.5$ units as found in this problem. l-glucose, an isomer of d-glucose, has $\alpha = -52.5$ units; levulose is a different sugar, with $\alpha = -88.5$ units.]

25-C9   Use the molecular weight (334) and the volume of the tube to find the concentration to be $(334 \times 10^{-6}\ \text{g})/(\pi)(0.1\ \text{cm})^2(20\ \text{cm}) = 5.32 \times 10^{-4}\ \text{g/cm}^3$. The rotation, for a tube length of 2 dm, is $2[(128\ \text{deg}/(\text{g/cm}^3)](5.32 \times 10^{-4}\ \text{g/cm}^3)$ $= 0.136°$. This small concentration of strychnine *could* be detected using the described polarimeter, assuming no other optically active solutes are present.

25-C10   If the O.A. is parallel to the surface, Fig. 25-55 is replaced by one in which the *major* axes of the ellipses in the slab are parallel to the direction of the E beam. The E beam travels faster than the O beam, but the beams do not diverge.

25-C11   The ratio of speeds equals the ratio of the indices of refraction. Hence the E ray in calcite is faster than the O ray, in the ratio $1.658/1.486 = 1.116$.

Chapter 26   Applied Optics

Questions

26-1   Spherical aberration, off-axis astigmatism, and chromatic aberration are discussed in Sec. 26-1. Although all these can be observed in the human eye, the aberration of greatest importance is not off-axis astigmatism, but a type of astigmatism associated with nonspherical shapes of cornea and lens (p. 621). See References 1, 5, and 6 at the end of the chapter concerning aberrations of the human eye.

26-2   Spherical aberration is reduced (see Fig. 26-1). However, stopping down the lens too far introduces loss of resolving power because of the diffraction pattern of the aperture (p. 633).

26-3   Hypermetropia refers to a condition, even in youth, where the image would be formed in back of the retina, usually because the retina is too close to the lens. In presbyopia, the image also would be formed in back of the retina, due to a loss of accommodation with aging.

26-4   The brain interprets the stimulus in an inverted sense, just as it has learned to reinvert the inverted image formed on the retina. See the footnote on p. 624 and also Reference 2 on the pinhead shadow inversion phenomenon.

26-5   A young person's muscle tone is usually good enough to allow the ciliary muscles to change the curvature of the lens surfaces, thus giving rise to accommodation.

26-6   Not much; see Example 26-1 on p. 626.

26-7   Both have an objective that makes a real image, which is viewed by using an eyepiece. In the telescope, the real image (in the barrel of the tube) is much smaller than the object; in the microscope the real image is much larger than the object.

26-8 If the size of the molecule is w, λ/w is not small (see p. 595, also pp. 628–29); in fact, $\lambda > w$ for this case.

26-9 Large diameter gives superior "light"-gathering power and the ability to "see" great distances. The low resolving power of a single dish is now being overcome by using several widely separated dishes in an interferometer arrangement (see References 14 and 15 at the end of the chapter).

26-10 The reflecting telescope is free of chromatic aberration (except for any that is introduced by the eyepiece), and a large mirror can be supported rigidly from beneath. The reflecting telescope is unwieldy and is not pointed directly at the object.

26-11 The Galilean telescope, or opera glass, is shorter than the astronomical telescope and gives an erect image.

26-12 Because they are images of a line-shaped slit.

26-13 Dispersion is the ability to spread apart two lines of nearly the same wavelength; resolving power is the ability to make the lines sharp, without regard to their angular separation. In symbols, dispersion is $\Delta\theta/\Delta\lambda$; resolving power is $\lambda/\Delta\lambda$.

26-14 See the discussion on p. 637.

Multiple Choice

26-15 (c);   26-16 (a);   26-17 (b);   26-18 (c);   26-19 (a);   26-20 (a).

Problems

26-A1 Player: θ = (2 m)/(80 m) = 0.025 rad; TV image: θ = (5 cm)/(300 cm) = 0.017 rad. The player in the stadium has the greater angular size.

26-A2 Satellite: (16 m)/(1600 × 10^3 m) = 10^{-5} rad; Saturn: (112 × 10^3 km)/(1.425 × 10^9 km) = 7.9×10^{-5} rad. Saturn is 7.9 times as large.

26-A3 f/D = (15 cm)/(5 cm) = 3; this is an $f/3$ lens.

26-A4 f/D = 2.8; f = (2.8)(3 cm) = 8.4 cm.

26-A5 M = (25 cm)/(0.125 cm) = 200.

26-A6 M = $(25/f)$ + 1 = 25/2.5 + 1 = 11.   [The magnifying power is between 10 and 11, depending on where the user places the virtual image.]

26-A7 M = (18)(15) = 270.

26-A8 $M = F/f$ = (240 cm)/(2 cm) = 120.   [Unless otherwise specified, we assume in all problems that a telescope or microscope is adjusted to place the virtual image at infinity; this is commonly called "relaxed vision" (but see p. 627, also Reference 7 at the end of the chapter).]

26-A9 $M = F/f$ gives (90 cm)/(2 cm) = 45, also (90 cm)/(0.75 cm) = 120.

26-A10 The moon's angular size is about $\frac{1}{120}$ rad (p. 625). Data from Table 7 on p. 805 give (3.48 × 10^6 m)/(3.84 × 10^8 m) = 0.0091 rad = 0.52°. (The sun also has an angular size of about 0.52°—this is what makes a total solar eclipse so spectacular.) A student's thumbnail, held at arm's length, subtends an angle of about 0.025 rad (1.5°), which is almost 3 times the angular size of the moon.

The large apparent size of the rising full moon is an optical illusion; the full moon easily fits behind even the little finger at arm's length.

26-B1 The diameter is now $\frac{1}{2}$ as large, the area is $\frac{1}{4}$ as large, so the exposure must be $4 \times \frac{1}{100}$ s = $\frac{1}{25}$ s.

26-B2 $f = 1/(60 \text{ m}^{-1}) = 0.0167$ m = 1.67 cm. The f-number is f/D = (1.67 cm)/(0.50 cm) = 3.3.

26-B3 The focal length of the lens (of power 55 diopters) is $\frac{1}{55}$ m = 1.82 cm.

Note: Probs. 26-B4 through 26-B8 deal with vision and the use of spectacle lenses. The method of curvatures (Sec. 24-9) is particularly useful in giving the student an intuitive understanding of how the eye lens and the spectacle lens (if any) combine to bring the wave front to a focus on the retina. We use P for the power of a lens, in diopters, and p for an object distance. The magnification, given by $-q/p$, need not be found. Similar results can, of course, be found by the ray method, using $1/p + 1/q = 1/f$, and solutions by both methods are given.

26-B4 *Curvature method:* Initial curvature + power of lens = final curvature becomes $0 + 57 = 57$. Either for the near point or for relaxed vision, the curvature of the wave front leaving the eye lens, heading for the retina, is $+57$ m^{-1}. (a) For the near point, by muscular effort the lens–cornea combination is given the maximum power $+65$ diopters. The extra $+8$ diopters can cancel the curvature -8 diopters of a wave front leaving an object that is $\frac{1}{8}$ m from the eye. The near point is at $\frac{1}{8}$ m, or 12.5 cm. (b) The retina is $\frac{1}{57}$ m, or 1.75 cm, from the lens. *Ray method:* (b) The relaxed lens, of power $+57$ diopters, has focal length $\frac{1}{57}$ m = 1.75 cm. This is the distance from the lens to the retina. (a) For the near point, $1/p + 1/q = 1/f$ becomes $1/p$ $+ 1/\frac{1}{57} = 1/\frac{1}{65}$; $1/p = 65 - 57 = 8$ m^{-1}; $p = \frac{1}{8}$ m = 12.5 cm.

26-B5 *Curvature method:* To see a distant object, he relaxes his eye, to a condition that can deal with a diverging wave front of curvature $-1/(2 \text{ m}) = -0.5$ diopter. The distant object supplies a wave front of curvature 0, so the top half of the bifocals operates thus: $0 + P_{\text{top}} = -0.5$; $P_{\text{top}} = -0.5$ diopter. To read the book, he can adjust his eye system to deal with a diverging wave front of curvature $-1/(0.5 \text{ m}) = -2$ diopters. However, the wave front from the book at 0.20 m has a diverging curvature -5 diopters. The bottom half of the bifocals operates thus: $-5 + P_{\text{bottom}} = -2$; $P_{\text{bottom}} = +3$ diopters. *Ray method:* The top half of the bifocals must form a virtual image 2 m from the eye lens. This image serves as an object for the eye lens. Thus, $1/p + 1/q$ $= 1/f$ becomes $1/\infty + 1/(-2) = 1/f$; $f = -2$ m; $P_{\text{top}} = -0.5$ diopter. The bottom half of the bifocals must form a virtual image 0.5 m from the eye lens; this image serves as an object for the eye lens. Now $1/p + 1/q = 1/f$ becomes $1/(0.2) + 1/(-0.5) = 1/f$; $1/f = 3$ m^{-1} = $+3$ diopters.

26-B6 *Curvature method:* For a sharp image on the retina, the wave front leaving the lens (inside the eye) must have curvature $1/(0.2 \text{ m}) = +50$ m^{-1}. (a) Relaxed eye: Initial curvature + power of spectacle lens + power of eye lens = final curvature becomes $0 + (-8) + P_{\text{eye}} = +50$; $P_{\text{eye}} = +58$ diopters. (b) For the near point without glasses, the power of the eye is now $58 + 5$ = 63 diopters. We have $-1/p + 63 = +50$; $p = 1/13 = 0.0769$ m = 7.69 cm. *Ray method:* (a) The negative lens forms a virtual image $\frac{1}{8}$ m from the eye lens; this image serves as a real object for the eye lens. Now $1/p + 1/q = 1/f$, applied to the eye lens, becomes $1/(\frac{1}{8}) + 1/(\frac{1}{50}) = 1/f$; $1/f = 58$ m^{-1}; $P_{eye} = +58$ diopters.   (b) For the near point without glasses, the eye lens has power 63 diopters, so $1/f = 63$ m^{-1}. The lens equation becomes $1/p + 1/(\frac{1}{50}) = 63$; $1/p = 13$ m^{-1}; $p = \frac{1}{13}$ m = 7.69 cm.

26-B7 *Curvature method:* When the newspaper is held at 24 cm, the wave front is too divergent to be handled by the eye lens, which can handle a curvature of $-1/0.60$ m^{-1}. Initial curvature + power of spectacle lens = final curvature becomes $-1/(0.24) + P_{lens} = -1/(0.60)$; $P = +2.5$ diopters, and $f = 1/(2.5$ m$^{-1})$ = 0.40 m = 40 cm.   *Ray method:* The spectacle lens forms a virtual image 60 cm from the eye lens; this image serves as a real object for the eye lens. The lens equation $1/p + 1/q = 1/f$ becomes $1/(24) + 1/(-60) = 1/f$; $f = +40$ cm, a converging lens.

26-B8 The child suffers from myopia; the relaxed eye lens is too powerful to form an image on the retina. For the near point, as well as for relaxed vision, the image distance inside the eye is 0.02 m, and the curvature of the wave front (inside the eye) is $+50$ diopters as it leaves the eye lens headed for the retina. *Curvature method:* (a) For the strongest power (near point), initial curvature + power of eye lens = final curvature becomes $-1/(0.10) + P = +50$; $P = +60$ diopters. For weakest power (far point), $-1/(1.25) + P = +50$; $P = +50.8$ diopters.   (b) For relaxed distant vision, $0 + P_{spectacle} + 50.8 = 50$; $P_{spectacle} = -0.8$ diopter. The negative sign indicates that the spectacle lens is diverging; it cancels some of the excess power of the eye lens.   *Ray method:* (a) Near point: $1/10 + 1/2 = 1/f$; $P = 1/f = 0.6$ cm$^{-1} = 60$ m$^{-1} = +60$ diopters. Far point: $1/125 + 1/2 = 1/f$; $P = 1/f = \frac{127}{250} = 0.508$ cm$^{-1} = 50.8$ m^{-1} = +50.8 diopters.   (b) The spectacle lens must form a virtual image 125 cm from the eye. Applied to the spectacle lens, $1/p + 1/q = 1/f$ becomes $1/\infty + 1/(-125) = 1/f$; $1/f = -0.008$ cm$^{-1} = -0.8$ m$^{-1} = -0.8$ diopter (a diverging lens).

26-B9 The focal length is $\frac{1}{40}$ m = 2.5 cm; $M = 25/f = (25$ cm$)/2.5$ cm$) = 10$.

26-B10 First find the object distance: $1/p + 1/(-100) = 1/2$; $p = \frac{100}{51}$ cm.   [*Curvature method:* $-1/p + 1/2 = -1/100$; $p = \frac{100}{51}$ cm.] The linear magnification is $-q/p = -(-100)/(\frac{100}{51}) = 51$, and the final image is of size $51h$, viewed at 100 cm. The unaided eye would view h at 25 cm. Hence

$$M = \frac{\text{angular size (aided)}}{\text{angular size (unaided)}} = \frac{(51h)/(100)}{(h)/(25)} = \frac{(51)(25)}{100} = 12.75$$

[As could be expected the answer lies between the values $1 + 25/f = 13.5$ and $25/f = 12.5$ (See Example 26-1 on p. 626-27).]

26-B11 Follow the method of Example 26-1a. First find the object distance: $1/p + 1/(-50) = 1/2$; $p = \frac{50}{26}$ cm.   [*Curvature method:* $-1/p + 1/2 = -1/50$; $p = \frac{50}{26}$ cm.] Now $h' = mh = -[(-50)/(\frac{50}{26})]h = 26h$.

$$M = \frac{\text{angular size (aided)}}{\text{maximum angular size (unaided)}} = \frac{(26h)/(50 \text{ cm})}{(h)/(50 \text{ cm})} = 26.$$

[This magnifier turns out to be about twice as useful to a person with a 50 cm near point as would be the same lens for a person with a "normal" near point. The far-sighted person starts off with a smaller unaided retinal image, so the improvement is relatively greater for him when the object is, in effect, brought near the focal point of the lens.]

26-B12 $M = 1 + 25/f = 8$; $f = 25/7$; $1/f = \frac{7}{25}$ cm$^{-1} = 0.28$ cm$^{-1} = 28$ m$^{-1} = +28$ diopters.

26-B13 $f/D = f/(5$ cm$) = 1.4$; $f = 7$ cm. $M = 1 + 25/f = 1 + (25$ cm$)/(7$ cm$) = 4.57$.

26-B14 $f = R/2 = 30$ cm; $1/20 + 1/q = 1/30$; $q = -60$ cm (a virtual image behind the mirror). [*Curvature method:* $-1/20 + 1/30 = 1/q$; $q = -60$ cm.] The image is 80 cm from the man's eye. The linear magnification is $-q/p$ $= -(-60$ cm$)/(20$ cm$) = +3$.

$$M = \frac{\text{angular size with aid}}{\text{angular size without aid}} = \frac{(3h)/(80 \text{ cm})}{(h)/(40 \text{ cm})} = 1.5$$

26-B15 (*a*) Objective lens: $1/0.40 + 1/q = 1/0.39$; $q = 15.6$ cm. This real image is the object for the eyepiece lens, and is 1.5 cm from the eyepiece. Distance between lenses $= (15.6 + 1.5)$ cm $= 17.1$ cm. (*b*) Real image is magnified by a factor $(15.6$ cm$)/(0.40$ cm$) = 39$. The eyepiece has magnification $25/f$ $= 25/1.5$; overall magnification is $(39)(25/1.5) = 650$.

26-B16 The real image, between the lenses, is 2 cm from the eyepiece, hence the image distance for the objective is $(21 - 2)$ cm $= 19$ cm. The object distance is found from $1/p + 1/19 = 1/1$; $p = \frac{19}{18}$ cm (just outside the focal point of the objective). The real image is larger than the object (in the ratio $19/\frac{19}{18} = 18$); the device is a microscope. [The overall magnification is $(18)(25/2)$ $= 225$.]

26-B17 (*a*) The focal length of the objective is 80 cm; the real image is $(82.5 - 80)$ cm $= 2.5$ cm from the eyepiece. When adjusted for minimum eyestrain, light leaves the eyepiece with zero divergence, hence the focal length is 2.5 cm. $M = F/f = (80$ cm$)/(2.5$ cm$) = 32$. (*b*) $(1000$ m$)/32 = 31.3$ m.

26-B18 (*a*) The real image is $(6 - 2)$ cm $= 4$ cm from the objective. The object distance for the objective lens is found from $1/p + 1/4 = 1/0.4$; $p = \frac{4}{9}$ cm $= 0.444$ cm. [*Curvature method:* $-1/p + 1/0.4 = 1/4$; $p = 0.444$ cm.] (*b*) Objective: $m = -q/p = -(4$ cm$)/(\frac{4}{9}$ cm$) = -9$; eyepiece: $M = 25/2 = 12.5$; overall magnifying power $= (-9)(12.5) = -112.5$ (inverted).

26-B19 (*a*) Focal length of mirror $= R/2 = 1.20$ m. The real image of a distant star is 120 cm from the objective; this is 1 cm from the eyepiece, giving a total length of 121 cm. (*b*) $M = F/f = (120$ cm$)/(1$ cm$) = 120$. (*c*) $(386\,000$ km$)/120 = 3217$ km.

26-B20 (*a*) The real image is 5 cm from the eyepiece and 45 cm from the objective; $M = F/f = (45$ cm$)/(5$ cm$) = 9$. (*b*) If $m = -1$, $p = q$ for the erecting lens, $1/p + 1/q = 1/f$ gives $1/p + 1/p = 1/f$; $p = 2f = 18$ cm. Also, $q = 18$ cm. The erecting lens adds 36 cm to the length of the instrument; the total length is now $(50 + 36)$ cm $= 86$ cm. [This is the long and slender "spy glass" used a century or more ago.]

26-B21 (*a*) $M = F/f = (1/f)/(1/F) = (12.5$ diopters$)/(2$ diopters$) = 6.25$. (*b*) Length $= F + f = 50$ cm $+ 8$ cm $= 58$ cm.

26-B22 The eyepiece has focal length $\frac{1}{25}$ m $= 4$ cm; the objective would have formed a real image of a distant object at a point 4 cm beyond the eyepiece, i.e., 24 cm from the objective. The focal length of the objective is 24 cm.

26-B23 $a = \left(\dfrac{1}{4000} \text{ cm}\right)\left(\dfrac{10^9 \text{ nm}}{10^2 \text{ cm}}\right) = 2500$ nm. Use $\sin \theta = n\lambda/a$. Yellow: $\sin \theta$ $= 3(580$ nm$)/(2500$ nm$)$; $\theta = 44.11°$. Blue: $\sin \theta = 3(470$ nm$)/(2500$ nm$)$; $\theta = 34.33°$. $\Delta\theta = 44.11° - 34.33° = 9.8°$.

26-B24 For each wavelength and order, compute $\sin \theta$ from $n\lambda/a$. For example, for the third red order, $\sin \theta = 3(700$ nm$)/(2500$ nm$) = 0.840$. All told, there are 13 values of $\sin \theta < 1$. The sequence is V_1, G_1, R_1, V_2, G_2, V_3, R_2, V_4, G_3, V_5, R_3, G_4, V_6. [The overlapping of orders is nicely illustrated by the grating spectrum of a mercury arc's blue, green, and yellow lines (there is no strong red line in the mercury spectrum).]

26-C1 (a) $1/1.10 + 1/q = 1/1$; $q = 11$ cm. This real image is 1.25 cm from the eyepiece, so the separation of the lenses is $(11 + 1.25)$ cm = 12.25 cm.   (b) The
linear size of the magnified bug is $(0.2$ mm$)(11/1.1) = 2.0$ mm, viewed at
1.25 cm (12.5 mm), so the magnified angular size is $(2$ mm$)/(12.5$ mm$)$
= 0.16 rad.   (c) The eyepiece is racked out so that its principal focus is
now beyond the real image formed by the objective. Considering the eyepiece
lens, with real object and real image, we have $1/p + 1/100 = 1/1.25$; $p = \frac{100}{79}$ cm
= 1.2658 cm, instead of 1.2500 cm when viewing the bug through the microscope in the normal fashion with minimum eyestrain. The lens must be moved
$(1.2658 - 1.2500)$ cm = 0.0158 cm away from the objective.   (d) $h' = h(q/p)$
= $(2.0$ mm$)[(100$ cm$)/(\frac{100}{79}$ cm$)] = 158$ mm.

26-C2 For the objective, $1/300 + 1/q = 1/20$; $q = \frac{300}{14}$ cm = 21.43 cm. The size of the
real image is $h(q/p) = h[(\frac{300}{14}$ cm$)/(300$ cm$)] = \frac{1}{14}h$. This image serves as a
real object for the eyepiece; its angular size, as viewed from the center of
the eyepiece lens, is $(\frac{1}{14}h)/(2$ cm$)$. The original object's distance from the eye
is $(300 + 21.43 + 2.0)$ cm = 323.4 cm.
$$M = \frac{\text{angular size with aid}}{\text{maximum angular size without aid}} = \frac{(\frac{1}{14}h)/(2\text{ cm})}{(h)/(323.4\text{ cm})} = 11.55.$$

26-C3 $F/f = 45$; $F + f = 92$. Solve simultaneously, obtaining $F = 90$ cm, $f = 2$ cm.

26-C4 (a) $1/4000 + 1/q = 1/8$; $q = \frac{4000}{499}$ cm
= 8.016 cm. $h' = h(q/p) = (30$ cm$)$
$\times [(\frac{4000}{499}cm)/(4000$ cm$)] = \frac{30}{499}$ cm = 0.060
cm.   (b) Since parallel rays emerge
from the eyepiece, the virtual object for
that lens, of height h', is 2.00 cm beyond
the eyepiece.   (c) Distance between
lenses = $(8.016 - 2.00)$ cm = 6.016 cm.
(d) The angular size of the image
formed by parallel rays leaving the

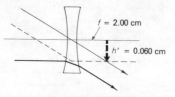

Prob. 26-C4

negative lens is given by $h'/f = (0.060$ cm$)/(2$ cm$) = 0.030$ rad. The unaided
angular size is about $(30$ cm$)/(4000$ cm$) = 0.0075$ rad. Thus, the overall angular magnification is $M = (0.030$ rad$)/(0.0075$ rad$) = 4.0$.   [A more sophis-
ticated analysis assumes the virtual object to be at a distance y to the right
of the eyepiece lens, forming a virtual image at a distance x to the left of that
lens. The lens equation gives $y = \dfrac{2}{1 - 2/x}$, and the linear size of the virtual
image is $h'' = h'(x/y) = h'(x/2 - 1)$. Here h' is the linear size of the image
formed by the objective of an object of height h at some large distance D
(which cancels out later); $h' = h(8/D)$. The angular magnification is, therefore,
$$M = \frac{\text{angular size with aid}}{\text{angular size without aid}} = \frac{\left[\frac{8h}{D}(x/2 - 1)\right]/x}{h/D}$$
which reduces to $M = 4 - 8/x$. As $x \to \infty$, $M \to 4$, as in this problem. Note
that the angular magnification of a Galilean telescope is a maximum when the
emerging rays are parallel (minimum eyestrain, $x \to \infty$); this is not true for
the astronomical telescope.]

26-C5 (a) The lens-maker's formula gives $P = 1/f = (n - 1)/R$, since the lenses
are plano-convex. For thin lenses in contact, $1/f = 1/f_1 + 1/f_2 = (n_C - 1)$
$\times (1/\infty + 1/R_C) + (n_F - 1)(-1/R_F + 1/\infty)$, which reduces to the desired equation for the combined power.   (b) For one color, $1/f$ can be written as

$$\frac{1}{f} = \frac{n_C}{R_C} - \frac{n_F}{R_F} - \left(\frac{1}{R_C} - \frac{1}{R_F}\right); \text{ for another color, } \frac{1}{f'} = \frac{n_C'}{R_C} - \frac{n_F'}{R_F} - \left(\frac{1}{R_C} - \frac{1}{R_F}\right).$$

Equate $1/f$ to $1/f'$ and obtain $(n_C - n_C')/R_C = (n_F - n_F')/R_F$, or $\Delta n_C/R_C$
$= \Delta n_F/R_F$.　　　(c) Use the result of part (b): $R_F = R_C(n_F - n_F')/(n_C - n_C')$
$= (20.00 \text{ cm})(0.0170)/(0.0095) = 35.7895$ cm. (To avoid rounding errors, calculations are carried to 5 or 6 significant figures; results can be rounded
later, if desired.)　　　(d) $1/f$ values (powers P in diopters) are calculated.
Red light: $P_C = (0.5145)/(0.2000) = +2.5725; \ P_F = (0.6221)/(-0.357895)$
$= -1.7382; \ P_{\text{net}} = +0.8343$ diopter. Blue light: $P_C = (0.5240)/(0.2000)$
$= +2.6200; \ P_F = (0.6391)/(-0.357895) = -1.7857; \ P_{\text{net}} = +0.8343$ diopter. It
is seen that the power of the lens is the same for red light and for blue light,
and the lens combination is achromatic for these two colors.

26-C6　The lines are not quite resolved. The formula for resolving power (implied
but not stated on p. 637) is $\lambda/\Delta\lambda = nN$, where n is the order and N is the total
number of lines (slits) of the grating. Here $n = 2$, $N = 90\,000$, and $nN = 180\,000$.
But we need a resolving power of $(600 \text{ nm})/(0.003 \text{ nm}) = 200\,000$. 　　[We can
also approach this problem without using a formula for resolving power (see
Fig. 25-14 on p. 593). Let $\lambda_1 = 600.000$ nm and $\lambda_2 = 600.003$ nm. There are
9×10^4 slits in the grating; therefore, for λ_1 in the second order, the segment
MM' is $(9 \times 10^4)(2\lambda_1) = (18 \times 10^4)(600.000)$ nm. The first minimum just beyond
this maximum (still for λ_1) is at a slightly greater angle for which MM' is
$(9 \times 10^4)(2\lambda_1) + \lambda_1$, which can be written as $(MM')_1 = (180\,000 + 1)(600.000)$ nm.
However, the second-order maximum for λ_2 is at an angle for which MM' is
$(9 \times 10^4)(2\lambda_2)$, which can be written as $(MM')_2 = (180\,000)(600.000 + 0.003)$ nm.
Subtracting, we find $(MM')_1 - (MM')_2 = 600$ nm $-$ 540 nm. The maximum of
λ_2 lies inside the first minimum of λ_1, and the lines are not quite resolved.]

26-C7　The angular separation of the lamps is $(1.5 \text{ m})/(8000 \text{ m}) = 1.875 \times 10^{-4}$ rad.
The angular radius of the diffraction disk of each headlight is $\lambda/0.82D$
$= (580 \times 10^{-9} \text{ m})/(0.82)(4 \times 10^{-3} \text{ m}) = 1.77 \times 10^{-4}$ rad. The headlights are just
barely separated.

26-C8　The angle subtended by the targets is $(300 \text{ m})/(40 \times 10^3 \text{ m}) = 0.0075$ rad. Use
$\sin\theta = \lambda/0.82D$, whence $D = \lambda/(0.82)(\sin\theta) = \lambda/(0.82)(0.0075); D = \lambda(162.6)$ for
this dish. 　　(a) $D = (0.102 \text{ m})(162.6) = 16.6$ m; 　　(b) $D = (0.03 \text{ m})(162.6)$
$= 4.9$ m.

26-C9　(a) $2\theta = 2\lambda/0.82D = \dfrac{2(416 \times 10^{-9} \text{ m})}{(0.82)(3 \times 10^{-3} \text{ m})} = 3.4 \times 10^{-4}$ rad $= 1.2'$. 　　(b) Linear

diameter $= r(2\theta) = (20 \times 10^{-3} \text{ m})(3.4 \times 10^{-4} \text{ rad}) = 6.8 \times 10^{-6}$ m $= 6.8 \ \mu$m.
(c) Area of diffraction disk $= \frac{1}{4}\pi(6.8 \times 10^{-6} \text{ m})^2 = 3.6 \times 10^{-11}$ m^2. Area of a
cone $= (1/250\,000) \text{ mm}^2 = 4 \times 10^{-12}$ m^2. The diffraction disk's area is 9 times
that of a cone. 　　(d) $(2.2 \times 10^{-6} \text{ m})/(20 \times 10^{-3} \text{ m}) = 1.1 \times 10^{-4}$ rad $= 0.4'$.
[The human eye has evolved with cones (at the region of most distinct vision)
small enough so that evolution toward smaller cones would serve no useful
function.]

Chapter 27   Electrons and Photons

Questions

27-1   Yes; no. (See the first paragraph of Sec. 27-1.)

27-2   Down. The electrons are moving to the left, equivalent to a conventional current to the right. Use $\mathbf{F} = q\mathbf{v} \times \mathbf{B}$.

27-3   All electrons have the same rest mass, 9.11×10^{-31} kg. The mass depends on velocity; faster electrons have greater mass (Eq. 7-6 on p. 158).

27-4   In broad outline, an exposed film absorbs light energy to raise a molecule to a stable excited state. During development, additional chemical energy is absorbed from the developer sufficient to complete the release of metallic silver in the emulsion. Red photons, of energy less than blue photons, have insufficient energy to establish the excited state, hence the film is insensitive to red light. Modern panchromatic emulsions utilize certain dyes and other complex molecules to absorb the low-energy red photons.

27-5   Copper has the higher work function, and also the higher photoelectric threshold frequency.

27-6   The KE is 10^5 eV.

27-7   From $\lambda = h/mv$, at a given speed the electron, of smaller mass, has a guide wave of longer wavelength.

27-8   No; aberrations of the magnetic lenses are the limiting factor.

27-9   Yes, on the average; no, when individual atoms are considered.

Multiple Choice

27-10   (a);   27-11   (c);   27-12   (b);   27-13   (b);   27-14   (a);   27-15   (c).

Problems

27-A1 $h\nu = (6.63 \times 10^{-34} \text{ J·s})\left(\dfrac{3 \times 10^8 \text{ m/s}}{310 \times 10^{-9} \text{ m}}\right) = 6.42 \times 10^{-19} \text{ J} = (6.42 \times 10^{-19} \text{ J})$

       $\times \left(\dfrac{1 \text{ eV}}{1.60 \times 10^{-19} \text{ J}}\right) = 4.0 \text{ eV}.$

Note: In this chapter, we often use the relation between E (in eV) and λ (in nm) given in Eq. 27-7: $E = (1240 \text{ eV·nm})/\lambda$. Here, using the "magic number" we calculate the energy directly in eV: $E = (1240 \text{ eV·nm})/(310 \text{ nm}) = 4.0 \text{ eV}.$

27-A2 $\lambda = (1240 \text{ eV·nm})/(2.10 \text{ eV}) = 590$ nm, equivalent to 5.90×10^{-9} m or 5900 Å.

27-A3 $(10^{-6} \text{ erg})\left(\dfrac{1 \text{ J}}{10^7 \text{ erg}}\right)\left(\dfrac{1 \text{ MeV}}{1.60 \times 10^{-13} \text{ J}}\right) = 0.625$ MeV.

27-A4 $mgh = (20 \times 10^{-6} \text{ g})\left(\dfrac{1 \text{ kg}}{10^3 \text{ g}}\right)\left(9.8 \ \dfrac{\text{N}}{\text{kg}}\right)(10^{-2} \text{ m}) = 1.96 \times 10^{-9}$ J;

       $(1.96 \times 10^{-9} \text{ J})\left(\dfrac{1 \text{ MeV}}{1.6 \times 10^{-13} \text{ J}}\right) = 1.23 \times 10^4$ MeV (12.3 GeV)

27-A5 $\lambda = h/mv = (6.63 \times 10^{-34} \text{ J·s})/(10^{-18} \text{ kg})(10^{-6} \text{ m/s}) = 6.63 \times 10^{-10} \text{ m} = 6.63 \text{ A}.$

27-A6 $\lambda = h/mv = (6.63 \times 10^{-34} \text{ J·s})/(9.11 \times 10^{-31} \text{ kg})(1.5 \times 10^{7} \text{ m/s}) = 4.8 \times 10^{-11} \text{ m}$
        $= 0.48 \text{ Å}.$ [The electron's speed is small enough so the rest mass can be used.]

27-B1   Equating the upward electric force to the weight of the drop gives $q(V/D)$
        $= mg$, where D is the separation of the plates. $(5 \times 1.6 \times 10^{-19} \text{ C})(600 \text{ V})/6$
        $\times 10^{-3} \text{ m}) = m(9.8 \text{ N/kg})$; $m = 8.16 \times 10^{-15} \text{ kg}$. The volume of the drop is m/d
        $= (8.16 \times 10^{-15} \text{ kg})/(900 \text{ kg/m}^3) = 9.07 \times 10^{-18} \text{ m}^3$. Finally, from the formula for
        the volume of a sphere, $9.07 \times 10^{-18} \text{ m}^3 = \frac{4}{3}\pi r^3$; $r = 1.29 \times 10^{-6} \text{ m} = 1.29 \ \mu\text{m}$.

27-B2 $F = q\left(\dfrac{V}{D}\right) = mg$; $m = \dfrac{qV}{gd} = \dfrac{(6 \times 1.6 \times 10^{-19} \text{ C})(400 \text{ V})}{(9.8 \text{ N/kg})(0.02 \text{ m})} = 1.96 \times 10^{-15} \text{ kg}.$

27-B3   The experimental value of e/m_0, given on p. 649, is 1.759×10^{11} C/kg. From
        Eq. 27-3,

$$R = \sqrt{\dfrac{2V}{B^2(e/m_0)}} = \sqrt{\dfrac{2(400 \text{ V})}{(4 \times 10^{-4} \text{ T})^2(1.759 \times 10^{11} \text{ C/kg})}} = 0.169 \text{ m}. \qquad \text{[This re-}$$

        sult is used in Prob. 27-C5.]

27-B4   Equate the centripetal force to the magnetic force: $mv^2/R = QvB$; $mv = BQR$.
        [Although the proof is nonrelativistic, the result is in fact valid for particles
        of any momentum, if the relativistic mass m is used.]

27-B5   From Eq. 27-3, $V = \frac{1}{2}R^2B^2(e/m) = \frac{1}{2}(0.40 \text{ m})^2(6 \times 10^{-5} \text{ T})^2(1.759 \times 10^{11} \text{ C/kg})$
        $= 50.7 \text{ V}.$

27-B6 $KE = qV = (2 \times 1.6 \times 10^{-19} \text{ C})(2 \times 10^9 \text{ V}) = 6.4 \times 10^{-10} \text{ J} = 640 \text{ pJ}.$ [The
        doubly charged He^{2+} ion has $KE = 2 \times 2 \text{ GeV} = 4 \text{ GeV}$, which converts to 640
        pJ. The *mass* of the ion does not enter into the problem.]

27-B7   Energy ratio = frequency ratio = $(3 \times 10^{18} \text{ Hz})/(98 \times 10^6 \text{ Hz}) \approx 3 \times 10^{10}$. The
        energy of the photons from a broadcasting station is so small that energy
        changes are essentially continuous.

27-B8   Using Eq. 7-8 (p. 162) for KE, the photoelectric equation becomes mc^2
        $- m_0c^2 = h\nu - w.$

Note: In problems 27-B9 through 27-B17, use $E = (1240 \text{ eV·nm})/\lambda$ to find photon energies.

27-B9   Photon energy = $1240/200 = 6.20$ eV; maximum $KE = (6.20 - 4.52) \text{ eV} = 1.68 \text{ eV}.$

27-B10   Photon energy is $1240/240 = 5.17$ eV; $KE = (5.17 - 2.40) \text{ eV} = 2.77 \text{ eV}.$
        [The metal surface is "thin," hence the photoelectrons all have the maximum
        possible energy, given by Eq. 27-6. In Probs. 27-B9, 27-B10, and 27-B12,
        the "maximum" KE refers to the KE of the electrons emitted near the surface
        of the metal (see footnote to column 2 of p. 649).]

27-B11   Photon energy is $1240/420 = 2.95$ eV; $w = (2.95 - 0.62) \text{ eV} = 2.33 \text{ eV}.$

27-B12   Photon energy is $1240/589 = 2.11$ eV; $w = (2.11 - 0.65) \text{ eV} = 1.46 \text{ eV}.$

27-B13 $\lambda = (1240 \text{ eV·nm})/(4.52 \text{ eV}) = 274$ nm.   [The threshold for tungsten is in
        the ultraviolet region. Visible light cannot emit photoelectrons from tungsten
        and many other common metals.]

27-B14 $w = 1240/450 = 2.76$ eV.

27-B15   The photoelectrons leave the surface with $KE = 1.04$ eV, and an additional
        1.22 eV is needed to overcome the work function. The photon energy is
        $(1.04 + 1.22) \text{ eV} = 2.26$ eV; $\lambda = 1240/2.26 = 549$ nm (green light).

27-B16   Photon energy is $1240/589 = 2.11$ eV. This is less than the work function of
        sodium metal, so no photoelectrons are emitted.

27-B17 The threshold is at 500 nm, so the work function is $1240/500 = 2.48$ eV. When λ reaches 400 nm, the photon energy is $1240/400 = 3.10$ eV; KE $= (3.10 - 2.48)$ eV $= 0.62$ eV.

27-B18 (a) $p = h/\lambda = (6.63 \times 10^{-34} \text{ J·s})/(1.54 \times 10^{-10} \text{ m}) = 4.31 \times 10^{-24}$ kg·m/s. (b) From $p = mv$, with $v = c$ in this case, we have $m = p/c = (4.31 \times 10^{-24}$ kg·m/s$)/(3 \times 10^8$ m/s$) = 1.44 \times 10^{-32}$ kg. [*Check:* Photon energy $= (12\,400 \text{ eV·Å})/(1.54 \text{ Å}) = 8052$ eV $= 1.288 \times 10^{-15}$ J. From $E = mc^2$, $m = E/c^2 = (1.288 \times 10^{-15} \text{ J})/(3 \times 10^8 \text{ m/s})^2 = 1.44 \times 10^{-32}$ kg. A photon has zero rest mass, and its energy may be considered to be entirely KE. This agrees with Eq. 7-6, which states that KE $= mc^2 - m_0c^2$ for any particle (including the particle known as the photon). If $m_0 = 0$, as is true for the photon, the formula reduces to KE $= mc^2$.]

27-B19 $p = h/\lambda = (6.63 \times 10^{-34} \text{ J·s})/(550 \times 10^{-9} \text{ m}) = 1.21 \times 10^{-27}$ kg·m/s. [See Eq. 27-8.]

27-B20 Original $\lambda = (12\,400 \text{ eV·Å})/(9000 \text{ eV}) = 1.378$ Å. For $90°$ scattering, $\lambda' = 0.0243$ Å (p.654). Hence the scattered wavelength is $\Delta\lambda = (1.378 + 0.024)$ Å $= 1.402$ Å. [Figure 27-9 is a record of the $90°$ scattering of the Pt $L\alpha$ line ($\lambda = 1.314$ Å) by a block of paraffin.]

27-B21 Use conservation of energy. $E = (12\,400 \text{ eV·Å})/(2.00 \text{ Å}) = 6200$ eV; $E' = (12\,400 \text{ eV·Å})/(2.02 \text{ Å}) = 6139$ eV. The recoiling electron's KE is $(6200 - 6139)$ eV $= 61$ eV. [$\Delta\lambda$ is different from 0.0243 Å because the scattering did not take place at $90°$.]

27-B22 $\lambda = h/mv = (6.63 \times 10^{-34} \text{ J·s})/(0.025 \text{ kg})(600 \text{ m/s}) = 4.4 \times 10^{-35}$ m. Wave behavior is unobservable because $\lambda/w \ll 1$ for any conceivable slit.

27-B23 (a) $\Delta p = h/\Delta x = (6.63 \times 10^{-34} \text{ J·s})/(2 \times 10^{-2} \text{ m}) = 3 \times 10^{-32}$ kg·m/s. (b) The uncertainty in the x component of momentum translates into an uncertainty in the x component of velocity: $\Delta v_x = (3 \times 10^{-32} \text{ kg·m/s})/(0.025 \text{ kg}) = 1.2 \times 10^{-30}$ m/s. The uncertainty in lateral target position is $(0.3 \text{ s})(1.2 \times 10^{-30}$ m/s$) \approx 4 \times 10^{-31}$ m. (c) On an atomic scale, the bullet fits loosely in the rifle barrel and emerges with some randomness of direction entirely unrelated to the uncertainty principle; this randomness is a consequence of Newtonian mechanics and could be calculated (in principle) if the exact structure of the gun and bullet were known precisely enough. For this classical uncertainty, $\Delta p \Delta x$ is much greater than h. There are also variations in the propulsive force of the gunpowder in different bullets. Air resistance and winds are variable. The rifle may not always be aimed precisely (to within 10^{-30} m of the target!); even if bolted down to a firing stand, the rifle and the target are not rigid to a degree that would make use of the uncertainty principle meaningful.

27-B24 From Prob. 27-B4, $p = BQR$. From $\lambda = h/p$, we obtain $\lambda = h/BQR$. [A dimensional check of this equation for λ is instructive.]

27-B25 The KE is 50 keV $= 8 \times 10^{-15}$ J. $p = mv = \sqrt{2m(\tfrac{1}{2}mv^2)} = \sqrt{2mE} = \sqrt{2(9.11 \times 10^{-31} \text{ kg})(8 \times 10^{-15} \text{ J})} = 1.21 \times 10^{-22}$ kg·m/s. $\lambda = h/p = (6.63 \times 10^{-34} \text{ J·s})/(1.21 \times 10^{-22} \text{ kg·m/s}) = 5.5 \times 10^{-12}$ m ≈ 0.05 Å. [Using the classical formula KE $= \tfrac{1}{2}mv^2$, we can find the velocity of the electron to be 1.32×10^8 m/s, momentum $= mv = 1.207 \times 10^{-22}$ kg·m/s, and $\lambda = 0.0549$ Å, as above. Since $v \approx 0.4c$, the outline of an exact (relativistic) treatment may be of interest: KE $= 50$ keV, $E_0 =$ rest energy of electron $= 511$ keV; total energy is 561 keV. Then from $m/m_0 = E/E_0$ we obtain $\sqrt{1 - v^2/c^2} = 511/561$, whence $v = 0.413c$. Finally, $p = mv = [m_0(561/511)]v = 1.239 \times 10^{-22}$ kg·m/s. This gives $\lambda = h/p = 0.0535$ Å. It is seen that the error in momentum (and wavelength) is less than 3% for v/c as great as 0.4.]

27-B26 $KE_{electron}/KE_{proton} = 1837.$ [If they have the same λ, they have the same momentum. Since $KE = \frac{1}{2}mv^2 = (mv)^2/2m = p^2/2m$, nonrelativistically, we see that KE is inversely proportional to m for a given momentum.]

27-B27 $p = \sqrt{2mE}$; $\lambda = \dfrac{h}{p} = \dfrac{h}{\sqrt{2mE}} = \dfrac{6.63 \times 10^{-34} \text{ J·s}}{\sqrt{2(1.67 \times 10^{-27} \text{ kg})(55 \times 10^3 \times 1.6 \times 10^{-19} \text{ J})}}$

      $= 1.22 \times 10^{-13}$ m.   [This is 0.00122 Å, or 122 fm.]

27-B28 From Example 16-1, $v = 460$ m/s. The mass of a single O_2 molecule is $(0.032 \text{ kg})/(6.02 \times 10^{23})$. Thus,

$$\lambda = \frac{h}{p} = \frac{(6.63 \times 10^{-34} \text{ J·s})(6.02 \times 10^{23})}{(0.032 \text{ kg})(460 \text{ m/s})} = 2.71 \times 10^{-11} \text{ m} = 0.27 \text{ Å}.$$

[The de Broglie wavelength is about $\frac{1}{4}$ the interatomic separation, indicating that quantum mechanics must be taken seriously in studying the molecule. There is an 8% inaccuracy in this solution, since the average (mean) v should be used, not the rms value 460 m/s from Example 16-1. (See footnote on p. 353.) Using $v = 425$ m/s would give $\lambda = 0.29$ Å.]

27-C1 Let λ be the threshold wavelength and $\lambda - 100$ be the photon wavelength (in nm). $1240/(\lambda - 100) - 1240/\lambda = 1$; solve for λ, obtaining 406 nm.

27-C2 Each photon's energy is $1240/555 = 2.234$ eV $= 3.57 \times 10^{-19}$ J. If N is the number of photons leaving the 100 W lamp each second, we have

$$\left(100 \, \frac{\text{J}}{\text{s}}\right)(0.01) = \left(N \, \frac{\text{photons}}{\text{s}}\right)(3.57 \times 10^{-19} \text{ J/photon}); \; N = 2.80 \times 10^{18} \text{ photons/s}.$$

The emitted photons pass through a spherical surface, centered on the moon, of radius 3.8×10^8 m; the mirror intercepts only a small fraction of the photons (proportional to r^2). Thus,

$$N' = \left(2.80 \times 10^{18} \, \frac{\text{photons}}{\text{s}}\right)\left(\frac{\pi(2.5 \text{ m})^2}{4\pi(3.8 \times 10^8 \text{ m})^2}\right) = 30 \text{ photons/s through the}$$

mirror.   [This flux of photons could be easily detected.]

27-C3 The electron is nonrelativistic; $p = \sqrt{2mE} = \sqrt{2(9.11 \times 10^{-31}\text{kg})(75 \times 1.6 \times 10^{-19} \text{ J})}$ $= 4.68 \times 10^{-24}$ kg·m/s. For the photon, $\lambda = h/p = (6.63 \times 10^{-34} \text{ J·s})/(4.68 \times 10^{-24}$ kg·m/s) $= 1.42 \times 10^{-10}$ m $= 1.42$ Å.   [The photon is in the x-ray region.]

27-C4 (a) The momentum of the incoming photon is $p = h/\lambda = (6.63 \times 10^{-34} \text{ J·s})/$ $(400 \times 10^{-9} \text{ m}) = 1.66 \times 10^{-27}$ kg·m/s.   (b) The momentum of the ejected electron is $mv = \sqrt{2m(\frac{1}{2}mv^2)} = \sqrt{2mE} = \sqrt{2(9.11 \times 10^{-31} \text{ kg})(0.64 \times 1.6 \times 10^{-19}\text{J})}$ $= 4.32 \times 10^{-25}$ kg·m/s.   (c) The seeming paradox is resolved by noting that the sodium metal recoils with enough momentum so that linear momentum, a vector quantity, is conserved.   [Even if the sodium is a particle of mass 10^{-6} kg (1 mg), its recoil energy is only about 10^{-43} J, utterly negligible compared with the energies of the photon and the photoelectron. The presence of the third body is required for momentum conservation; a photon cannot give up its energy to a free electron.]

27-C5 In Prob. 27-B3, the radius of the semicircular path is found to be 0.169 m. The electron's speed is found from its KE: $\frac{1}{2}(9.11 \times 10^{-31} \text{ kg})v^2 = (400 \text{ V})$ $\times (1.60 \times 10^{-19} \text{ C})$; $v = 1.19 \times 10^7$ m/s. Time of flight $= \pi R/v = \pi(0.169 \text{ m})/$ $(1.19 \times 10^7 \text{ m/s}) = 4.46 \times 10^{-8}$ s. The uncertainty principle $(\Delta p_x)(\Delta x) \geq (h)$ can be written (using the equality sign) as $(m\Delta v_x)(\Delta x) = h$; $\Delta v_x = h/m(\Delta x)$ $= (6.63 \times 10^{-34} \text{ J·s})/(9.11 \times 10^{-31} \text{ kg})(10^{-6} \text{ m}) = 728$ m/s. Thus the horizontal velocity of the beam, perpendicular to the path, is not exactly 0; there is an uncertainty of at least 728 m/s. In 4.46×10^{-8} s this leads to an uncertainty in the horizontal position at the collector given by $\Delta x' = (728 \text{ m/s})$ $\times (4.46 \times 10^{-8} \text{ s}) = 3.3 \times 10^{-5}$ m $= 33$ μm. This is much larger than the entrance slit width (1 μm), so we conclude that the uncertainty principle *would* be significant in this experiment.

27-C6   The energy levels are proportional to n^2; the next one in the list is (37.7 eV)(5^2) = 942 eV.

27-C7   Solving the equation for E_n to obtain L gives

$$L = \frac{nh}{\sqrt{8mE_n}} = \frac{(1)(6.63 \times 10^{-34} \text{ J·s})}{\sqrt{8(9.11 \times 10^{-31} \text{ kg})(10 \times 1.6 \times 10^{-19} \text{ J})}} = 1.94 \times 10^{-10} \text{ m}$$

= 1.94 Å.   [The size of this ''box'' is comparable to the spacing between atoms in a crystal (Fig. 2-1 on p. 19).]

Chapter 28   The Outer Atom

Questions

28-1   A line spectrum gives information about chemical composition; a continuous (blackbody) spectrum gives information about the temperature of a solid, a liquid, or a dense gas (see Table 28-1, also Fig. 14-4 on p. 323).

28-2   A neon sign is red because most of the intense lines of Ne are in the red and orange region; it is a physiological fact that a mixture of colors in the orange-red region gives the sensation of a pure spectrum color in the same region (not true when violet and green are mixed, which gives a desaturated blue). Thus a neon sign matches some spectral shade of red. A helium sign is pearly white, because the intense spectrum lines of He are spread throughout the spectrum [red, yellow, green, blue (Fig. 28-2c)].

28-3   The bright lines are a comparison spectrum, made with the same spectroscope and a local iron arc. The lines that match indicate the presence of iron vapor in the sun's atmosphere. Lines that do *not* match up are due to elements other than iron. The conspicuous broad dark lines in the top segment are due to calcium, very abundant in the solar atmosphere. The hydrogen line Hδ at 4101 Å is the subject of Prob. 28-B4.

28-4   No; infrared photons have less energy than any visible photons.

28-5   No difference in energy; the difference is in the way it is caused or allowed to take place.

28-6   All except (*a*) are possible. Spontaneous emission of a photon by the normal electric dipole transition is ''forbidden'' (see Fig. 23-7, which represents an antenna as a dipole; also see Sec. 23-8). Strictly speaking, radiation by transitions from a metastable state such as this one is possible, with extremely low probability, by emission of a photon of magnetic dipole radiation, electric quadrupole radiation, etc. See p. 680.

28-7   The laser is described in Sec. 28-5.

28-8   At room temperature, not very many H atoms are in the E_2 state (10.20 eV above the ground state); hence, absorption from E_2 to E_3 is not likely. In a star, thermal agitation increases the population of the E_2 state sufficiently to allow a significant absorption. The absorption $E_2 \rightarrow E_6$ (410.1 nm) in the sun's atmosphere is shown in the photograph on p. 671. (See Prob. 28-B4.)

Multiple Choice

28-9 (a);   28-10 (b);   28-11 (c);   28-12 (a);   28-13 (c);   28-14 (b).

Problems

28-A1   404.59 nm; 406.36 nm; 407.18 nm.

28-A2 $E = (5.67 - 3.46)$ eV $= 2.21$ eV.   [The wavelength is $1240/2.21 = 561$ nm.]

28-A3 $E = (7.73 - 4.67)$ eV $= 3.06$ eV; $\lambda = (1240$ eV·nm$)/(3.06$ eV$) = 405$ nm.
[This is one of the strong violet lines that help give a mercury arc its characteristic color.]

28-A4   If the KE of the electron is less than 10.20 eV, there is no way that the H atom's energy can be increased, the electron bounces off the H atom with all of its original KE, and the collision is surely elastic. The energy is 10.20 eV, or 1.63×10^{-18} J.

28-A5   The required energy is $(10.44 - 4.67)$ eV $= 5.77$ eV.

28-B1 $\lambda = 1240/10.20 = 122$ nm; the line is in the far ultraviolet and is not visible. [The Lyman α line is the strongest component of the hydrogen spectrum of the sun; it is (fortunately for us) absorbed by the ozone layer and does not reach the earth's surface.]

28-B2 $\lambda = 1240/13.60 = 91.2$ nm; ultraviolet.

28-B3 $E = E_5 - E_3 = (13.06 - 12.09)$ eV $= 0.97$ eV; $\lambda = 1240/0.97 = 1280$ nm (infrared).

28-B4 (c) In the photograph on p. 671, Hδ is at 4101 Å, near the left end of the lowest segment of the spectrum. (d) The lowest level is E_2 (10.20 eV), as is true for all Balmer-series lines. The photon energy is $1240/410 =$ $= 3.02$ eV. Hence the upper level has excitation energy $(10.20 + 3.02)$ eV $= 13.22$ eV.   [The energy levels are inversely proportional to n^2; for $n = 6$, $E_6 = (-13.60)/6^2 = -0.38$ eV below the ionization energy (see Fig. 28-6). The excitation energy is 13.60 eV $- 0.38$ eV $= 13.22$ eV, as deduced in this problem from the spectrum line's wavelength.]

28-B5 $E = 1240/546 = 2.27$ eV. By trial, we find that the transition $E_6 \rightarrow E_4$ has energy $(7.73 - 5.46)$ eV $= 2.27$ eV.

28-B6 $E = 1240/436 = 2.84$ eV. By trial, we find that the transition $E_6 \rightarrow E_3$ has energy $(7.73 - 4.89)$ eV $= 2.84$ eV. This is one of the strong lines in the blue-violet region that give a mercury arc its characteristic naked-eye color.

28-B7   At room temperature, almost all H atoms are in the ground state E_1. The least energetic photon that can be absorbed is the Lyman α line, of energy 10.20 eV.

28-B8 $\Delta E = 1240/254 = 4.88$ eV $= 7.81 \times 10^{-19}$ J. The mass equivalent of this energy is $\Delta m = \Delta E/c^2 = (7.81 \times 10^{-19}$ J$)/(3 \times 10^8$ m/s$)^2 = 8.68 \times 10^{-36}$ kg. The mass of a single Hg atom is $(0.2006$ kg$)/(6.02 \times 10^{23}) = 3.33 \times 10^{-25}$ kg. The fractional change is $\Delta m/m = (8.68 \times 10^{-36}$ kg$)/(3.33 \times 10^{-25}$ kg$) = 2.6 \times 10^{-11}$. [This change, less than one part in 10 billion, cannot be observed.]

28-B9   In its orbital motion, the earth is a "particle" moving in a circle, with moment of inertial $I = M(R_{\text{orbit}})^2$. The angular speed is 2π rad/year. The Bohr postulate is $I\omega = nh$, whence we obtain the "quantum number":

$$n = \frac{I\omega}{h} = \frac{mR^2\omega}{h} = \frac{(5.98 \times 10^{24}\ \text{kg})(1.49 \times 10^{11}\ \text{m})^2[(2\pi\ \text{rad})/(31.6 \times 10^6\ \text{s})]}{6.63 \times 10^{-34}\ \text{J·s}}$$

$= 4 \times 10^{73}$. This huge quantum number means that one additional quantum of orbital energy would be hopelessly unobservable. The earth's orbital motion is precisely described in classical terms.

28-B10 From $n\lambda = 2\pi r$, we obtain $nh/mv = 2\pi r$; $nh/2\pi = mvr = mr^2\omega = I\omega$.

28-B11 The radius of the first Bohr orbit is 0.529×10^{-10} m (p. 677). From Eq. 18-5 (p. 409),

$$V = \frac{kQ}{r} = \frac{(9 \times 10^9\ \text{N·m}^2/\text{C}^2)(1.6 \times 10^{-19}\ \text{C})}{0.529 \times 10^{-10}\ \text{m}} = +27.2\ \text{V}$$

[The potential energy of a (negative) electron at this point is -27.2 eV. From the statement just after Eq. 28-8, it follows that the KE is half as large as the PE, and positive. Therefore, KE $= +\frac{1}{2}(27.2\ \text{eV}) = +13.6$ eV. The total energy is KE + PE $= -27.2$ eV + 13.6 eV $= -13.6$ eV, in agreement with the value at the top of p. 678, and the right-hand portion of Fig. 28-6.]

28-B12 Calculate the ratio of $(1/2^2 - 1/3^2)$ to $(1/2^2 - 1/4^2)$.

28-B13 From Eq. 28-6, $r_n = n^2 r_1$; $n = \sqrt{\dfrac{r_n}{r_1}} = \sqrt{\dfrac{400 \times 10^{-9}\ \text{m}}{0.529 \times 10^{-10}\ \text{m}}} = 87$.

28-B14 See Prob. 17-B1. Let m = mass of electron and M = mass of proton. Analogously to Eq. 28-8, $\text{PE}_{\text{grav}} = +GmM/r$, found by integrating the repulsive force of gravitation when the electron moves from ∞ to r. The ratio of the magnitudes of the two energies is $(ke^2/r)/(GmM/r)$, or ke^2/GmM, which works out to be 2.3×10^{39} for the ratio of electric PE to gravitational PE.

28-C1 (a) $\sin\theta = \lambda/0.82D = (694.3 \times 10^{-9}\ \text{m})/(0.82)(0.1\ \text{m})$; $2\theta = 1.69 \times 10^{-5}$ rad.
(b) $r(2\theta) = (3.8 \times 10^8\ \text{m})(1.69 \times 10^{-5}\ \text{rad}) = 6.4 \times 10^3\ \text{m} = 6.4$ km.

28-C2 From Eq. 28-5, with $n = 1$ and $Z = 1$, $v/c = 2\pi ke^2/hc$, which works out to be $0.00728 \approx 1/137$. This is the dimensionless *fine structure* constant α. (In the cgs system, still used by many researchers, $k = 1$ and the formula is $\alpha = 2\pi e^2/hc$.) Relativistic effects are proportional to v^2/c^2, which is less than 10^{-4} even for $n = 1$.

28-C3 $E = \frac{3}{16}(13.60\ \text{eV}) = 2.55$ eV; $\lambda = (1240\ \text{eV·nm})/(2.55\ \text{eV}) = 486$ nm.
[The line is emitted by ionized helium, which has one electron; it is not seen in Fig. 28-2c, the spectrum of ordinary neutral helium, which has two electrons.]

28-C4 (a) $v = r\omega_{\text{orbital}} = 2\pi r\nu_{\text{orbital}}$; $\nu_{\text{orbital}} = v/2\pi r$. Use Eqs. 28-5 and 28-6, obtaining $\nu_{\text{orbital}} = 4\pi^2 mk^2 Z^2 e^4/n^3 h^3$. (b) When values for hydrogen are substituted, the equation becomes $\nu_{\text{orbital}} = (1/n^3)(6.55 \times 10^{15})\ \text{s}^{-1}$. The orbital frequencies are $\nu_1 = 6.55 \times 10^{15}\ \text{s}^{-1}$; $\nu_2 = 0.82 \times 10^{15}\ \text{s}^{-1}$. (c) From Fig. 28-3 or 28-6, the energy of the emitted photon is 10.20 eV $= 1.632 \times 10^{-18}$ J; $\nu_{\text{photon}} = E/h = (1.632 \times 10^{-18}\ \text{J})/(6.63 \times 10^{-34}\ \text{J·s}) = 2.46 \times 10^{15}\ \text{s}^{-1}$. From part (b), the average orbital frequency is $\frac{1}{2}(6.55 + 0.82) \times 10^{15}\ \text{s}^{-1} = 3.7 \times 10^{15}\ \text{s}^{-1}$. [This problem illustrates the Bohr Correspondence Principle: In the limit, as the quantum numbers n and m both $\to \infty$, $\nu_{\text{orbital}} \to \nu_{\text{photon}}$. The principle states that in the limit of high quantum numbers, the energy is continuous and the laws of classical physics are approximated. Here, of course, we have $n = 1$ and $m = 2$ (hardly equal to ∞!) and the agreement is for order of magnitude only. As expected, ν_{photon} for the Lyman α line of energy 10.20 eV lies between the two classically computed orbital frequencies.]

28-C5   (a) $\nu = c/\lambda = (3 \times 10^8 \text{ m/s})(905 \times 10^{-9} \text{ m}) = 3.31 \times 10^{14}$ Hz. The number of waves emitted in 200 ns is $(3.31 \times 10^{14} \text{ Hz})(200 \times 10^{-9} \text{ s}) = 6.6 \times 10^7$ waves. (b) $s = ct = (3 \times 10^8 \text{ m/s})(200 \times 10^{-9} \text{ s}) = 60$ m.

28-C6   The first lens would form a real image at 17 mm; this serves as a virtual object 7 mm beyond the second lens. $1/p + 1/q = 1/f$ becomes $1/(-7) + 1/q = 1/17$; $q = 5.0$ mm.   [*Curvature method:* $+1/7 + 1/17 = 1/q$; $q = 5.0$ mm.]

28-C7   As discussed on p. 628, the resolving power is given by $\theta = \lambda/0.82D = (905 \times 10^{-9} \text{ m})/(0.82)(12.7 \times 10^{-3} \text{ m}) = 8.7 \times 10^{-5}$ rad $= 0.005°$. The lens is entirely adequate to separate the two incident beams, which differ by $0.89°$.

28-C8   The angular separation is $0.89°$, or 1.55×10^{-2} rad. The linear separation is $\Delta s = r \Delta\theta = (9.6 \times 10^{-3} \text{ m})(1.55 \times 10^{-2} \text{ rad}) = 0.15$ mm.

28-C9 $(600 \times 10^{-3} \text{ J/s})(3 \times 3600 \text{ s}) = 6480 \text{ J} = 6.48$ kJ.

28-C10 (a) The torque condition, with axis at the tip of the cane, gives $(4 \text{ N})(90 \cos\theta$ cm$) = F(120 \cos\theta$ cm$)$. The angle θ that the cane makes with the pavement cancels out, and $F = 3$ N.   (b) From $\Sigma F_y = 0$, the upward force of the pavement is found to be 1 N.

Chapter 29   Atomic Structure

Questions

29-1   The first two postulates are used in quantum mechanics.

29-2   The principal quantum number n determines, to a large extent, the energy of an electron in an atom. Some extremely small effects are not included in this statement; for example, the direction of the electron's spin relative to its orbital motion affects the energy slightly (spin-orbit coupling); the energy levels are split (p. 693). For an electron in a many-electron atom, the energy of the *atom* cannot be neatly subdivided into the sum of the energies of the individual electrons.

29-3   The orbital quantum number l designates the magnitude of the orbital angular momentum, in units of $h/2\pi$.

29-4   The magnetic quantum number m_l designates the component of orbital angular momentum (in units of $h/2\pi$) parallel to any preassigned direction (usually designated as the z axis).

29-5   The magnetic spin quantum number m_s designates the component of spin angular momentum (in units of $h/2\pi$) parallel to any preassigned direction (usually designated as the z axis). Since $m_s = +\frac{1}{2}$ or $-\frac{1}{2}$, the magnitude of the component of spin angular momentum can only be $+h/4\pi$ or $-h/4\pi$ for any single electron in an atom.

29-6   Angular momentum averages to zero (the electron is in an s state).

29-7   Because of spin-orbit coupling (internal Zeeman effect—see p. 693).

29-8 The differences among the lanthanides are mainly due to the number of electrons in the $4f$ subshell—but chemical properties are mainly determined by the outer electrons. Each lanthanide has two $5s$ electrons, six $5p$ electrons, and two $6s$ electrons (Table 29-4).

29-9 A high-speed electron strikes a target of copper; an electron is ejected from the K shell by collision; the atom settles down by transferring an electron from a higher shell (such as the L shell) to the vacancy in the K shell. The excess energy is emitted as an x-ray photon. Another method of producing an x-ray photon is by fluorescence; the vacancy in the K shell (for example) can be produced by absorption of another x-ray photon of energy sufficient to cause ionization by removing a K electron.

29-10 Yes, but the intensity is probably very low unless a very copius beam of α particles is used.

Multiple Choice

29-11 (b);   29-12 (c);   29-13 (b);   29-14 (c);   29-15 (c);   29-16 (c).

Problems

29-A1 n, l, m_l, m_s values are 1, 0, 0, $\frac{1}{2}$ for one electron; 1, 0, 0, $-\frac{1}{2}$ for the other electron.

29-A2 Using Eq. 29-1, with $l = 3$, gives $I\omega = \sqrt{3(4)}\,(6.63 \times 10^{-34}\text{ J·s})/2\pi = 3.66 \times 10^{-34}$ kg·m^2·s^{-1}.   [The value of n does not enter into the calculation. It is instructive to make a dimensional check to show that J·s = kg·m^2·s^{-1}.]

29-A3 Equation 29-2 shows that $E_{K\alpha} = 0$ when $Z = 1$; the graph crosses the Z axis at $Z = 1$.

29-A4 50; not likely.   [The configuration could be $5s^2 5p^6 5d^{10} 5f^{14} 5g^{18}$, but this O shell would not be filled until some of the more tightly bound electrons with $n = 6, 7$, or 8 are added. Thus, in Table 29-4, even $_{74}$W has only 12 electrons with $n = 5$. Glenn Seaborg predicts that the superheavy element with $Z = 126$ will have a ground configuration (with 60 electrons in full K, L, M, and N shells) terminating with $5s^2 5p^6 5d^{10} 5f^{14} 5g^2 6s^2 6p^6 6d^{10} 6f^2 7s^2 7p^6 8s^2 8p^2$, where only 34 of the possible 50 $n = 5$ electrons survive competition with certain electrons having $n = 6, 7$, or 8. Reference: "Transuranic Elements," article by G. Seaborg in The Encyclopedia of Physics, 2nd ed. (Van Nostrand Reinhold Co., New York, 1974).]

29-B1 (a) The valence electron in $_{19}$K has $n = 4$ (Table 29-3), for which the maximum value of l is 3.   (b) Because of screening, the effective nuclear charge is about $1e$, as in Example 29-1. For a circular orbit with $n = 4$, Eq. 28-6 shows that $r \approx 4^2(0.53$ Å$) = 8.5$ Å.

29-B2 $E_1 = 1240/656.273 = 1.889458$ eV; $E_2 = 1240/656.285 = 1.889423$ eV. $\Delta E = 3.5 \times 10^{-5}$ eV $= 35\ \mu$eV.

29-B3 Energy differences given in Table 29-5 are used to deduce the values of the energy levels in Fig. 29-7: $E_L = 20.00$ keV $- 17.50$ keV $= 2.50$ keV; $E_M = 20.00$ keV $- 19.80$ keV $= 0.20$ keV. Hence the energy of the Mo $L\alpha$ line is $(2.50 - 0.20)$ keV $= 2.30$ keV; the wavelength is $\lambda = (12\ 400$ Å$)/(2300$ eV$) = 5.4$ Å.   [This is in the "soft" x-ray region.]

29-B4 E = 200 keV; λ = (12 400 eV·Å)/(200 × 10^3 eV) = 0.062 Å.
29-B5 E = 30 keV; λ = (12 400 eV·Å)/(30 × 10^3 eV) = 0.41 Å.

Chapter 30   The Nucleus

Questions

30-1   Seemingly, the law of conservation of energy was contradicted by the continuous production of energy in a sample of uranium. This objection is no longer valid, because we now know that some of the rest mass of the sample is being converted into energy according to $\Delta E = (\Delta m)c^2$.

30-2 α rays: low penetrating power, charge +2e, mass (4 × 1836)m_e, deflected by magnetic field. β rays: medium penetrating power, charge ±1e, mass m_e, deflected by magnetic field. γ rays: high penetrating power, no charge, mass (entirely relativistic) given by E/c^2, not deflected by magnetic field.

30-3   Approximately 4(1836):1, or about 7300.

30-4   The naturally occurring elements are mixtures of isotopes; the isotopes themselves are nearly (but not quite) integral multiples of the unified atomic mass unit. See, for example, mass data given in Table 9 of the Appendix and also (for heavier elements), in Probs. 30-B16, 30-B19, and 30-B20.

30-5 ^{222}Rn is the daughter of the much longer-lived ^{226}Ra.

30-6   One of the two nuclides would have greater mass than the other, so decay by β^- emission or by electron capture would be energetically possible.

30-7   The ionization chamber, surface barrier detector, Geiger counter, scintillation counter, cloud chamber, bubble chamber, spark chamber, and photographic emulsion are described, in greater or less detail, in Sec. 30-9.

30-8   A γ-ray photon has mass given by E/c^2, momentum given by E/c, and no charge.

30-9   The mass balances are unfavorable for the decays $^{16}_{8}$O → $^{16}_{9}$F + $_{-1}^{0}$e (β^- emission), and for $^{16}_{8}$O + $_{-1}^{0}$e → $^{16}_{7}$N (electron capture). See the first paragraph of Sec. 30-7.   [The latter case can be checked using data from Table 9 in the Appendix; the mass of the electron is not used, since masses of neutral atoms are given.]

30-10   The IR drop in R makes the wire negative relative to ground while the Geiger tube is conducting.

30-11   A neutrino has mass given by E/c^2, no rest mass, and linear momentum given by E/c. All the energy of the neutrino can be considered to be KE.

30-12   The almost complete insensitivity to external conditions of temperature, pressure, and chemical environment shows that radioactive decay is a nuclear process. The fact that unstable isotopes of an element (all with the same electron clouds) have different radioactive behavior also shows that radioactivity is a nuclear process.

30-13 Neutrons are electrically neutral and can approach the positive nucleus of a target atom without experiencing a Coulomb repulsion.

Multiple Choice

30-14 (*b*);   **30-15** (*b*):   **30-16** (*c*);   **30-17** (*c*);   **30-18** (*a*);   **30-19** (*b*).

Problems

30-A1 Zn; He; Ca; U.

30-A2 C; Na; Hg; Cu.

30-A3 6; 12; 120; 36.

30-A4 47 protons, 60 neutrons, 107 nucleons.

30-A5 $r = (1.2 \times 10^{-15})A^{1/3} = (1.2 \times 10^{-15})(125)^{1/3} = 6 \times 10^{-15}$ m = 6 fm.

30-A6 $A = [r/(1.2 \times 10^{-15} \text{ m})]^3 = (4.8/1.2)^3 = 64.$

30-A7 (0.020 u)(931 MeV/u) = 18.6 MeV.

30-A8 (200 MeV)/(931 MeV/u) = 0.214 u.

30-A9 In 5 half-lives, $1/2^5 = 1/32$ of the ^{55}Fe remains.

30-A10 1/4 (= $1/2^2$) of the material has survived for 3 h. Thus, 2 half-lives = 3 h; $T_{1/2}$ = 1.5 h = 90 min.

30-A11 (256 μg)/(16 μg) is a factor of 16 (= 2^4); 3 d = $4T_{1/2}$; $T_{1/2}$ = 0.75 d = 18 h.

30-A12 12 d is 3 half-lives, i.e. $1/2^3 = 1/8$ of the ^{100}Pd remains; (1.776 g)/8 = 0.222 g.

30-A13 If about 1 atom remains at 12:55 P.M., at 1:15 P.M. 20 additional half-lives have elapsed; $2^{-20} = 1/1\,048\,576.$

30-A14 (*a*) $^{63}_{30}$Zn + $^{0}_{-1}$e → $^{63}_{29}$Cu;   (*b*) $^{40}_{19}$K → $^{40}_{20}$Ca + $^{0}_{-1}$e;   (*c*) $^{60}_{29}$Cu → $^{60}_{28}$Ni + $^{0}_{+1}$e;

(*d*) $^{230}_{90}$Th → $^{226}_{88}$Ra + $^{4}_{2}$He;   (*e*) $^{113}_{48}$Cd → $^{113}_{48}$Cd + γ.

30-A15 (*a*) $^{22}_{11}$Na → $^{22}_{10}$Ne + $^{0}_{+1}$e;   (*b*) $^{38}_{17}$Cl → $^{38}_{18}$Ar + $^{0}_{-1}$e;   (*c*) $^{218}_{84}$Po → $^{214}_{82}$Pb + $^{4}_{2}$He;

(*d*) $^{59}_{28}$Ni + $^{0}_{-1}$e → $^{59}_{27}$Co.

30-A16 $^{64}_{30}$Zn; $^{64}_{28}$Ni; $^{64}_{28}$Ni.

30-A17 The parent has greater mass; Δm = (0.436 MeV)/(931 MeV/u) = 0.000468 u.

30-B1 The total mass of the fragments (8 $^{1}_{1}$H atoms and 8 neutrons) is 8(1.007825) + 8(1.008665) = 16.13192 u. From Table 9 in the Appendix, the mass of a neutral $^{16}_{8}$O atom is 15.994915 u. The BE is given by Δm = 16.13192 − 15.994915 u = 0.137005 u = 127.55 MeV. BE per nucleon is (127.55 MeV)/(16 nucleons) = 7.97 MeV/nucleon.   [The mass of 8 *neutral* $^{1}_{1}$H atoms is used, rather than the mass of 8 protons, because the original mass of $^{16}_{8}$O in Table 9 also is for a neutral atom, containing 8 electrons.]

30-B2 The fragments are a $^{13}_{6}$C nucleus and a $^{1}_{1}$H nucleus. In the calculations, the masses of neutral atoms are used because the masses of 14 electrons are included in the fragments as well as in the $^{14}_{7}$N atomic mass. BE = (^{13}C + ^{1}H) − ^{14}N = (13.003354 + 1.007825) − 14.003074 = 0.008105 u = 7.55 MeV. [Note that this is much less than the 18.7 MeV binding energy of the least strongly bound neutron in ^{12}C (Example 30-1 on p. 712). As pointed out on p. 713, ^{12}C is exceptionally stable, consisting of three α particles. See also Prob. 30-B3.]

30-B3 (*a*) ^{12}C − 3(^{4}He) = 12.000000 − 3(4.002603) = −0.007809 = −7.27 MeV. The spontaneous decay of ^{12}C into three α particles is energetically impossible;

at least 7.27 MeV must be supplied to cause the breakup of ^{12}C, which is therefore stable.   (b) ^{8}Be $-$ 2(^{4}He) = 8.005308 $-$ 2(4.002603) = +0.000102 u = +0.095 MeV. The spontaneous decay of ^{8}Be releases 0.095 MeV; this energy is shared equally by the two α particles, which each have 0.047 MeV of KE and travel in opposite directions (to conserve momentum).

30-B4   (a) (^{3}He + ^1n) $-$ ^{4}He = (3.016030 + 1.008665) $-$ 4.002603 = 0.022092 u = 20.6 MeV.   (b) (^{6}Li + ^1n) $-$ ^{7}Li = (6.015125 + 1.008665) $-$ 7.016004 = 0.007786 u = 7.25 MeV.

30-B5 $T_{1/2}$ = 24 min; λ = 0.693/$T_{1/2}$ = 0.0289 min^{-1}. Now use Eq. 30-3: $N = (4 \times 10^{20})\,e^{-(0.0289\ \text{min}^{-1})(15\ \text{min})}$ = 2.59 $\times$ 10^{20} nuclei.

30-B6   The amount remaining is 0.75 the original amount. From Eq. 30-3, $e^{-(0.693/14)t}$ = 0.75; $-(0.693/14)t$ = ln (0.75) = -0.287; t = 5.81 d. [Noting that -0.693 = ln ($\frac{1}{2}$), the equation to be solved could be written $t/14$ = (ln 0.75)/(ln 0.50). Thus, t = 14(ln 0.75)/(ln 0.50), which relates the time, half-life, and fraction remaining in a simple way that is adapted to the use of electronic calculators.]

30-B7   The fraction is $e^{-(0.693/1.3)(4.5)}$ = $e^{-2.40}$ = 9.1%.

30-B8   The fraction is $e^{-(0.693/13)(5)}$ = $e^{-0.267}$ = 77%.

30-B9 λ = 10^{-6} s^{-1}; $T_{1/2}$ = 0.693/λ = 6.93 $\times$ 10^5 s = 8.02 d.

30-B10   (a) $\lambda = \left(\dfrac{0.693}{8 \times 10^4\ \text{y}}\right)\left(\dfrac{1\ \text{y}}{3.156 \times 10^7\ \text{s}}\right)$ = 2.7 $\times$ 10^{-13} s^{-1}.   (b) $\Delta N = N\lambda\,\Delta t$ = (10^{13} atoms)(2.7 $\times$ 10^{-13} s^{-1})(60 s) = 164.72 = "about 160 atoms" (rounded, in view of the crude estimate of $T_{1/2}$).

30-B11   (a) Co;   (b) ^{60}Fe;   (c) ^{57}Ni;   (d) All β^- decays shown are accompanied by γ rays with the possible exception of ^{62}Fe, which has not been well investigated, although some nuclides such as ^{32}P do decay by β^- emission without any γ ray; ^{61}Zn decays by β^+ emission without a γ ray 80% of the time; ^{56}Ni decays only by electron capture; the isomer of ^{58}Co decays only by γ-ray emission (I.T. means isomeric transition);   (e) ^{56}Mn, ^{59}Fe.

30-B12 ^1n $-$ ^{1}H = 1.008665 $-$ 1.007825 = 0.000840 u = 0.78 MeV.   [The mass of the neutral ^{1}H atom includes the mass of the negatron that is created in the decay. The mass and energy of the neutrino are negligible since we are asked for the "maximum" energy of the emitted negatrons.]

30-B13 $^3_1$H $\rightarrow$ $^3_2$He + $^0_{-1}$e + $\bar{\nu}_e$; the daughter nuclide is $^3_2$He. Using masses of neutral atoms gives ^{3}H $-$ ^{3}He = 3.016050 $-$ 3.016030 = 0.000020 u = 0.02 MeV.

30-B14 ^{14}C $-$ ^{14}N = 14.003242 $-$ 14.003074 = 0.000168 u = 0.16 MeV.   [The low energy of the negatrons from this very useful ^{14}C isotope makes its detection difficult. Liquid scintillation detectors are often used, in which the material containing the ^{14}C-labeled atoms is dissolved or suspended in the scintillant.]

30-B15 ^{59}Fe $-$ ^{59}Co = 58.93488 $-$ 58.93319 = 0.00169 u = 1.57 MeV. The most energetic β^- from ^{59}Fe is given in the chart as having energy 1.56 MeV (albeit emitted with very low probability).   [See Prob. 30-C5, where an energy-level diagram for ^{59}Co is constructed.]

30-B16   The nuclide ^{50}Cr is stable in an absolute sense, since the probability of *any* decay is zero. None of the following modes of decay is energetically possible (in each test, use the masses of neutral atoms): β^- decay, ^{50}Cr $\rightarrow$ ^{50}Mn + $^0_{-1}$e; α decay, ^{50}Cr $\rightarrow$ ^{46}Ti + ^{4}He; electron capture, ^{50}Cr + $^0_{-1}$e $\rightarrow$ ^{50}V; neutron emission, ^{50}Cr $\rightarrow$ ^{49}Cr + ^1n.

30-B17 (a) Maximum available energy: $^{56}\text{Mn} - {}^{56}\text{Fe} = 55.93891 - 55.93494 = 0.00397$ u $= 3.70$ MeV.   (b) The 2.86 MeV β ray and 0.845 γ ray add up to 3.71 MeV.

30-B18 The mass of a bare α particle is $^4\text{He} - 2m_e = 4.002603 - 2(0.000549)$
$= 4.0015$ u $= \left(\dfrac{4.0015 \text{ u}}{12.000 \text{ u}}\right)\left(\dfrac{0.012000 \text{ kg/mol}}{6.02 \times 10^{23} \text{ atoms/mol}}\right) = 6.647 \times 10^{-27}$ kg.
KE $= \frac{1}{2}mv^2 = \frac{1}{2}(6.647 \times 10^{-27} \text{ kg})(1.50 \times 10^7 \text{ m/s})^2 = 7.48 \times 10^{-13}$ J $= 4.67$ MeV.

30-B19 $^{226}\text{Ra} - ({}^{222}\text{Rn} + {}^4\text{He}) = 226.0254 - (222.0175 + 4.0026) = 0.0053$ u $= 4.9$ MeV. [Use the mass of neutral ^4He so that 88 electrons are included on each side of the equation.]

30-B20 Yes, decay is possible. The energy of the α particle is found from the masses of neutral atoms: $^{209}\text{Bi} - ({}^{205}\text{Tl} + {}^4\text{He}) = 208.9804 - (204.9745 + 4.0026) = 0.0033$ u $= 3.1$ MeV.   [Strictly speaking, the available energy is not entirely given to the ejected α particle; a small fraction of the energy is given to the recoiling daughter nucleus.]

30-B21 Incoming particles: $^2\text{H} + {}^2\text{H} = 2.014102 + 2.014102 = 4.028204$ u. Outgoing particles: $^3\text{He} + {}^1n = 3.016030 + 1.008665 = 4.024695$ u. The products have less mass than the incoming particles; $\Delta m = 0.003509$ u $= 3.27$ MeV. If the bombarding particle has negligible KE, 3.27 MeV is available for the KE of the fragments.   [This is an exothermic nuclear reaction.]

30-B22 $^{10}\text{B}(d,n)^{11}\text{C}$; $\quad ^{35}\text{Cl}(n,p)^{35}\text{S}$; $\quad ^{55}\text{Mn}(p,n)^{55}\text{Fe}$; $\quad ^{65}\text{Cu}(d,2n)^{65}\text{Zn}$; $\quad ^{59}\text{Co}(n,\gamma)^{60}\text{Co}$.

30-B23 $^{10}\text{B}(n,\alpha)^7\text{Li}$; $\quad ^{27}\text{Al}(\alpha,n)^{30}\text{P}$; $\quad ^1\text{H}(n,\gamma)^2\text{H}$; $\quad ^{25}\text{Mg}(\gamma,p)^{24}\text{Na}$; $\quad ^{113}\text{Cd}(n,\gamma)^{114}\text{Cd}$.

30-B24 The reaction is $^{10}\text{B}(n,\alpha)^7\text{Li}$. $\quad ^{10}\text{B} + {}^1n - ({}^4\text{He} + {}^7\text{Li}) = 10.012939 + 1.008665 - (4.002603 + 7.016004) = 0.002997$ u $= 2.8$ MeV.   [The reaction is between bare nuclei. Neutral atomic masses are used, since the mass of 5 electrons is included both before and after the reaction.]

30-B25 $^{14}\text{N} + {}^4\text{He} - ({}^1\text{H} + {}^{17}\text{O}) = 14.003074 + 4.002603 - (1.007825 + 16.99133)$
$= 0.001281$ u $= 1.19$ MeV.

30-B26 $^9\text{Be} + {}^4\text{He} - ({}^1n + {}^{12}\text{C}) = 9.012186 + 4.002603 - (1.008665 + 12.000000)$
$= 0.006124$ u $= 5.70$ MeV. Adding the KE of the incoming α particle gives the total KE of the products: $(5.70 + 5.30)$ MeV $= 11.0$ MeV.   [The reaction is between bare nuclei. Neutral atomic masses are used, since the mass of 6 electrons is included both before and after the reaction.]

30-C1 (a) The masses of the bare nuclei are found by subtracting the mass of Z electrons from the masses of the neutral atoms given in the chart. $^{57}_{27}\text{Co}$ nucleus: $56.93630 - 27(0.000549) = 56.9214$ u; $^{57}_{26}\text{Fe}$ nucleus: $56.93540 - 26(0.000549) = 56.92113$ u. The mass difference between the bare nuclei is $\Delta m = 0.00035$ u, less than the mass needed to create a positron. Thus, positron emission is energetically impossible. However, electron capture, $^{57}_{27}\text{Co} + {}^{0}_{-1}\text{e} \rightarrow {}^{57}_{26}\text{Fe}$, is energetically possible; the available energy can be found using masses of the neutral atoms, since the $^{57}_{27}\text{Co}$ atom already includes the mass of the captured electron. The available energy during electron capture is $\Delta m = 56.93630 - 56.93540 = 0.00090$ u $= 0.84$ MeV. [Another, less tedious, approach is the following: The masses of the bare nuclei must differ by more than the mass of an electron if a positron is to be created. Using underlines to represent bare nuclei, the mass equation is $\underline{^{57}\text{Co}} - \underline{^{57}\text{Fe}} > e$. Add 27 electrons to the Co nucleus, making neutral Co; add 26 electrons to the Fe nucleus, making neutral Fe. The net result is to add one electron to the left side of the equation, so we add one electron to the right side, and the inequality becomes ^{57}Co − ^{57}Fe > 2e, where the masses are now those of the neutral atoms. This leads to the conclusion that for positron decay, the masses of the neutral atoms must differ by more than two electron masses (1.02 MeV). For the decay of ^{57}Co, the mass difference between neutral atoms (0.84 MeV) is less than 1.02 MeV, so positron decay is not possible. The fact that the difference is *positive* (even though less than 1.02 MeV) tells us that electron capture is possible. These conclusions are verified by reference to the chart (Fig. 30-4 on p. 720).]   (b) Positron emission from ^{56}Co is possible, and is so listed in Fig. 30-4. For the neutral atoms ^{56}Co − ^{56}Fe = 55.93985 − 55.93494 = 0.00491 u = 4.57 MeV, much greater than 1.02 MeV mentioned above. Electron capture is also possible, as must be the case whenever positron emission is possible.

30-C2   (a) The mass difference is ^{56}Mn − ^{56}Fe = 55.93891 − 55.93494 = 0.00397 u = 3.70 MeV, which, as it happens, is not equal to the energy of any of the observed particles.   (b) The energy-level diagram shows β^--particle emission as slanting arrows and γ-ray emission as vertical arrows.

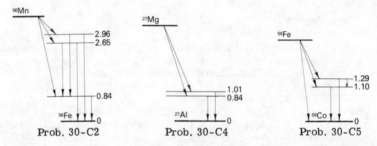

Prob. 30-C2   Prob. 30-C4   Prob. 30-C5

30-C3   (a) ^{60}Co − ^{60}Ni = 59.93381 − 59.93079 = 0.00302 u = 2.81 MeV.   (b) The observed energies are given in the chart, Fig. 30-4 on p. 720. Most of the time, the energy is apportioned between a 0.31 MeV β^- particle, and 1.17 MeV and 1.33 MeV γ rays (0.31 + 1.17 + 1.33 = 2.81). Very rarely, 0.05% of the time, the energy is apportioned between a 1.48 MeV β^- particle and a 1.33 MeV γ ray (1.48 + 1.33 = 2.81).

30-C4   (a) ^{27}Mg − ^{27}Al = 26.98435 − 26.98154 = 0.00281 u = 2.62 MeV.   (b) All four of the observed energy differences are accounted for by the energy-level diagram.

30-C5 ^{59}Fe − ^{59}Co = 58.93488 − 58.93319 = 0.00169 u = 1.57 MeV. This agrees with the energy of the most energetic observed β^- ray, so we conclude that ^{59}Fe can decay by β emission directly to the ground state of ^{59}Co. (Not true in the decay schemes for Probs. 30-C2 and 30-C4.)

30-C6   (a) $1 \dfrac{\text{MeV}}{c^2} = \dfrac{1.60 \times 10^{-13} \text{ J}}{(3 \times 10^8 \text{ m/s})^2} = 1.78 \times 10^{-30}$ kg.   (b) Mass = $931A$ MeV/c^2; volume = $\frac{4}{3}\pi r^3 = \frac{4}{3}\pi(1.2)^3 A = 7.24A$ fm^3; density = $M/V = (931A)/(7.24A) = 129$ (MeV/c^2)/fm^3. In SI units, using the result of part (a), we have for the density of nuclear matter
$$\left(129 \, \frac{\text{MeV}/c^2}{\text{fm}^3}\right)\left(\frac{1.78 \times 10^{-30} \text{ kg}}{1 \text{ MeV}/c^2}\right)\left(\frac{1 \text{ fm}}{10^{-15} \text{ m}}\right)^3 = 2.3 \times 10^{17} \text{ kg/m}^3$$
[A cancels out; the density agrees with the value given on p. 21.]

30-C7 $p = \sqrt{2mE} = \sqrt{2\left(\dfrac{4 \times 10^{-3}\ \text{kg}}{6.02 \times 10^{23}}\right)(7.68 \times 1.60 \times 10^{-13}\ \text{J})} = 1.28 \times 10^{-19}\ \text{kg·m/s}.$

$\lambda = h/p = (6.63 \times 10^{-34}\ \text{J·s})/(1.28 \times 10^{-19}\ \text{kg·m/s}) = 5.2 \times 10^{-15}\ \text{m} = 5.2\ \text{fm}.$
[The de Broglie wavelength is about equal to the radius of a gold nucleus, as calculated from Eq. 30-1 (see also p. 758), thus ensuring the success of Rutherford's scattering experiment. See the second paragraph of Sec. 31-8, also the discussion of resolving power in Sec. 26-5, according to which λ/w must be less than 1.]

30-C8 The initial KE of the α particle is equivalent to 7.68/931 = 0.00825 u. ^{12}C $+ {}^4$He + energy of α particle = 12.000000 + 4.002603 + 0.00825 = 16.01085 u. After the reaction, ^{1}H + ^{15}N = 1.007825 + 15.000108 = 16.007933 u (neutral atomic masses are used, since the mass of 8 electrons is included both before and after the reaction). This reaction has a threshold, since rest mass has increased. After collision, the energy available for KE of the fragments is 16.01085 − 16.00793 = 0.00292 u = 2.72 MeV.   [The KE of the fragments is less than the KE brought into the reaction by the α particle.]

30-C9 $N = \frac{2}{60}$ mol = 2.01×10^{22} nuclei present. The disintegration constant is $\lambda = 0.693/T_{1/2} = 0.693/(5.27 \times 3.156 \times 10^7\ \text{s}) = 4.17 \times 10^{-9}\ \text{s}^{-1}$. Equation 30-6 gives the disintegration rate as $\lambda N = (2.01 \times 10^{22})(4.17 \times 10^{-9}\ \text{s}^{-1})$ = 8.38×10^{13} dis/s. From Prob. 30-C3a (the answer is available to the student on p. 816), each disintegration gives 2.81 MeV, i.e., 4.50×10^{-13} J. Power = $(4.50 \times 10^{-13}\ \text{J/s})(8.38 \times 10^{13}\ \text{dis/s}) = 38\ \text{J/s} = 38\ \text{W}$.   [The outside surface of the container of a strong cobalt source used in therapy is warm to the touch.]

30-C10 The disintegration constant is $0.693/T_{1/2} = 0.693/(5730 \times 3.156 \times 10^7\ \text{s})$ = $3.83 \times 10^{-12}\ \text{s}^{-1}$. The number of ^{14}C atoms in the sample is $\frac{70}{12}(6.02 \times 10^{23})$ $\times (10^{-12}) = 3.51 \times 10^{12}$ atoms. The disintegration rate is $\lambda N = (3.83 \times 10^{-12}\ \text{s}^{-1})$ $\times (3.51 \times 10^{12}\ \text{atoms}) = 13$ dis/s.   [Use of ^{14}C for radioactive dating is discussed on p. 740, and is the subject of Prob. 31-C1.]

30-C11 ^{48}V: 1 or 0; ^{48}Cr: 2, 1, or 0.

30-C12 The reaction is $^A_Z\text{X} + {}^{\ 0}_{-1}\text{e} \rightarrow {}^{\ \ A}_{Z-1}\text{Y} + ?$ The number of nucleons has not changed, so X and Y have the same total spin, or their spins differ by 1 unit (if one nucleon's spin changed from $+\frac{1}{2}$ to $-\frac{1}{2}$ or *vice versa*), or, in general, their spins differ by an integral number of units (if several nuclear spins "flip"). The electron on the left has a spin $\frac{1}{2}$, and this half-integral spin must be carried away by a neutrino. If a γ-ray photon is emitted during the process, its spin is 1 (Table 31-4 on p. 761), and the neutrino is still needed to conserve angular momentum.

30-C13 21 and 28.

Chapter 31 Applied Nuclear Physics

Questions

31-1 ^{15}O could be used as a radioactive tracer in some experiments where its short half-life of 2.05 min (Table 9 in the Appendix) would not be a limitation. Oxygen enriched in one of the heavier stable isotopes, ^{17}O or ^{18}O, could be used; a mass spectrometer would be needed for analysis of the oxygen released by the plant.

31-2　The relativistic mass increase, given by $m = m_0/\sqrt{1 - v^2/c^2}$, causes the time for one revolution to increase (Eq. 31-1). In the synchrotron, the magnetic field is caused to increase as m increases, so T remains constant.

31-3　For a highly energetic particle moving almost at the speed of light, the equation at the top of column 2 of p. 741 becomes $c = Bqr/m$; $mc^2 = Bcqr$. For a given magnetic field (limited by the magnetic properties of iron), the energy mc^2 can be increased only by increasing the radius of the synchrotron orbit.

31-4　The system of two particles has zero linear momentum in the laboratory frame of reference. After collision, each proton is at rest in the laboratory frame. See Sec. 31-3.

31-5　The beam path is straight for only a few meters and begins to curve again when it enters the region where the bending magnets are located.

31-6　Fission reactors supply heat to turn electric generators, thus making nuclear power available; they also supply radioactive isotopes for research and for therapy. Major disadvantages are concerned with waste disposal, security of nuclear materials, and thermal pollution.

31-7　The cross section of ^{1}H for capture of slow neutrons is 500 times as great as that of ^{2}H; captured neutrons are not available for continuing the chain reaction. (See Table 31-2.)

31-8　The half-life is too short.

31-9　Advantages and disadvantages of fusion power are summarized on p. 753.

31-10　The patient receives more than 100 mrem, but only once or twice a year. Through scattering or improper shielding, the dentist would receive a small fraction of this exposure, but the exposure would be repeated many times a day.

31-11　A radiation dose lower than the threshold causes no lasting somatic damage to the tissue or organism.

31-12　About 2×931 MeV, or 1.86 GeV.

31-14　π^0 and η decay into two γ-ray photons. We interpret these decays to be mediated by the e-m interaction for two reasons. The photon is the field particle for the e-m interaction (p. 404, also top of p. 760). Also, none of the particles in Table 31-4 decay exclusively by the strong interaction (for then their half-lives would be of the order of 10^{-23} s). The e-m interaction, next strongest according to Table 31-3, makes the half-lives of π^0 and η much shorter than the half-lives of the other mesons.

31-15　All the mesons and baryons are hadrons.

31-16　If the particle is a π^+, the decays are $\pi^+ \rightarrow \mu^+ + \nu_\mu$ and (later) $\mu^+ \rightarrow e^+ + \nu_e + \bar{\nu}_\mu$. The stable end results of two decays are e, ν_μ, ν_e, and $\bar{\nu}_\mu$. The three neutrinos leave no tracks because they are uncharged and create no ions when they approach atoms of the liquid contained in the bubble chamber.

31-17   A cosmic-ray star is a group of particles created simultaneously as a single event at a single point (Figs. 31-14, 31-15). A cosmic-ray shower is a cascade effect consisting of many events (Fig. 31-16).

Multiple Choice

31-18 (c);   31-19 (c);   31-20 (b);   31-21 (c);   31-22 (c);   31-23 (a).

Problems

31-A1 $T = \dfrac{\pi m}{Bq} = \dfrac{\pi(1.67 \times 10^{-27}\text{ kg})}{(1\text{ T})(1.60 \times 10^{-19}\text{ C})} = 3.28 \times 10^{-8}$ s = 32.8 ns.   [The time is independent of the path radius, as long as $v/c \ll 1$, as is the case here.]

31-A2 T = circumference/speed = $(2\pi)(10^3\text{ m})/(3 \times 10^8\text{ m/s}) = 2.09 \times 10^{-5}$ s = 20.9 μs.

31-A3   From Table 31-1, $E \approx 10$ GeV.   [The exact (relativistic) solution, for $v/c = 0.996$, uses the rest mass of the proton (938 MeV/c^2) from Table 31-4.

$E = \dfrac{m_0 c^2}{\sqrt{1 - v^2/c^2}} = \dfrac{938\text{ MeV}}{\sqrt{1 - (0.996)^2}} = 1.05 \times 10^4$ MeV = 10.5 GeV.]

31-A4 T for half a revolution is $\frac{1}{2}(10^{-7}$ s) = 5×10^{-8} s.

$B = \dfrac{\pi m}{Tq} = \dfrac{\pi(1.67 \times 10^{-27}\text{ kg})}{(5 \times 10^{-8}\text{ s})(1.60 \times 10^{-19}\text{ C})} = 0.656\,T.$

31-A5 (a) $(0.6 \times 10^9\text{ eV})/(0.05 \times 10^6\text{ eV per rev}) = 12\,000$ rev. (b) $s = (12\,000) \times (2\pi)(1\text{ m}) = 7.54 \times 10^4$ m = 75 km.   [The given average path radius takes account of the fact that the proton's radius of revolution increases as it spirals out.]

31-A6 ^{238}U + ^{1}n − ^{239}U = 238.0508 + 1.008665 − 239.0543 = 0.0052 u = 4.8 MeV available for the KE of the ^{239}U and the energy of the γ rays.

31-A7 ^{235}U + ^{1}n = 235.0439 + 1.008665 = 236.0526 u. ^{141}Ba + ^{92}Kr + 3^1n = 140.9140 + 91.9250 + 3(1.008665) = 235.8650 u. Δm = 0.1876 u = 175 MeV.

31-A9 $\lambda = \dfrac{h}{p} = \dfrac{h}{mc} = \dfrac{hc}{mc^2} = \dfrac{(6.63 \times 10^{-34}\text{ J·s})(3 \times 10^8\text{ m/s})}{(21 \times 10^9\text{ eV})(1.60 \times 10^{-19}\text{ J/eV})} = 5.92 \times 10^{-17}$ m = 0.06 fm.
[It is through study of inelastic scattering of electrons such as these that some evidence for partons (quarks?) was obtained at SLAC (p. 758).]

31-B1   The proton gains (400 − 8) GeV = 392 GeV; $N = (392 \times 10^9\text{ eV})/(2.5 \times 10^6$ eV per rev) = 1.57×10^5 rev. The proton's energy is much larger than its rest energy (0.94 GeV), so we know that it is highly relativistic, traveling at almost the speed of light. Thus, $(1.57 \times 10^5)(2\pi)(1.00 \times 10^3\text{ m}) = (3 \times 10^8$ m/s)(t); $t = 3.28$ s.

31-B2 (a) $\frac{1}{2}mv^2 = \frac{1}{2}(1.67 \times 10^{-27}\text{ kg})(2 \times 10^7\text{ m/s})^2 = 3.34 \times 10^{-13}$ J = 2.09 MeV.
(b) $qvB = \dfrac{mv^2}{r}$; $B = \dfrac{mv}{qr} = \dfrac{(1.67 \times 10^{-27}\text{ kg})(2 \times 10^7\text{ m/s})}{(1.60 \times 10^{-19}\text{ C})(0.6\text{ m})} = 0.348$ T.

31-B3 $I = (1.5 \times 10^{13}\text{ s}^{-1})(1.6 \times 10^{-19}\text{ C}) = 2.4 \times 10^{-6}$ A = 2.4 μA. Power = VI = $(400 \times 10^9\text{ V})(2.4 \times 10^{-6}\text{ A}) = 9.6 \times 10^5$ W = 960 kW.   [Dissipation of thermal energy in the target of a large accelerator is an engineering challenge.]

31-B4 (a) From Table 31-4, or from mc^2, the rest energy of a proton is 939 MeV = 0.94 GeV. (b) KE = total energy − rest energy = (18.00 − 0.94) GeV = 17.06 GeV.

31-B5 (a) The rest mass of a bare deuteron is $^2\text{H} - 1m_e = 2.014102 - 0.000549$ = 2.0136 u = 1874.6 MeV = 1.87 GeV. (b) Total energy = rest energy + KE = (1.87 + 17.20) GeV = 19.07 GeV.

31-B6 (a) $\left(20 \times 10^6 \frac{\text{J}}{\text{s}}\right)\left(\frac{1 \text{ MeV}}{1.60 \times 10^{-13} \text{ J}}\right) = \left(201 \frac{\text{MeV}}{\text{fission}}\right)\left(N \frac{\text{fissions}}{\text{s}}\right)$, whence $N = 6.22 \times 10^{17}$ fissions/s. (b) In 1 y, there are $(6.22 \times 10^{17}$ fissions/s$) \times (3.156 \times 10^7 \text{ s}) = 1.963 \times 10^{25}$ fissions. (c) Mass consumed = $(1.963 \times 10^{25}$ atoms$)\left(\frac{0.235 \text{ kg}}{6.02 \times 10^{23} \text{ atoms}}\right) = 7.66$ kg. (d) $(7.66 \text{ kg})/(0.72 \times 10^{-2})$ = 1064 kg.

31-B7 The total energy equivalent of a single ^{235}U atom is
$$m_0c^2 = \left(\frac{0.235 \text{ kg}}{6.02 \times 10^{23} \text{ atoms}}\right)(3 \times 10^8 \text{ m/s})^2\left(\frac{1 \text{ MeV}}{1.60 \times 10^{-13} \text{ J}}\right) = 2.20 \times 10^5 \text{ MeV}.$$
The fraction consumed is (201 MeV)/$(2.20 \times 10^5$ MeV$) = 9.1 \times 10^{-4} \approx 0.1\%$.

31-B8 (a) $\left(180 \frac{\text{MeV}}{\text{nucleus}}\right)\left(\frac{6.02 \times 10^{23} \text{ nuclei}}{1 \text{ mol}}\right)\left(\frac{1.60 \times 10^{-13} \text{ J}}{1 \text{ MeV}}\right) = 1.73 \times 10^{13}$ J/mol
$= \left(1.73 \times 10^{13} \frac{\text{J}}{\text{mol}}\right)\left(\frac{1 \text{ kcal}}{4184 \text{ J}}\right) = 4.14 \times 10^9$ kcal/mol
$= \left(1.73 \times 10^{13} \frac{\text{J}}{\text{mol}}\right)\left(\frac{1 \text{ mol}}{0.239 \text{ kg}}\right) = 7.25 \times 10^{13}$ J/kg
(b) $(10^6 \text{ kWh})(3.6 \times 10^6 \text{ J/kWh}) = (7.25 \times 10^{13} \text{ J/kg})(m)(0.20)$; $m = 0.248$ kg.

31-B9 A is $^{13}_7\text{N}$; B is $^{13}_6\text{C}$; C is $^{14}_7\text{N}$; D is $^{15}_8\text{O}$; E is $^{15}_7\text{N}$; the final reaction is $^{15}_7\text{N}(p, \alpha)^{12}_6\text{C}$.

31-B10 Use Eq. 16-5 (p. 354): KE $= \frac{3}{2}nRT$, where here the number of moles n is $1/N_A$ for a single particle.
KE $= \frac{3}{2}\left(\frac{1 \text{ mol}}{6.02 \times 10^{23} \text{ atoms}}\right)\left(8.31 \frac{\text{J}}{\text{mol·K}}\right)(50 \times 10^6 \text{ K}) = 1.03 \times 10^{-15}$ J/atom
$= 0.0065$ MeV/atom. [See the last paragraph of p. 750.]

31-B11 The power is $\left(10^9 \frac{\text{J}}{\text{s}}\right)\left(\frac{1 \text{ MeV}}{1.60 \times 10^{-13} \text{ J}}\right)\left(\frac{86\,400 \text{ s}}{1 \text{ d}}\right) = 5.40 \times 10^{26}$ MeV/d.
Using reaction c, the fuel requirement is
$\left(5.40 \times 10^{26} \frac{\text{MeV}}{\text{d}}\right)\left(\frac{1 \text{ atom}}{17.6 \text{ MeV}}\right)\left(\frac{3.01 \times 10^{-3} \text{ kg}}{6.02 \times 10^{23} \text{ atoms}}\right) = 0.154$ kg/day.

31-B12 (a) $(1.2 \times 10^9 \text{ kg})\left(11 \times 10^6 \frac{\text{J}}{\text{kg}}\right)\left(\frac{1 \text{ kWh}}{3.6 \times 10^6 \text{ J}}\right)\left(\frac{\$0.01}{1 \text{ kWh}}\right)(0.32) = \$11.7 \times 10^6$.
(b) To find the mass of uranium needed to supply the same energy as the garbage, we have $(1.2 \times 10^9 \text{ kg})(11 \times 10^6 \text{ J/kg}) = (m)(5.9 \times 10^{11} \text{ J/kg})$; $m = 22.4 \times 10^3$ kg = 22.4 metric tons of uranium.

31-B13 $(0.1 \ \mu\text{Ci})\left(\frac{3.7 \times 10^4 \text{ dis/s}}{1 \ \mu\text{Ci}}\right) = 3700$ dis/s. [Check: $\lambda = 0.693/T_{1/2}$
$= (0.693)/(1.3 \times 10^9 \times 3.156 \times 10^7 \text{ s}) = 1.69 \times 10^{-17} \text{ s}^{-1}$; $dN/dt = N\lambda$
$= (130 \text{ g})\left(\frac{6.02 \times 10^{23} \text{ atoms}}{40 \text{ g}}\right)(0.012 \times 10^{-2})(1.69 \times 10^{-17} \text{ s}^{-1}) \approx 4000$ dis/s.
The factor 0.012×10^{-2} is the relative abundance of the ^{40}K isotope.]

31-B14 (a) The number of ion pairs is $(\frac{1}{3} \times 10^{-9} \text{ C})\left(\frac{1 \text{ ion pair}}{1.60 \times 10^{-19} \text{ C}}\right) = 2.083 \times 10^9$ ion pairs. The energy corresponding to 1 R is $(2.083 \times 10^9)(35 \times 1.6 \times 10^{-19} \text{ J}) = 11.7 \times 10^{-9} \text{ J} = 11.7$ nJ. (b) If we assume that air and "tissue" absorb energy equally, per gram, then 1 rad = $\left(100\ \dfrac{\text{ergs}}{\text{g}}\right)$

$\times \left(1.293 \times 10^{-3}\ \dfrac{\text{g}}{\text{cm}^3}\right)\left(\dfrac{10^{-7}\ \text{J}}{1\ \text{erg}}\right) = 1.29 \times 10^{-8}$ J $= 12.9$ nJ, absorbed in 1 cm^3 of air. Thus 1 rad $\approx$ 1.1 R.

31-B15 (a) 500 rad, since the RBE for γ radiation is 1.   (b) We recall that 1 rad $= 100$ erg/g $= (100 \times 10^{-7}$ J$)/(10^{-3}$ kg$) = 10^{-2}$ J/kg. Thus, the dose is $(500 \times 10^{-2}$ J/kg$)(70$ kg$) = 350$ J. A fall from a height of 1 m would give KE = PE $= mgh = (70$ kg$)(9.8$ N/kg$)(1$ m$) = 686$ J.

31-B16 (a) $V = \frac{4}{3}\pi\,(7 \times 10^{-15}$ m$)^3 = 1.44 \times 10^{-42}$ m^3.   (b) Mass of a single nucleus (electron cloud has negligible mass) is $(0.197$ kg$)/(6.02 \times 10^{23}) = 3.27 \times 10^{-25}$ kg. Density $= M/V = 2.3 \times 10^{17}$ kg/m^3.   (c) If $V \propto A$, then $r \propto A^{1/3}$; $(7$ fm$)(262/197)^{1/3} = 7.7$ fm.   (d) $(197/A)^{1/3} = 2$; $A = 197/8 = 24.6$. Table 9 in the Appendix gives ^{24}Mg or ^{25}Mg as possible stable nuclides of atomic mass number about 25.

31-B17 $(^{3}\text{He} + {}^{3}\text{He}) - ({}^{4}\text{He} + {}^{1}\text{H} + {}^{1}\text{H}) = 6.032060 - 6.018253 = 0.013807$ u $= 12.85$ MeV.

31-B18 The reaction is between bare nuclei. Proton: ^{1}H $- 1m_e = 1.007825 - 0.000549$ $= 1.007276$ u. Deuteron: ^{2}H $- 1m_e = 2.014102 - 0.000549 = 2.013553$ u. The mass of the positron is 0.000549 u. A mass check shows that the reaction is possible: $1.007276 + 1.007276 - (2.013553 + 0.000549) = 0.000450$ u $= 0.42$ MeV released.   [Since the reaction is energetically possible, and ordinary hydrogen ^{1}H is plentiful, it would seem that here is a possible abundant energy source. However, the reaction does not take place spontaneously at ordinary temperatures because electrostatic (Coulomb) repulsion prevents two low-energy protons from coming close enough to interact.]

31-B19 (a) The muon's rest mass is about 207 times that of the electron. To avoid rounding errors, we use values to 4 significant figures (see *Physics Today*, Sept. 1974, p. 19, and the detachable card opposite p. 81 of that issue): $(206.8)(0.0005486) = 0.1134$ u for the muon. The mass of a proton is ^{1}H $- 1m_e$ $= 1.007825 - 0.000549 = 1.007276$ u. The neutrino must bring in an energy equivalent to p $+ \mu^- -$ n $= 1.007276 + 0.1134 - 1.008665 = 0.1120$ u $= 104$ MeV.   (b) The neutrino must bring in an energy equivalent to n $+ e^+ -$ p $= 1.008665 + 0.000549 - 1.007276 = 0.00194$ u $= 1.8$ MeV.

31-B20 (a) From the recording, 8 cycles of 1024 counts take place in about 6.0 s; rate $= 8(1024)/6.0 \approx 1350$ counts/s.   (b) 24 cycles of 1024 counts in about 5.5 s; rate $= 24(1024)/5.5 \approx 4500$ counts/s.

31-C1 The specimen, 10 moles of carbon, contains 6.02×10^{24} atoms of ^{12}C and, when living, had 6.02×10^{12} atoms of ^{14}C (the abundance 10^{-12} is given in Sec. 31-1). From the half-life 5730 y, the disintegration constant for ^{14}C is $\lambda = (0.693)/(5730$ y$) = 1.209 \times 10^{-4}$ y$^{-1} = 3.83 \times 10^{-12}$ s^{-1}. By Eq. 30-6, the original activity of ^{14}C was $A_0 = \lambda N_0 = (3.83 \times 10^{-12}$ s$^{-1})(6.02 \times 10^{12}) = 23.06$ dis/s. The present activity is $(900/60) = 15.00$ dis/s. Thus, $e^{-\lambda t} = A/A_0$ $= (15.00/23.06) = 0.6505$; $\lambda t = 0.430$, whence $t = 0.430/(1.209 \times 10^{-4}$ y$^{-1})$ $= 3560$ y, about 36 centuries ago.   [The result is subject to several uncertainties, in addition to the problem of counting low-level activities. The abundance 10^{-12} is not exact, nor was it necessarily the same 36 centuries ago as it is today, since the cosmic-ray flux that creates ^{14}C in the atmosphere (Sec. 30-8, item 5) has not necessarily remained constant. The abundance ratio has also been upset by mankind's burning of fossil fuel in the past few centuries.]

31-C2   If $v \approx c$, the KE is $mc^2 - m_0c^2 \approx mc^2$ since the rest mass is negligible. Thus, $Vq \approx mc^2$. Also, $mv^2/R = qvB$ gives $R = mv/qB$, valid at any speed since mv is the correct relativistic expression for linear momentum. Thus, $R \approx mc/qB$. Combine these equations; m and q cancel out, yielding $V = RBc$.

31-C3 $B = V/Rc = (400 \times 10^9 \text{ V})/(10^3 \text{ m})(3 \times 10^8 \text{ m/s}) = 1.33$ T.   [The actual B for the Fermilab accelerator (Fig. 31-4) is 1.8 T, but the bending magnets are installed over only 75% of the orbit, to allow room for rf accelerating cavities and the focusing magnets. During bending, R is less than 1.000 km.]

31-C4   (a) $(20 \times 10^3 \text{ A})(20 \times 10^{-9} \text{ s})(10^6 \text{ J/C}) = 400$ J.   (b) $(20 \times 10^3 \text{ A})(20 \times 10^{-9} \text{ s})/(1.60 \times 10^{-19} \text{ C}) = 2.5 \times 10^{15}$ electrons.   (c) KE $= mc^2 - m_0c^2$; $mc^2 = 1$ MeV $+ 0.511$ MeV $= 1.511$ MeV. From $m = m_0/\sqrt{1 - v^2/c^2}$, we have $\sqrt{1 - v^2/c^2} = (0.511)/(1.511)$; $v/c = 0.8856$; $v = (0.8856)(3 \times 10^8 \text{ m/s}) = 2.66 \times 10^8$ m/s. (d) Pulse length $= vt = (2.66 \times 10^8 \text{ m/s})(20 \times 10^{-9} \text{ s}) = 5.31$ m.   (e) The electrons in one pulse are distributed in a column 10 cm^2 ($= 10^{-3}$ m^2) in cross section and 5.31 m long; V $= 5.31 \times 10^{-3}$ m^3. The volume associated with each electron is $(5.31 \times 10^{-3} \text{ m}^3)/(2.5 \times 10^{15}) = 2.12 \times 10^{-18}$ m^3; average spacing $\approx (2.12 \times 10^{-18} \text{ m})^{1/3} \approx 1.3 \times 10^{-6}$ m.

31-C5 $(4 \text{ kg})\left(\dfrac{6.02 \times 10^{23} \text{ atoms}}{0.018 \text{ kg}}\right)(2)(0.015 \times 10^{-2})(\tfrac{1}{2})\left(\dfrac{4.0 \text{ MeV}}{1 \text{ atom}}\right)\left(\dfrac{1.60 \times 10^{-13} \text{ J}}{1 \text{ MeV}}\right)$
$= 1.3 \times 10^{10}$ J.   [The factor 2 is because there are 2 H atoms in each H$_2$O molecule; the factor $\tfrac{1}{2}$ is because 2 protons are used in each reaction event.]

31-C6   The tritium formed in two reactions of type a can release 11.3 MeV by reaction d. But two reactions a release 8.0 MeV. Hence, using the answer to Prob. 31-C5 (available to the student on p. 816), we find that the energy still available is $(11.3/8.0)(1.3 \times 10^{10} \text{ J}) = 1.8 \times 10^{10}$ J.

31-C7 $(10^3 \text{ kg shale})(60 \times 10^{-6})\left(\dfrac{6.02 \times 10^{23} \text{ atoms}}{0.238 \text{ kg}}\right)\left(\dfrac{200 \text{ MeV}}{1 \text{ atom}}\right)\left(\dfrac{1.60 \times 10^{-13} \text{ J}}{1 \text{ MeV}}\right)$
$= 4.86 \times 10^{12}$ J.   [Use the number of ^{238}U atoms, since a perfectly efficient breeder reactor is supposed to be available to convert it to ^{239}Pu, with an estimated 200 MeV/fission similar to the fuel value of ^{235}U.]

31-C8   The number of C atoms at the face of the column, 1 m^2 in area, would be $(1 \text{ m}^2)/(0.0037 \times 10^{-28} \text{ m}^2) = 2.70 \times 10^{30}$ atoms. The length of the column is found from volume = mass/density:
$(2.70 \times 10^{30} \text{ atoms})\left(\dfrac{0.012 \text{ kg}}{6.02 \times 10^{23} \text{ atoms}}\right)\left(\dfrac{1 \text{ m}^3}{2250 \text{ kg}}\right) = L(1 \text{ m}^2)$; $L = 24$ m.

31-C10   Equation 28-8 gives kZe^2/r for the PE of a positive charge of magnitude e at a distance r from a nucleus of charge $+Ze$. The potential is
$V = \dfrac{\text{work}}{\text{charge}} = \dfrac{kZe}{r} = \dfrac{(9 \times 10^9 \text{ N·m}^2/\text{C}^2)(50)(1.60 \times 10^{-19} \text{ C})}{8 \times 10^{-15} \text{ m}} = +9.0 \times 10^6$ V
$= +9.0$ MV.

31-C11   (a) The falling photon gains energy; its frequency is increased. The detector must be moved away from the source (downward) so that the apparent frequency is decreased to its original value by the Doppler effect.
(b) $\Delta E/E = mgH/E = (h\nu/c^2)gH/h\nu = gH/c^2$. Since $E = h\nu$, $\Delta E/E = \Delta\nu/\nu$. For the very small v/c encountered here, we can use the approximate Doppler effect equation (Eq. 10-8 on p. 239); $v/c = \Delta\nu/\nu = \Delta E/E$, whence $v/c = gH/c^2$. $v = gH/c = (9.8 \text{ m/s}^2)(22 \text{ m})/(3 \times 10^8 \text{ m/s}) = 7.2 \times 10^{-7}$ m/s.
(c) $t = s/v = (10^{-3} \text{ m})/(7.2 \times 10^{-7} \text{ m/s}) = 1390$ s $= 23$ min.

C
D 0
E 1
F 2
G 3
H 4
I 5
J 6